COMPACT CALCULUS

Philip Franklin

*Professor of
Mathematics*

*Massachusetts
Institute of
Technology*

COMPACT
CALCULUS

McGraw-Hill
Book Company, Inc.

New York
San Francisco
Toronto
London

COMPACT CALCULUS

PREFACE

This book is a rigorous introduction to elementary calculus. It is shorter than most standard introductory texts, but contains much of the modern spirit. The reader is assumed to have studied trigonometry and to have done some work with graphs in his course in algebra.

The treatment is rigorous in the sense that the proofs are carried out in logical order from basic definitions, assumptions, or a few theorems from higher analysis which are stated without proof at this stage. Arguments based on geometric intuition are largely avoided.

The notation f for a function whose value at x is f(x) is used consistently. In the few places where the discussion is clarified by so doing, notations such as $\int_a^b f$ and $D \sin = \cos$ are used.

This book is only about half the size of many introductory texts. But practically all the topics usually treated in a one-year course are included. This is accomplished by a systematic arrangement which avoids undue repetition. Before explaining any detailed technique, the first two chapters present the concept of the derivative as a slope or rate and of the definite integral as a limit of sums. Thus the student studying physics and calculus concurrently will have some basic knowledge of these concepts when they are used in the physics course. There is a restriction in the number of worked-out examples. But this leaves something for the average student to learn from his instructor and something for the more ambitious student to investigate for himself. Thus the author has attempted to make this calculus text a reasonable sequel to the present-day reformed high-school mathematics courses.

Philip Franklin

CONTENTS

1

FUNCTIONS, DERIVATIVES, LIMITS

Calculus is a branch of analysis. The distinguishing feature of analysis is the free use of limits and other processes involving an *infinite* number of steps. As the reader will recall, algebra is for the most part concerned with *finite* sequences of operations.

One part of our subject, the differential calculus, was invented to solve the geometric problem of finding the tangent to a curve, or the problem of finding velocities and other rates of change in physical problems. The other part, the integral calculus, was invented to solve the problems in geometry of finding areas and lengths of arcs, or to find centers of gravity and similar quantities, or to calculate the orbits of moving bodies from the laws of motion in mechanics.

The basic notions of the calculus were known in crude form to the Greeks, for example, Archimedes (c. 200 B.C., Greek). But their organization into a useful method was accomplished only in relatively recent times, independently by I. Newton (1642–1727, English) and G. W. von Leibniz (1646–1716, German).

1—THE REAL-NUMBER SYSTEM

The numbers used in counting are the positive integers, or *natural numbers*. To measure lengths in geometry we need the fractions, obtained from the integers by division, and the positive irrational numbers. These positive numbers and their negatives, together with zero, make up the *real-number system*.

The reader has encountered the *complex-number system*, made up of ordered pairs of real numbers, in his study of quadratic equations. Although it originally had a more literal meaning, at present the word "real" in the phrase "real number" is used in a technical sense only, in contradistinction to "natural number" or to "complex number". Since elementary calculus is primarily concerned with real numbers, we shall frequently omit the word real. Thus in this book, unless otherwise explicitly qualified, the word number will mean real number.

A complete set of axioms characterizing the real numbers can be given, but is often omitted from elementary treatments of algebra. We do assume that the reader will have acquired a working knowledge of the four fundamental operations of addition, subtraction, multiplication, and division, as well as the relations of order and inequality which hold for real numbers.

Although the reader has already encountered the plotting of points $P(x,y)$ in the cartesian plane, we briefly describe the basis of this association of ordered pairs of real numbers with points in the plane. As in Fig. 1, we take two straight lines which intersect at right angles as an x axis and a y axis. Using the same unit on each axis, we plot the pair (x,y) or point $P(x,y)$ by means of its signed projections on the axes. In this system the point $P(x,0)$, for x positive, is a point on the x axis whose distance to the right of the origin is x units of the common scale. For $x = 0$, the point $P(0,0)$ is the origin itself. And for x negative, the point $P(x,0)$ is a point on the x axis whose distance to the left of the origin is measured by $|x| = -x$.

The construction just described sets up a representation of numbers x on the x axis. In this representation of real numbers by points on an indefinite straight line, the relation is one-to-one. For this reason, we often use geometric language and speak of numbers a, b, x as points a, b, x.

Let $(b - a)$ be a positive number. Then $a < b$; that is, a "is less than" b. Here the point a lies to the left of the point b (Fig. 2). Also, $b > a$, or b "is greater than" a. And the point b lies to the right of the point a. The points x between a and b make up the *open interval* (a,b). This is defined by

$$x \text{ is in } (a,b) \rightleftarrows a < x < b, \tag{1}$$

where the symbol $\rightleftarrows$ is read "if and only if", or "implies and is

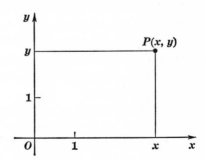

FIGURE 1

FIGURE 2

implied by". The symbol $(-\infty, \infty)$ represents the infinite interval consisting of all points of the line.

The symbol $\leq$ means "is less than or equal to", while $\geq$ means "is greater than or equal to". With these we may define the *closed interval* $[a,b]$, which includes its end points:

$$x \text{ is in } [a,b] \rightleftarrows a \leq x \leq b. \tag{2}$$

We also define the *half-open intervals* $[a,b)$ and $(a,b]$ by x is in $[a,b) \rightleftarrows a \leq x < b$ and x is in $(a,b] \rightleftarrows a < x \leq b$.

We recall the symbol for absolute or numerical value defined by

$$|x| = x \text{ if } x \geq 0 \qquad |x| = -x \text{ if } x < 0. \tag{3}$$

For any two points a and b, the distance between them, or length of the interval having these as end points, is

$$|b - a| = |a - b|. \tag{4}$$

2—VECTORS

Let $P_1(x_1,y_1)$ and $P_2(x_2,y_2)$ be any two distinct points of the cartesian plane, taken in this order. Then they determine a directed segment, or *vector* $\overrightarrow{P_1P_2}$. Its projections on the axes, or components, are the directed distances $x_2 - x_1$ and $y_2 - y_1$. If we think of a point originally at P_1, and later at P_2, these signed distances represent the algebraic increments or changes in the coordinates. In the calculus these changes are denoted by Δ, read "delta". Thus (Fig. 3)

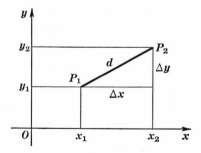

FIGURE 3

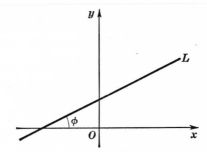

FIGURE 4

$$\Delta x = x_2 - x_1 \qquad \Delta y = y_2 - y_1. \tag{5}$$

By the Pythagorean theorem, the distance d from P_1 to P_2, or length of the vector $\overrightarrow{P_1P_2}$, is

$$d = |\overrightarrow{P_1P_2}| = \sqrt{(\Delta x)^2 + (\Delta y)^2}$$
$$= \sqrt{(x_2 - x_1)^2 + (y_2 - y_1)^2}. \tag{6}$$

As an illustration, the locus of the equation

$$(x - h)^2 + (y - k)^2 = a^2 \tag{7}$$

is a circle with center at (h,k) and radius $|a|$, since the equation asserts that the distance d from (h,k) to (x,y) satisfies $d^2 = a^2$, and hence $d = |a|$. For example, the locus of the equation $(x - 2)^2 + (y + 3)^2 = 16$ is the circle with center $(2, -3)$ and radius 4.

We note that the vector $\overrightarrow{P_2P_1}$ has components $x_1 - x_2$ and $y_1 - y_2$, the negatives of those of $\overrightarrow{P_1P_2}$. We write $\overrightarrow{P_2P_1} = -\overrightarrow{P_1P_2}$.

3—THE STRAIGHT LINE

Let L be any straight line in the cartesian plane (Fig. 4). The angle ϕ $(0 \le \phi < 180°)$ measured counterclockwise from the positive x axis to the line L is called the *inclination* of the line.

Let us first assume that the line is not parallel to the y axis, so that $\phi \ne 90°$. Then if P_1 and P_2 are any two distinct points on the line, $\Delta x \ne 0$, and we have

$$m = \frac{\Delta y}{\Delta x} = \tan \phi. \tag{8}$$

We call m the *slope* of the line L. Since it equals $\tan \phi$, it is the same for all pairs of distinct points on L. Let P_1 and P_2 be two fixed points on the line, and $P(x,y)$ any point on the line L distinct from P_1. Then it follows that

$$\frac{y - y_1}{x - x_1} = m = \frac{y_2 - y_1}{x_2 - x_1}. \qquad (9)$$

From this we may derive the relation

$$y - y_1 = \frac{y_2 - y_1}{x_2 - x_1}(x - x_1). \qquad (10)$$

Since this holds if and only if $P(x,y)$ is on L, it is one form of an equation of L, or equation having L as its locus. This equation is known as the *two-point form*.

The *point-slope* form is

$$y - y_1 = m(x - x_1). \qquad (11)$$

We also have the *slope-intercept form*

$$y = mx + b. \qquad (12)$$

Here $b = -mx_1 + y_1$ is the intercept on the y axis, since $(0,b)$ satisfies Eq. (12). In distinction from Eq. (9), Eqs. (10) to (12) remain valid even when $(x,y) = (x_1,y_1)$. Thus they hold if and only if (x,y) lies on L, and so each has the entire line L as its locus.

For $\phi = 90°$, we have $\Delta x = 0$. Here $1/m = \cot \phi = \Delta x / \Delta y = 0$. And the equation of the line may be written

$$x = x_1. \qquad (13)$$

4—FUNCTIONS

Let X and Y be two arbitrary sets of real numbers. As typical examples of the sets we shall often use, the reader may think of all the real numbers on some interval, all positive numbers, or the totality of real numbers. If a set contains only a single element, then the letter, such as a or b, used to represent this element is called a *constant*.

Suppose that a rule is given which assigns to each element x of X a single element y of Y. Then the set f of ordered pairs (x,y) thus generated is called a *function*. And we write

$$f : X \to Y \qquad \text{or} \qquad f : (x,y), \tag{14}$$

read "the function f which maps X onto Y", or "the function f whose ordered pairs are (x,y)", respectively.

The definition of a function without reference to its possible expression by a simple mathematical formula is due to P. G. Lejeune Dirichlet (1805–1859, German). But the definition given here in terms of a mapping or set of ordered pairs and with emphasis on the uniqueness of y was not widely used in elementary textbooks until 1953.

The *domain of definition* of the function f is the set X. The *range* of the function f is the set Y. A letter, such as x or y, used to represent an arbitrary element of a set is called a *variable*. The letter x, which represents an element of the domain X, is called the *independent variable of f*. The letter y, which represents an element of the range Y, is called the *dependent variable*, or the *value of the function f at x*. It is denoted by $f(x)$, read "f of x".

The rule which defines a function may take the form of a simple algebraic expression by means of which $y = f(x)$ may be calculated for any element x of X. In such a case, unless X is explicitly restricted otherwise, we shall assume that X is the largest subset of the real numbers for which the expression determines a real value.

For example, we may use the polynomial $x^2 + 3$ to define a function f by writing $f : (x, x^2 + 3)$. Usually it is simpler to write $f(x) = x^2 + 3$, understanding $f : (x,y)$, where $y = f(x)$. Or we may write $y = x^2 + 3$, understanding $f : (x,y)$. For this function the domain X is the infinite interval $(-\infty, \infty)$, or $-\infty < x < \infty$. The range Y is the half-open interval $[3, \infty)$, or $3 \le y < \infty$. From the definition of this function f, we find the following particular ordered pairs:

$f(x) = x^2 + 3,\ (x, x^2 + 3)$

$f(3) = 3^2 + 3 = 12,\ (3,12)$

$f(-2) = (-2)^2 + 3 = 7,\ (-2,7)$

$f(4 + h) = (4 + h)^2 + 3 = 19 + 8h + h^2 \qquad (4 + h, 19 + 8h + h^2)$

5—OPERATIONS ON FUNCTIONS

Let f and g be two functions defined by the respective equations $y = f(x)$ and $y = g(x)$. Then we may define new functions in terms of these by applying the four fundamental operations of algebra. Thus we write $f + g$ for the function such that $y = f(x) + g(x)$. Similarly, for $f - g$, $y = f(x) - g(x)$. For fg, $y = f(x) g(x)$. And for f/g, $y = f(x)/g(x)$. Also, for f^n, $y = [f(x)]^n$. In particular, if c is a constant, cg is defined by $y = cg(x)$. For combinations involving both f and g, the domain consists of the elements common to X_f, the domain of f, and X_g, the domain of g. For f/g we must exclude the numbers for which $g(x) = 0$.

We may also form the composite[1] function $f(g)$ defined by the relation $y = f[g(x)]$. Here the domain consists of those numbers x in X_g for which the corresponding $y = g(x)$ is in X_f.

For some combinations, the final form of the rule for computing y from x may have a wider domain than those just described, under the convention mentioned above. Thus let f be defined by $f(x) = x^2$, and g be defined by $g(x) = \sqrt{1 - x^2}$, indicating the positive square root. Here X_g is the closed interval $[-1,1]$, or $-1 \le x \le 1$, which is the domain for $f(g)$ as obtained in this way. But the rule for this composite function is the polynomial $P(x) = 1 - x^2$, and the function P such that $y = P(x)$ has the infinite interval $(-\infty, \infty)$ as its domain.

6—RELATIONS

Suppose that a rule is given which assigns to each element x of X *one or more* elements of Y. Then the set of ordered pairs thus generated is called a *relation*. Its domain is X, and its range Y. The rule may take the form of an equation, such as

$$x^2 + y^2 = a^2. \tag{15}$$

---

[1] Some writers use $f \circ g$ in place of $f(g)$. It has some advantages if several stages are used, for example, $f \circ g \circ h$ in place of $f[g(h)]$. (It is easy to establish the validity of the associative law $f \circ (g \circ h) = (f \circ g) \circ h$ for composition.)

Let the constant a be positive, $a > 0$. Then the domain is $[-a,a]$, or $-a \le x \le a$, and the range is $[-a,a]$, or $-a \le y \le a$. For any x in the domain, either

$$y = \sqrt{a^2 - x^2} \qquad \text{or} \qquad y = -\sqrt{a^2 - x^2}. \tag{16}$$

Each of these equations defines a function. Call the first function f and the second g. Then the ordered pairs which make up the set generated by Eq. (15) are all the pairs which make up f as well as those other than $(a,0)$ and $(-a,0)$ which make up g.

The set of points in the cartesian plane (x,y) corresponding to the pairs of the relation constitute the graph of the relation, or the locus of the equation defining it. In the case of Eq. (15), the graph is a circle with center at the origin and radius a.

7—SECOND-DEGREE RELATIONS

Let a and b be positive constants with $a \ge b > 0$. Then the relation defined by

$$\frac{x^2}{a^2} + \frac{y^2}{b^2} = 1 \tag{17}$$

has as its graph the *ellipse* shown in Fig. 5. Here the domain is $[-a,a]$, or $-a \le x \le a$, and the range is $[-b,b]$, or $-b \le y \le b$.

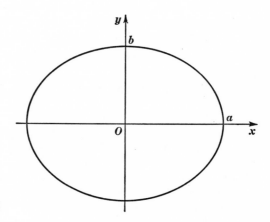

FIGURE 5

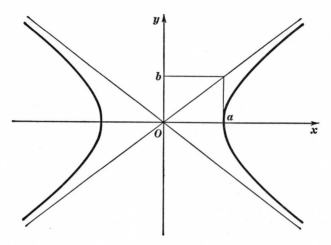

FIGURE 6

The upper half of the ellipse is the graph of the function defined by $y = (b/a)\sqrt{a^2 - x^2}$, which shows that it could be obtained from the upper half of a circle by foreshortening each ordinate in the same ratio.

For a and b any two positive constants, the relation defined by

$$\frac{x^2}{a^2} - \frac{y^2}{b^2} = 1 \tag{18}$$

has as its graph the *hyperbola* shown in Fig. 6. The upper half is the graph of the function defined by $y = (b/a)\sqrt{x^2 - a^2}$. For this function, as well as for the relation determined by Eq. (18), the domain consists of two parts, $(-\infty, -a]$, or $x \le -a$, and $[a, \infty)$, or $x \ge a$. For parts far from the origin the locus closely approximates the asymptotes, the straight lines having $y = bx/a$ and $y = -bx/a$ as their equations.

For p any positive number, the relation defined by

$$y^2 = 4px \tag{19}$$

has as its graph the *parabola* shown in Fig. 7. The upper half is the graph of the function given by $y = 2\sqrt{px}$. The domain is $[0, \infty)$, or $0 \le x$.

In connection with quadratic equations, the student has plotted graphs of the relation given by

$$y = ax^2 + bx + c. \tag{20}$$

These are all parabolas when $a \neq 0$, since the equation is equivalent to

$$(y - k) = a(x - h)^2 \quad \text{with } h = -\frac{b}{2a}, \, k = c - \frac{b^2}{4a}. \tag{21}$$

If A, B, C are not all zero, the general equation

$$Ax^2 + Bxy + Cy^2 + Dx + Ey + F = 0 \tag{22}$$

is of the second degree. If it represents a real, nondegenerate locus, that locus is a hyperbola, parabola, or ellipse (including the circle as a special ellipse). The degenerate cases may mean no real locus, a single point, or two straight lines which may be intersecting, parallel, or coincident.

If A and B are not both zero, the general equation

$$Ax + By + C = 0 \tag{23}$$

is of the first degree and its locus is a straight line.

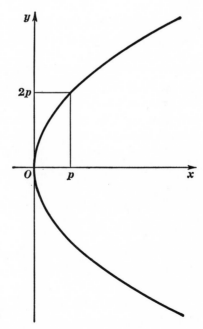

FIGURE 7

8—SLOPE OF A CURVE

Consider the function $f : (x,y)$ defined by $y = f(x)$. Suppose that a portion of its graph is a curved arc, such as AB in Fig. 8. Let $P_1(x_1,y_1)$ be any fixed point on this arc. Then the straight line P_1T tangent to the curve at P_1 is defined by the following construction. Let $P_2(x_2,y_2)$ be any point on the curve near, but not at, P_1. The segment P_1P_2 is the *chord*, and the indefinite straight line P_1S_2 is a *secant* determined by P_1 and P_2. Now imagine P_2 to move along the curve toward P_1. Then the secant P_1S_2 will revolve about P_1. If there is a fixed straight line through P_1, P_1T, such that as P_2 approaches P_1, the angle between P_1S_2 and P_1T, or $\angle S_2P_1T$, approaches zero, then the line P_1T is the *tangent* to the curve at P_1.

From Eq. (8), we find that the slope of the secant is

$$m_S = \tan \phi_S = \frac{y_2 - y_1}{x_2 - x_1} = \frac{\Delta y}{\Delta x}. \tag{24}$$

Let $m_1 = \tan \phi_1$ be the slope of the tangent line P_1T. We indicate that P_2 tends to P_1, or that x_2 tends to x_1, by writing $x_2 \to x_1$, or $\Delta x \to 0$. And to indicate that as this happens, $|\phi_S - \phi_1|$ approaches zero, or that ϕ_S tends to ϕ_1 and m_S tends to m_1, we write

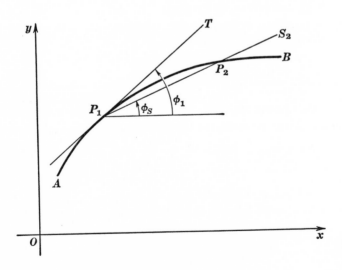

FIGURE 8

$$m_1 = \lim_{x_2 \to x_1} m_S = \lim_{x_2 \to x_1} \frac{y_2 - y_1}{x_2 - x_1} = \lim_{\Delta x \to 0} \frac{\Delta y}{\Delta x}. \tag{25}$$

The *slope of the curve* at P_1 is defined to be the slope of the tangent line at P_1, or m_1. Since $y_1 = f(x_1)$ and $y_2 = f(x_2)$, we have

$$m_1 = \lim_{x_2 \to x_1} \frac{f(x_2) - f(x_1)}{x_2 - x_1}. \tag{26}$$

For example, let $f(x) = x^2$. Then $y = x^2$, and the curve is a parabola. Here $y_1 = x_1^2$, $y_2 = x_2^2$, and

$$m_S = \frac{y_2 - y_1}{x_2 - x_1} = \frac{x_2^2 - x_1^2}{x_2 - x_1} = x_2 + x_1 \qquad \text{for } x_2 \neq x_1. \tag{27}$$

When x_2 tends to x_1, m_S approaches the value of the last expression with $x_2 = x_1$, or $2x_1$. Hence $m_1 = 2x_1$.

By Eq. (11) the equation of the tangent line at (x_1, y_1), with $y_1 = x_1^2$, is

$$y - x_1^2 = 2x_1(x - x_1) \qquad \text{or } y = 2x_1 x - x_1^2$$
$$\text{or } y + y_1 = 2x_1 x. \tag{28}$$

To draw the tangent line at P_1, after m_1 is known, we select any convenient value of $a \neq 0$ and plot the point $P_T = (x_1 + a,\ y_1 + m_1 a)$. Then the line joining P_1 and P_T is the tangent at P_1, since it passes through P_1 and has m_1 as its slope.

Since $\Delta x = x_2 - x_1$, $x_2 = x_1 + \Delta x$. Hence $\Delta y = y_2 - y_1 = f(x_1 + \Delta x) - f(x_1)$, and

$$m_1 = \lim_{\Delta x \to 0} \frac{\Delta y}{\Delta x} = \lim_{\Delta x \to 0} \frac{f(x_1 + \Delta x) - f(x_1)}{\Delta x}. \tag{29}$$

Since x_2 does not appear explicitly in this equation, we may drop the subscript 1. Thus we write for the slope at $(x, f(x))$

$$m = \lim_{\Delta x \to 0} \frac{f(x + \Delta x) - f(x)}{\Delta x}. \tag{30}$$

Here x is the fixed value previously denoted by x_1.

We often write a single letter h in place of Δx, so that

$$m = \lim_{h \to 0} \frac{f(x + h) - f(x)}{h}. \tag{31}$$

The notation $h \to 0$ implies that h is never zero, but may be positive or negative as it approaches zero.

With this notation, if $y = x^2$, we should write $y + \Delta y = (x + h)^2 = x^2 + 2xh + h^2$, and by subtraction $\Delta y = 2xh + h^2$. Since $\Delta x = h$, $\Delta y / \Delta x = 2x + h$. And

$$m = \lim_{h \to 0} (2x + h) = 2x. \tag{32}$$

Note that, if we wished to find the equation of the tangent to the graph of $y = x^2$, with $P(x,y)$ used for an arbitrary point on this tangent line, we should again introduce the subscript 1 for $P_1(x_1,x_1^2)$ for the point of contact on the graph. Then from Eq. (32) we should deduce $m_1 = 2x_1$ as the slope and again find Eq. (28).

9—DERIVATIVE

Besides its geometric meaning as a slope, the right-hand member of Eq. (30) or (31) has other useful interpretations. We shall describe some of these in the next section. We denote the right-hand member by $f'(x)$, read "f prime of x", so that

$$f'(x) = \lim_{h \to 0} \frac{f(x + h) - f(x)}{h} = \lim_{\Delta x \to 0} \frac{f(x + \Delta x) - f(x)}{\Delta x} \tag{33}$$

Starting with a function f, defined by $y = f(x)$, this yields a new function f', defined by $y = f'(x)$. The domain of f' is the set of all numbers x in X_f for which the limit exists. The function f' is called the *derivative* of the function f with respect to x. And $f'(x)$ is the value of this derivative at x. The process by which f' is obtained from f is called *differentiation*. Other notations for the value of the derivative at x, besides $f'(x)$, are $D_x y$, $D_x f(x)$, and y'. The symbol $f'(x)$ was introduced by J. L. Lagrange (1736–1813, French), and the symbol $D_x f(x)$ was introduced by A. L. Cauchy (1789–1857, French). We often omit the subscript x and write Dy or Df. And at times we write $D_x f$ to mean the function f'.

Thus in the example $f(x) = x^2$, we found $f'(x) = D_x(x^2) = 2x$. But from $y = x^2$ we should also write $D_x y = 2x$, or $y' = 2x$.

In general, if $y = f(x)$, we have

$$y' = D_x y = \lim_{\Delta x \to 0} \frac{\Delta y}{\Delta x} = f'(x). \tag{34}$$

Since Δy is the change in y corresponding to a change Δx in x, the ratio of these changes, or the quotient obtained by dividing Δy by Δx, is called the *average rate of change* of y with respect to x, over the interval from x to $x + \Delta x$. And the limit of this quotient as $\Delta x \to 0$ is called the *true rate of change* of y with respect to x at x. This true rate equals $f'(x)$.

EXAMPLE 1.   Find $D_x y$ if $y = x^3$.

SOLUTION.   With $\Delta x = h$, $y + \Delta y = (x + h)^3 = x^3 + 3x^2 h + 3xh^2 + h^3$, so that

$$\frac{\Delta y}{\Delta x} = \frac{3x^2 h + 3xh^2 + h^3}{h} = 3x^2 + 3xh + h^2.$$

Taking the limit as $\Delta x = h \to 0$, we find that $D_x(x^3) = 3x^2$.

EXAMPLE 2.   Find $D_x y$ if $y = \sqrt{x}$ and $x > 0$.

SOLUTION.   With $\Delta x = h$, $y + \Delta y = \sqrt{x + h}$, so that

$$\frac{\Delta y}{\Delta x} = \frac{\sqrt{x + h} - \sqrt{x}}{h} = \frac{\sqrt{x + h} - \sqrt{x}}{h} \frac{\sqrt{x + h} + \sqrt{x}}{\sqrt{x + h} + \sqrt{x}},$$

where the factor multiplied in rationalizes the *numerator*, yielding

$$\frac{\Delta y}{\Delta x} = \frac{(\sqrt{x + h})^2 - (\sqrt{x})^2}{h(\sqrt{x + h} + \sqrt{x})} = \frac{x + h - x}{h(\sqrt{x + h} + \sqrt{x})}$$

$$= \frac{1}{\sqrt{x + h} + \sqrt{x}}.$$

Taking the limit as $\Delta x = h \to 0$, we find that $D_x y = 1/2\sqrt{x}$. This may be written $D_x(x^{1/2}) = \frac{1}{2}x^{-1/2}$.

10—INTERPRETATIONS OF THE DERIVATIVE

Let a particle move along the x axis in such a way that the particle is at the point $(s,0)$ at time t. And let f be the function $f : (s,t)$ defined by $s = f(t)$. Then $\Delta s/\Delta t$ is the average velocity of the particle for the interval from t to $t + \Delta t$, and the true *velocity* at time t is the limit of this as $\Delta t \to 0$. Thus

$$v = \lim_{\Delta t \to 0} \frac{\Delta s}{\Delta t} = f'(t) = D_t s. \tag{35}$$

Let $g : (v,t)$ be the function defined by $v = g(t) = f'(t)$. Then the *acceleration* a at time t is

$$a = \lim_{\Delta t \to 0} \frac{\Delta v}{\Delta t} = g'(t) = D_t v. \tag{36}$$

If the quantity of consumer goods produced by a company is q, and the price at which it can be sold depends on q, then the gross revenue R is a function f of q, so that $R = f(q)$. Then the *marginal revenue* for quantity q is

$$M = \lim_{\Delta q \to 0} \frac{\Delta R}{\Delta q} = f'(q) = D_q R. \tag{37}$$

When our interest in the function defined by the equation $y = f(x)$ results from its graph as a geometric curve, the scales for x and y must be taken with the same unit of length. And in this case $D_x y$ is a number equal to the trigonometrical tangent of the slope angle, $\tan \phi$. But if $s = f(t)$ refers to a motion, although we could still plot a graph, there is no reason for taking the unit on the s axis, which might represent one foot, equal to the unit on the t axis, which might represent one second. In this case the units of the velocity $v = D_t s$ are feet per second. For any graph, the angle of inclination ϕ for a line tangent to the graph would depend on the scales used and would have little interest. But the "slope" of such a line, calculated as $(s_2 - s_1)/(t_2 - t_1)$ by reading on their proper scales (t_1, s_1) and (t_2, s_2) for any two distinct points on the tangent line, would equal the velocity in feet per second for the value of t at the point of tangency. Similar remarks apply to the scales and units for $a = D_t v$ with units feet per second divided by seconds, or feet per second squared, and to $D_q R$ with units dollars per unit of goods. If the context makes it clear that we consider s a function of t and R a function of q, we can write Ds for $D_t s$ and DR for $D_q R$.

11—DEFINITION OF LIMIT

Let $F : (x,y)$ be defined by $y = F(x)$. Suppose that its domain includes some *neighborhood* of x_1, that is, some open interval having x_1 as one of its points. Then we say that y *approaches a limit L as x* tends to x_1 and write

$$L = \lim_{x \to x_1} F(x), \tag{38}$$

provided that *for any positive number ϵ, no matter how close to zero, there exists a positive number δ_ϵ which is such that*

$$|F(x) - L| < \epsilon \quad \text{for all } x \text{ satisfying } 0 < |x - x_1| < \delta_\epsilon. \tag{39}$$

Let us apply this to Eq. (31). We must take $h,0$ in place of x,x_1, and

$$F(h) = \frac{f(x + h) - f(x)}{h} \tag{40}$$

with x fixed. And for each ϵ, there corresponds a δ_ϵ such that

$$\left| \frac{f(x + h) - f(x)}{h} - m \right| < \epsilon \quad \text{for all } h \text{ such that } 0 < |h| < \delta_\epsilon. \tag{41}$$

In the example with $f(x) = x^2$, Eq. (32), we may take $\delta_\epsilon = \epsilon$, since here

$$m = 2x \quad \text{and} \quad \frac{f(x + h) - f(x)}{h} = 2x + h.$$

As $x \to x_1$, let $F(x) \to L_1$ and $G(x) \to L_2$. And let k be any constant. Then it may be proved from the definition of limit that

$$\lim k\, F(x) = k \lim F(x) = kL_1, \tag{42}$$

$$\lim [F(x) + G(x)] = \lim F(x) + \lim G(x) = L_1 + L_2, \tag{43}$$

$$\lim [F(x)\, G(x)] = [\lim F(x)]\, [\lim G(x)] = L_1 L_2, \tag{44}$$

$$\lim \frac{F(x)}{G(x)} = \frac{\lim F(x)}{\lim G(x)} = \frac{L_1}{L_2} \quad \text{provided that } L_2 \neq 0. \tag{45}$$

In each of these Eqs. (42) to (45), the limits are taken as $x \to x_1$. We shall use these without explicit reference to them. It follows from them that if $P(x)$ is any polynomial, then

$$\lim_{x \to x_1} P(x) = P(x_1). \tag{46}$$

And if $Q(x)$ is any polynomial for which $Q(x_1) \neq 0$, then

$$\lim_{x \to x_1} \frac{P(x)}{Q(x)} = \frac{P(x_1)}{Q(x_1)} \text{ for } Q(x_1) \neq 0. \tag{47}$$

12—CONTINUITY AND DIFFERENTIABILITY

Let $f : (x,y)$ be defined by $y = f(x)$. Suppose that its domain includes some neighborhood of x_1, that is, all points of some open interval having x_1 as one of its points. This ensures that

(a) $f(x_1)$ exists. (48)

Suppose further that

(b) $\lim_{x \to x_1} f(x) = f(x_1).$ (49)

That is, the limit in the left-hand member exists and is equal to the value given in (a).

Definition. The function f is *continuous* at $x = x_1$ if and only if the properties (a) and (b) above are both satisfied.

If a function is continuous at each point of an interval, it is said to be *continuous in the interval*. A function that is not continuous at $x = x_1$ is said to be *discontinuous* at $x = x_1$, provided that the domain of the function includes some points in every neighborhood of x_1.

From the sentence ending with Eq. (46), it follows that if the function f is defined by $y = P(x)$, with $P(x)$ a polynomial, then f is continuous for all values of x. And if f is defined by $y = P(x)/Q(x)$, where $P(x)$ and $Q(x)$ are each polynomials, then by Eq. (47) f is continuous at all points at which $Q(x) \neq 0$ and discontinuous at those points x_i at which $Q(x_i) = 0$, since these do not lie in its domain. For example, if $f(x) = 1/x^2$, then f is discontinuous at $x = 0$. Note that here neither condition is satisfied. We indicate the behavior of this function near zero by writing

$$\lim_{x \to 0^-} \frac{1}{x^2} = +\infty,$$
(50)

but the limit on the left does not exist in the sense of our definition. Likewise, if $f(x) = 1/x$, then f is discontinuous at $x = 0$. We indicate the behavior of this function by writing

$$\lim_{x \to 0^-} \frac{1}{x} = -\infty \qquad \text{and} \qquad \lim_{x \to 0^+} = +\infty.$$
(51)

Here x tends to zero through negative values when $x \to 0-$, and through positive values when $x \to 0+$.

Again, let us consider f defined by $f(x) = (x^2 - 1)/(x - 1)$. This function is discontinuous at $x = 1$, since it is not defined there. But

$$\lim_{x \to 1} \frac{x^2 - 1}{x - 1} = \lim_{x \to 1} (x + 1) = 2.$$
(52)

Hence the function f defined by

$$f(x) = \frac{x^2 - 1}{x - 1} \qquad \text{for } x \neq 1 \text{ and } f(1) = 2$$
(53)

is continuous for all values of x. In fact, it is the same as the function defined by $f(x) = x + 1$ for all values of x.

We note that if f and g are each continuous at $x = x_1$, so are $f + g$, $f - g$, and fg. The same is true of f/g if $g(x_1) \neq 0$. And if f is continuous at $x_2 = g(x_1)$, then $f(g)$ is continuous at $x = x_1$.

As another example, consider the function f defined by $y = |x|/x$. This function is discontinuous at $x = 0$, since it is not defined there. Near zero, we have

$$\lim_{x \to 0^-} \frac{|x|}{x} = \lim_{x \to 0^-} (-1) = -1,$$
(54)

$$\lim_{x \to 0^+} \frac{|x|}{x} = \lim_{x \to 0^+} (1) = 1.$$
(55)

Definition. The function f is *differentiable* at $x = x_1$ if

$$\lim_{h \to 0} \frac{f(x_1 + h) - f(x_1)}{h}$$

exists.

If a function is differentiable at x_1, it is necessarily continuous at x_1.

PROOF. If $f(x_1 + h) - f(x_1)$ is defined for all sufficiently small h, $f(x)$ must be defined in some neighborhood of x_1. And we have

$$\lim_{h \to 0} [f(x_1 + h) - f(x_1)] = \lim_{h \to 0} (h) \lim_{h \to 0} \frac{f(x_1 + h) - f(x_1)}{h}$$

$$= 0 \cdot f'(x_1) = 0. \ \blacksquare† \tag{56}$$

The converse statement is not always true. For example, let f be defined by $f(x) = |x|$. Then f is continuous for all values of x, including $x = 0$ since $f(0) = 0 = \lim_{x \to 0} |x|$. But f is not differentiable at $x = 0$. For here we have

$$f(0 + h) - f(0) = |h|. \tag{57}$$

It follows from this and Eqs. (54) and (55) that

$$\lim_{h \to 0-} \frac{|h|}{h} = -1 \quad \text{and} \quad \lim_{h \to 0+} \frac{|h|}{h} = 1. \tag{58}$$

Thus the limit with h unrestricted as to sign does not exist. This is a case where the graph has a corner. The function has -1 as its *left-hand derivative* and 1 as its *right-hand derivative*.

In fact, functions which are continuous throughout an interval but nowhere differentiable have been constructed. But such functions are rarely met in practice.

PROBLEMS

Section 1

1. Show that the inequalities $3x + 2 > 5$ and $2x + 3 < 7$ both hold if and only if x is in the open interval (1,2).
2. Show that $|x - 2| \leq 5$ if and only if x lies in the closed interval $[-3,7]$.
3. Show that $|ab| = |a| \, |b|$.
4. Show that if $a < b$, then $a < (a + b)/2 < b$.
5. Show that if $0 < a < b$, then $a < \sqrt{ab} < b$.

† We shall frequently use this sign ■ to denote the completion of a proof.

Section 2

6. Let ϕ be the angle from the positive direction on the x axis to the direction of $\overrightarrow{P_1P_2}$. Let d be the distance of Eq. (6). Verify that $\cos \phi = \Delta x/d$, $\sin \phi = \Delta y/d$, and for $\Delta x \neq 0$, $\tan \phi = \Delta y/\Delta x$.

7. Verify that an equation of the circle with center (a,b) and radius r is

$$(x - a)^2 + (y - b)^2 = r^2.$$

8. Verify that the locus of $x^2 + y^2 + Ax + By + C = 0$ is a circle of radius $r = \sqrt{-C + A^2/4 + B^2/4}$ (assumed to be real) and center $(-A/2, -B/2)$.

Section 3

9. Find an equation representing a straight line passing through the point $(2,3)$ and making an angle of $60°$ with the x axis.

10. Find an equation of a line passing through $(2,1)$ and rising three y units for each forward x unit.

11. Find an equation of the line parallel to the line given by $y = 2x$ and such that each ordinate y is two units more than the ordinates of this line for the same x.

12. Show that the line through $(a,0)$ and $(0,b)$, with $ab \neq 0$, is the locus of $x/a + y/b = 1$.

13. Show that $Ax + By - Ax_1 - By_1 = 0$ is an equation of the straight line through (x_1,y_1) parallel to the locus of $Ax + By + C = 0$.

Section 4

In each of Probs. 14 to 19, a function $f : (x,y)$ is defined by an equation $y = f(x)$. Verify the stated values of the largest possible domain and corresponding range in each case.

14. $y = 4x - 2$, all x, all y.

15. $y = x^2 - 2x$, all x, $-1 \leq y$.

16. $y = \sqrt{4 - 2x}$, $x \leq 2$, $0 \leq y$.

17. $y = 1/x$, $x \neq 0$, $y \neq 0$.

18. $y = \sqrt{\dfrac{x}{1 - x}}$, $0 \leq x < 1$, $0 \leq y$.

19. $y = \sqrt{\dfrac{x+2}{x}}$, $x \le -2$ or $0 < x$, $0 \le y < 1$ or $1 < y$.

Section 5

20. Let f be defined by $f(x) = x^2 - 2x$, and g be defined by $g(x) = 2x$. Verify that $F = f + g$ may be defined by $F(x) = x^2$ and that $G = fg$ may be defined by $G(x) = 2x^3 - 4x^2$.

21. Let $f(x) = 3 - x$. Verify that $f(x) + 3 = 6 - x$ but that $f(x + 3) = -x$.

22. Let $f(x) = (x + a)/(ax + 1)$ and $g(x) = 1/x$. Verify that $f(g) = g(f)$ unless $x = 0$, $-a$, or $-1/a$.

23. Let $f(x) = x + 1$, and $g(x) = x^2$. Verify that $F = f(g)$ may be defined by $F(x) = x^2 + 1$ and that $G = g(f)$ may be defined by $G(x) = x^2 + 2x + 1$.

24. Let $f(x) = (ax + b)/(x - a)$ with $a^2 + b \ne 0$. Verify that $F = f(f)$ may be defined by $F(x) = x$, unless $x = a$.

Section 6

25. Plot the locus of $x^2 + y^2 = 25$, a circle.

26. Plot the locus of $|x| + |y| = 1$, a square.

27. Plot the locus of $|y| - |x| = 1$, four half lines forming a V and an inverted V.

28. Plot the locus of $|x| + |y| + |x + y| = 2$, a hexagon.

Section 7

Plot the graphs of each of the following relations:

29. $9x^2 + 16y^2 = 144$.

30. $9(x - 2)^2 + 16(y - 3)^2 = 144$.

31. $9x^2 - 16y^2 = 144$.

32. $9(x - 4)^2 - 16(y - 3)^2 = 144$.

33. $y^2 = 20x$.

34. $20y = x^2 - 4x + 24$.

Section 8

Let (x_1y_1) be a point on the graph of $y = ax^2 + bx + c$. Verify that at this point each of the following statements is valid:

35. The slope $m_1 = 2ax_1 + b$.

36. The equation of the tangent line may be written $y = 2axx_1 + bx - ax_1^2 + c$ or $y + y_1 = 2axx_1 + bx + bx_1 + 2c$.

Section 9

37. Prove that if $F = f + g$, then $F' = f' + g'$.

38. Prove that if $F = cg$, where c is a constant, then $F' = cg'$.

39. Prove that if $f(x) = 1/\sqrt{x}$, then $f'(x) = -\tfrac{1}{2}x^{-3/2}$.

40. Prove that if $f(x) = 1/x$, then $f'(x) = -1/x^2$.

41. From Examples 1 and 2 of Sec. 9 and Probs. 35, 39, and 40, it follows that the result $D_x(x^n) = nx^{n-1}$ is correct for $n = 1, 2, 3, \tfrac{1}{2}, -\tfrac{1}{2}, -1$, and 0. Deduce from Prob. 38 that $D_x(cx^n) = cnx^{n-1}$ for these same values of n.

42. From Example 1 of Sec. 9 and Probs. 35, 37, and 38, deduce that $D_x(Ax^3 + Bx^2 + Cx + D) = 3Ax^2 + 2Bx + C$.

43. Suppose that we define a new kind of derived function f_2, such that

$$f_2(x) = \lim_{h\to 0} \frac{[f(x + h)]^2 - [f(x)]^2}{h}.$$

For this derived function show that if $F = cg$, then $F_2 = c^2 g_2$. Also deduce this relation from Prob. 38, after showing that $f_2 = (f^2)' = 2ff'$. And from Prob. 37 deduce that if $F = f + g$, then $F_2 = 2(f + g)(f' + g') = f_2 + g_2 + 2fg' + 2gf' = (F/f)f_2 + (F/g)g_2$.

44. As in Prob. 43, define a new kind of derived function $f_{1/2}$ such that

$$f_{1/2}(x) = \lim_{h\to 0} \frac{\sqrt{f(x + h)} - \sqrt{f(x)}}{h}.$$

By the procedure of Example 2 of Sec. 9, show that $f_{1/2} = f'/2\sqrt{f}$. Deduce from Prob. 38 that if $F = cg$, then $f_{1/2} = \sqrt{c}g_{1/2}$. And from Prob. 37 deduce that if $F = f + g$, then

$$F_{1/2} = \frac{1}{2\sqrt{F}}(f' + g') = \frac{\sqrt{f}}{\sqrt{F}}f_{1/2} + \frac{\sqrt{g}}{\sqrt{F}}g_{1/2}.$$

Section 10

In Probs. 45 to 47 the derivatives need not be calculated from first principles, but may be found from Prob. 42 with a suitable change of letters.

45. Verify that if distance s is given by $s = 20 + 50t - 16t^2$, then the velocity v is given by $v = 50 - 32t$, and acceleration a by $a = -32$.

46. Verify that if $s = 2t^2 + 4t^3$, then $v = 4t + 12t^2$ and $a = 4 + 24t$.

47. Verify that if the gross revenue for quantity q is $R = 1{,}000q - q^2$, then the marginal revenue is $M = 1{,}000 - q$.

Section 11

48. Prove Eq. (42). And show that if δ_ϵ for F is defined by Eq. (39) and a corresponding δ_ϵ' for kF is defined, we may take

$$\delta_\epsilon' = \delta_\epsilon \quad \text{if } |k| < 1 \quad \text{and} \quad \delta_\epsilon' = \frac{1}{|k|}\,\delta_\epsilon \quad \text{if } |k| > 1.$$

49. Prove Eq. (43). And show that if δ_ϵ for F is defined by Eq. (39), and a corresponding δ_ϵ' for G and δ_ϵ'' for $F + G$ are defined, then we may take $\delta_\epsilon'' =$ the smaller of $\delta_{\epsilon/2}$ and $\delta_{\epsilon/2}'$.

Section 12

50. Show that the function f defined by $f(x) = 1/(2 - x)$ is discontinuous at $x = 2$ and that $\lim\limits_{x \to 2-} f(x) = +\infty$, $\lim\limits_{x \to 2+} f(x) = -\infty$.

51. Show that the function f defined by $f(x) = (x + 2)/(4 - x^2)$ is discontinuous at $x = 2$ and at $x = -2$. But also show that if we let the given definition hold for $x \neq -2$ and, in addition, take $f(-2) = \frac{1}{4}$, then the new function is continuous at $x = -2$ and is identical with the function of Prob. 50.

52. Plot the graph of the function defined by

$$y = f(x) = \frac{\sqrt{3}}{2}\,(4 - |x - 1| - |x - 3|) \qquad \text{for } 0 \le x \le 4$$

(half of a regular hexagon).

Verify that f is continuous in this range and differentiable except at $x = 1$ and $x = 3$.

53. A function f is defined by $f(x) = 2x + 4$ for $x < 0$ and by $f(x) = a + bx + x^2$ for $x > 0$. Show that if f is to be made continuous at $x = 0$, we must define $f(0) = 4$ and take $a = 4$. Show further that to make f differentiable at $x = 0$, we must take $a = 4$, $b = 2$.

54. A function f is defined by $f(x) = x^3$ for $x < 1$ and $f(x) = a + bx + x^2$ for $x \ge 1$. Show that if f has a derivative at $x = 1$, then $a = -1$ and $b = 1$.

2

THE DEFINITE INTEGRAL
AS A LIMIT

In this chapter we are concerned with a special limiting process, integration. Integration may be applied to certain functions to yield the definite integral, which plays a central role in the integral calculus and its applications. We shall eventually use the definite integral as a means of defining precisely such geometrical quantities as area, volume, and arc length, as well as such physical quantities as center of gravity and moment of inertia. This makes it desirable initially to develop the definite integral as an abstract mathematical concept.

After defining integration, we shall show that it is always applicable to continuous functions, which were defined in Sec. 12. But before this we shall state certain properties of continuous functions, as well as a criterion for the convergence of a sequence. These theorems are proved in advanced courses in analysis.

13—PROPERTIES OF CONTINUOUS FUNCTIONS

Let the function f be continuous at each point of the closed interval $[a,b]$, or $a \leq x \leq b$. Then the function has a least and a greatest value in $[a,b]$; that is, *there exist values u and v of x in $[a,b]$ such that $f(u) = m$ and $f(v) = M$, with $m \leq f(x) \leq M$ for any x in $[a,b]$.* We refer to this as the *extreme-value* property of continuous functions.

Note that this property and the others discussed below, in this section, are concerned with *continuous* functions on a *closed* interval. Thus the continuous function f given by $f(x) = x$ on the open interval $(0,1)$ has neither a maximum nor a minimum value. And if we extend the definition to the closed interval $[0,1]$ by taking $f(0) = f(1) = \frac{1}{2}$, then the resulting discontinuous function still has neither a maximum nor a minimum.

The *intermediate-value* property of continuous functions states that, *if f is continuous on $[x_1,x_2]$ and K_0 is any number between $f(x_1)$ and $f(x_2)$, then there is at least one point x_0 of $[x_1,x_2]$ such that $f(x_0) = K_0$.* It follows from this that if K is any number between m and M, $m \leq K \leq M$, where M and m are the extreme values of f for $[a,b]$, then there is at least one point x such that $f(x) = K$.

The difference $M - m$ is called the *oscillation* of f on $[a,b]$. If x_1 and x_2 are any two points of $[a,b]$, then

$$|f(x_1) - f(x_2)| \leq M - m. \tag{1}$$

This follows from $m \leq f(x_1) \leq M$ and $m \leq f(x_2) \leq M$. The second relation leads to $-M \leq -f(x_2) \leq -m$, and by adding this to the first we get $-(M - m) \leq f(x_1) - f(x_2) \leq M - m$. This is equivalent to Eq. (1).

On any closed subinterval of $[a,b]$, there will be a greatest value M_1, a least value m_1, and an oscillation $M_1 - m_1$. And on $[a,b]$ the function f is *uniformly continuous: Given any positive number ϵ, there exists another positive number $\delta(\epsilon)$ such that in every subinterval of $[a,b]$ of length not exceeding δ, the oscillation of f is at most ϵ.* Thus, from Eq. (1), if x_1 and x_2 are any two points on $[a,b]$, we have

$$|f(x_1) - f(x_2)| \leq \epsilon \qquad \text{if } |x_1 - x_2| \leq \delta(\epsilon). \tag{2}$$

14—THE CAUCHY CONVERGENCE CRITERION

We shall also use a condition for the convergence of a sequence to a limit, originally due to Cauchy. One modern formulation of this result is the following:

A necessary and sufficient condition for a sequence a_t, $t = 1, 2, 3, \ldots$, to approach a finite limit as t tends to infinity is that for any given positive number η, there exists some corresponding positive integer t_η such that the difference of any two values of a_t, each with $t > t_\eta$, is numerically at most η.

That is,

$$|a_{t_1} - a_{t_2}| \leq \eta \qquad \text{for } t_1 > t_\eta, \ t_2 > t_\eta. \tag{3}$$

For example, this criterion can readily be applied to the sequence

$$a_1, a_2, \ldots, a_t, \ldots = 1 - \tfrac{1}{2}, 1 - \tfrac{1}{4}, \ldots, 1 - \frac{1}{2^t}, \ldots$$

15—PARTITION OF AN INTERVAL

For a given interval $[a,b]$ let us choose any positive integer n and select $(n - 1)$ points $x_1, x_2, \ldots , x_{n-1}$, which satisfy the relation

$$a = x_0 < x_1 < x_2 < \cdots < x_{n-1} < x_n = b, \qquad (4)$$

but are otherwise arbitrary. Then we may use these to partition the interval $[a,b]$ into n subintervals $[x_0,x_1], [x_1,x_2], \ldots , [x_{n-1},x_n]$. Let ξ_i be any point in, and Δx_i be the length of, the ith subinterval $[x_{i-1},x_i]$. Then

$$x_{i-1} \leq \xi_i \leq x_i \qquad \text{and} \qquad \Delta x_i = x_i - x_{i-1}. \qquad (5)$$

We note that for any partition we have

$$\Delta x_i > 0 \qquad \text{and} \qquad \sum_{i=1}^{n} \Delta x_i = b - a. \qquad (6)$$

We shall use the notation $[n,x_i,\xi_i]$ to designate a partition into n subintervals, together with a particular selection of n intermediate points.

16—DEFINITION OF THE DEFINITE INTEGRAL

Let f be a given function on the interval $[a,b]$ whose value at x is $f(x)$. Consider $[n,x_i,\xi_i]$, the partition of $[a,b]$ determined by points x_i, with a choice of intermediate points ξ_i satisfying Eqs. (4) and (5). Now form the sum

$$S = f(\xi_1) \, \Delta x_1 + f(\xi_2) \, \Delta x_2 + \cdots + f(\xi_n) \, \Delta x_n$$

$$= \sum_{i=1}^{n} f(\xi_i) \, \Delta x_i. \qquad (7)$$

The value of S depends on the number n, the choice of the x_i, and the choice of the ξ_i.

Let δ_M denote the maximum of the n positive quantities Δx_i,

$$\delta_M = \max (\Delta x_i). \qquad (8)$$

And consider any infinite sequence of sums labeled S_t with $t = 1$, 2, 3, . . . , for which

$$\lim_{t \to \infty} \delta_M = 0. \tag{9}$$

If, for any sequence of this type, the values of S_t approach a finite limit, and if this limit has the same value J for all such sequences, then J is called the *definite integral* of f for the interval $[a,b]$. We then say that the function f is *integrable* over this interval $[a,b]$, and we write

$$\int_a^b f = \int_a^b f(x)\ dx = J = \lim S_t. \tag{10}$$

The process by which J was obtained from f is called *integration*. In the first and second expressions for J, we call f or $f(x)$ the *integrand* and a and b the *limits* of the integral. In the second expression, x is the *variable of integration*. The use of the word limit as applied to a and b, the end points of the interval over which the integral is taken, is well established. This is related more to the popular use of "limit" to mean "boundary" than to other technical meanings of limit in mathematics, such as that of Sec. 11.

The first precise abstract presentation of integration was given by B. Riemann (1826–1866, German). The process described here is sometimes referred to as *Riemann integration,* to distinguish it from other types of integration such as the ones due to T. J. Stieltjes (1856–1894, Dutch) and to H. Lebesgue (1875–1941, French).

17—MATHEMATICAL INDUCTION

For certain specific sequences S_t, the limit may be obtained from an expression for S_t as found by a suitable summation formula. One method of proving such formulas is the use of mathematical induction, which we proceed to describe. The method is based on the following property of the natural numbers:

Principle of Mathematical Induction. Let S be a set of the natural numbers such that:
  (*a*) S contains 1.

(*b*) If S contains a natural number n, then it also contains the number $n + 1$.

Then S is the set of *all* natural numbers.

To prove that a statement is true for all positive integers n by means of this principle, it will be sufficient to do the following:

(*a*) Verify that the statement is true for $n = 1$.

(*b*) Assume that the statement is true for $n = 1, 2, \ldots , k - 1$, and on this basis prove that it is true for $n = k$.

EXAMPLE 1.   Prove that

$$1^2 + 2^2 + 3^2 + \cdots + n^2 = \frac{n(n + 1)(2n + 1)}{6}.$$

SOLUTION.   (*a*) For $n = 1$, the equation $1^2 = (1 \cdot 2 \cdot 3)/6$, or $1 = 1$, is true.

(*b*) For $n = k - 1$, the equation

$$1^2 + 2^2 + 3^2 + \cdots + (k - 1)^2 = \frac{(k - 1)k(2k - 1)}{6}$$

is assumed to be true.   Hence, adding k^2 to both sides, we find that

$$\sum_{i=1}^{k} i^2 = \left(\sum_{i=1}^{k-1} i^2 \right) + k^2 = \frac{(k - 1)k(2k - 1)}{6} + k^2$$

$$= \frac{k(k + 1)(2k + 1)}{6}.$$

EXAMPLE 2.   For what value of c is the statement $1 + 3 + 5 + \cdots + (2n + 1)^2 = n^2 + 2n + c$ true for all n?

SOLUTION.   To prove (*b*), we assume

$$\sum_{i=1}^{k-1} (2i + 1) = k^2 + c - 1.$$

Adding $(2k + 1)$ to both sides leads to

$$\sum_{i=1}^{k} (2i + 1) = k^2 + 2k + c,$$

which follows for any value of c. However, for (a) to hold, we must have $1 + 3 = 3 + c$. Thus the statement holds for all n if $c = 1$, and for no n if $c \neq 1$.

18—INTEGRALS OF CONTINUOUS FUNCTIONS

We shall now show that the procedure of Sec. 16 necessarily leads to a unique limit J for all sequences S_t with $\delta_M \to 0$ if the function f is continuous on $[a,b]$. The theorem follows:

A function f is integrable over any closed interval throughout which it is continuous.

Let f be continuous over the closed interval $[a,b]$. Then, by Sec. 13, it is uniformly continuous in the closed interval. Thus, for any given fixed positive quantity η, we may select a δ_0 such that

$$|f(x_2) - f(x_1)| \leq \epsilon \qquad \text{if } |x_2 - x_1| \leq \delta_0 \tag{11}$$

where

$$\epsilon = \frac{\eta}{b - a}. \tag{12}$$

Now consider two partitions and the corresponding sums,

$$S = \sum_{i=1}^{n} f(\xi_i)\,\Delta x_i \qquad \text{and} \qquad S' = \sum_{j=1}^{n} f(\xi_j')\,\Delta x_j', \tag{13}$$

such that

$$\delta_M = \max\,(\Delta x_i) \qquad \text{and} \qquad \delta_M' = \max\,(\Delta x_j') \tag{14}$$

are each less than $\delta_0/2$,

$$\delta_M < \frac{\delta_0}{2} \qquad \delta_M' < \frac{\delta_0}{2}. \tag{15}$$

Next mark *all* the points of subdivision of *each* set x_i and x_j' to form a new partition. Let these points, taken in order, with a point in both sets counted only once, be called x_k'', so that

$$a = x_0'' < x_1'' < x_2'' < \cdots < x_p'' = b. \tag{16}$$

And let

$$\Delta x_k = x_k'' - x_{k-1}'' \tag{17}$$

denote the length of the kth interval. Then, as in Eq. (6),

$$\Delta x_k > 0 \quad \text{and} \quad \sum_{k=1}^{p} \Delta x_k = b - a. \tag{18}$$

The difference of the two sums S and S' may be written

$$S - S' = \sum_{k=1}^{p} [f(\xi_i) - f(\xi_j')] \Delta x_k, \tag{19}$$

where ξ_i is in that interval of the first partition which includes the points x_{k-1}'' and x_k'', and ξ_j' is in that interval of the second partition which includes the points x_k'' and x_{k-1}''. Thus ξ_i and ξ_j' lie in overlapping intervals of the first two partitions, since they each contain the kth interval $[x_{k-1}'', x_k'']$ of the third subdivision. From this and Eq. (14) we have

$$|\xi_i - \xi_j'| < \delta_i + \delta_j' \leq \delta_M + \delta_M'. \tag{20}$$

In view of Eq. (15), we have

$$|\xi_i - \xi_j'| < \delta_0. \tag{21}$$

This, combined with Eq. (11), shows that

$$|f(\xi_i) - f(\xi_j')| \leq \epsilon. \tag{22}$$

Since this is true for each term of the sum in Eq. (19), we may deduce from this and the first part of Eq. (18) that

$$|S - S'| \leq \sum_{k=1}^{p} |f(\xi_i) - f(\xi_j')| \Delta x_k \leq \sum_{k=1}^{p} \epsilon \Delta x_k. \tag{23}$$

Hence it follows from the second part of Eq. (18) and from Eq. (12) that

$$|S - S'| \leq \epsilon(b - a) \leq \eta. \tag{24}$$

Let us now apply this to a sequence S_t. For such a sequence Eq. (9) holds. Hence there is a positive integer t_0 such that $\delta_M < \delta_0/2$ for $t > t_0$. Hence the difference of any two values of S_t with

$t > t_0$ will be numerically at most η, since we may take these two sums S_t as the S and S' of Eq. (24).

Thus the sequence S_t approaches a finite limit J_1 by the Cauchy convergence criterion of Sec. 14.

Next, consider any second sequence S_t'. This approaches a finite limit J_2 by the argument just given. Thus

$$\lim (S_t - S_t') = J_1 - J_2. \tag{25}$$

For the second sequence, let $\delta_M' < \delta_0/2$ for $t > t_0'$. Then, for $t > \max (t_0, t_0')$, we may take S_t and S_t' as the S and S' of Eq. (24). Thus

$$|S_t - S_t'| \leq \eta \qquad \text{for } t > \max (t_0, t_0'). \tag{26}$$

Equations (25) and (26) show that

$$|J_1 - J_2| \leq \eta, \tag{27}$$

and hence, since η is *any* positive number,

$$J_1 - J_2 = 0. \tag{28}$$

Thus the limit J_2 is the same as J_1, and there is a common limit J for all sequences. ■

Let us return to Eq. (24), with S any finite sum for which $\delta_M < \delta_0/2$ and with S' replaced by any value of S_t, with $t > t_0$. Then we have

$$|S - S_t| \leq \eta \qquad \text{for } t > t_0. \tag{29}$$

If we let $t \to \infty$, or increase indefinitely, in this relation, and recall that the limit of S_t is J_1, or J, we have

$$|S - J| \leq \eta. \tag{30}$$

Thus, for a *continuous function*, with δ_0 determined by Eqs. (11) and (12), and $\delta_M = \max (\Delta x_i) < \delta_0/2$ as in Eqs. (14) and (15), *any sum in Eq. (7) approximates the value of the integral to within η.*

The argument of this section has not only shown the existence of the definite integral of any continuous function over a closed interval, but also has provided a (theoretical) method of calculating a numerical approximation to its value.

19—LINEAR PROPERTIES OF THE INTEGRAL

The definition of integration on $[a,b]$ was made on the assumption that $b > a$. Thus the symbol $\int_a^b f$ has so far been defined only if $b > a$.

Assuming that f is integrable over the intervals used, we may extend the meaning of the symbol $\int_a^b f$ by *defining*

$$\int_a^b f = -\int_b^a f \quad \text{if } a > b \quad \text{and} \quad \int_a^a f = 0. \tag{31}$$

These definitions make

$$\int_a^b f = -\int_b^a f \tag{32}$$

true for all values of a and b.

If the values a, b, c are such that $a < b < c$, it follows from the original definition of the integral in Sec. 16 that

$$\int_a^b f + \int_b^c f = \int_a^c f, \tag{33}$$

since we may evaluate the integral on the right by using a sequence of sums, for each of which the point b is one of the x_i.

If $a = b$ or $b = c$, Eq. (33) is an identity in view of the second part of Eq. (31). And by Eq. (32), Eq. (33) may be written

$$\int_a^b f + \int_b^c f + \int_c^a f = 0. \tag{34}$$

This is symmetrical in a, b, c and so holds without any restriction on the order of the three quantities.

The definitions in Eq. (31) are motivated by the desire to have Eq. (34) hold for all values of a, b, c.

By a repeated application of Eq. (33), we may show that the integral of a function depends linearly on the interval of integration in the sense that if a finite number of intervals are added or subtracted to form a new set of intervals, the integrals combine in the same way.

For a fixed interval of integration, the integral depends linearly on the function, in the sense that, if k is a constant and f and g are two functions, each integrable for the interval, then

$$\int_a^b kf = k \int_a^b f \tag{35}$$

and

$$\int_a^b (f + g) = \int_a^b f + \int_a^b g. \tag{36}$$

These relations follow from the linear character of the sum in Eq. (7) from which the integral was obtained by a limiting process, and the definitions in Eq. (31).

Each of the results of this section may be written in an alternative form by defining

$$\int_a^b f(x) \, dx = \int_a^b f \tag{37}$$

for all values of a and b. For example, Eq. (32) becomes

$$\int_a^b f(x) \, dx = - \int_b^a f(x) \, dx. \tag{38}$$

20—MEAN-VALUE THEOREM

Let f be continuous over the closed interval $[a,b]$. Then, by the extreme-value property of Sec. 13, there are values $m = f(u)$ and $M = f(v)$, with u,v in $[a,b]$, such that $m \leq f(x) \leq M$ for each x on $[a,b]$. In particular, this is true of the values ξ_i used in Eq. (7), so that

$$m \leq f(\xi_i) \leq M \qquad \text{and} \qquad m \, \Delta x_i \leq f(\xi_i) \, \Delta x_i \leq M \, \Delta x_i. \tag{39}$$

It follows that

$$m \sum_{i=1}^n \Delta x_i \leq \sum_{i=1}^n f(\xi_i) \, \Delta x_i \leq M \sum_{i=1}^n \Delta x_i. \tag{40}$$

In view of Eq. (6), second part, and Eq. (7), this may be written

$$m(b - a) \leq S \leq M(b - a). \tag{41}$$

Taking the limit for any sequence shows that

$$m(b - a) \leq \int_a^b f(x) \, dx \leq M(b - a). \tag{42}$$

The number K defined by

$$K = \frac{1}{b-a} \int_a^b f(x)\, dx \quad \text{or} \quad \int_a^b f(x)\, dx = (b-a)K \qquad (43)$$

is called the *average*, or *mean*, value of the function $f(x)$ for the interval a,b. It follows from Eqs. (42) and (43) that

$$m \leq K \leq M. \qquad (44)$$

Hence, by the intermediate-value property of continuous functions stated in Sec. 13, there is at least one number x^* between a and b such that $K = f(x^*)$. Thus Eq. (43) can be written as

$$\int_a^b f(x)\, dx = (b-a)f(x^*). \qquad (45)$$

This result still holds for $a = b$, or $a > b$, by Eq. (31).

We have thus proved the *mean-value theorem for integrals:*

Let a and b be any two numbers. And let the function f be continuous on [a,b] (or [b,a] if a > b). Then there is at least one number x* on this closed interval for which Eq. (45) holds.

21—DUMMY INDICES AND VARIABLES

In a finite summation, abbreviated by the symbol Σ with an index of summation i, the precise letter used for the index of summation is of no importance, since it does not appear in the sum when this is written out in full. Thus

$$\sum_{i=1}^{3} a_i = \sum_{j=1}^{3} a_j = \sum_{k=1}^{3} a_k, \qquad (46)$$

since each is an abbreviation for $a_1 + a_2 + a_3$. We call such an index a *dummy index*. We may always replace a dummy index by some other letter, and to do so sometimes clarifies an argument and avoids confusion. This was the case in Sec. 18, where we replaced i by j in the sum S'.

In the sum for S in Eq. (7), we may in particular take $\xi_i = x_i$, in which case the sum is

$$S = \sum_{i=1}^{n} f(x_i) \, \Delta x_i. \tag{47}$$

This is the form which gave rise to the notation for an integral $\int_a^b f(x) \, dx$, the sign of integration being a modified S, and the replacement of the Greek letters Σ and Δ by the Latin letters S and d, indicating that we have performed a limiting process. This is analogous to replacing Δ by d to indicate that dy/dx is obtained from $\Delta y/\Delta x$ by a limiting process, as Leibniz did when using dy/dx as a symbol for $D_x y$.

When $a < b$, the limits a and b of an integral are analogous to the initial and final values of the index of summation. As we have replaced x_i by x, the index of summation no longer appears, but the letter x itself plays an analogous role. In fact, if we had taken the values of the function f as $f(u)$ instead of $f(x)$, using a value of u such that $a < u < b$, we could carry out the entire process of Sec. 16, regarding the x_i as intermediate values of u. Thus we should find the same values for the sums S and S_t and the limiting value J. This fact is emphasized by the abbreviated notation $\int_a^b f$.

Thus the variable of integration is a *dummy variable* and it may be replaced by any other letter. Then we have

$$\int_a^b f = \int_a^b f(x) \, dx = \int_a^b f(u) \, du = \int_a^b f(y) \, dy. \tag{48}$$

The value of the integral depends on the choice of the interval of integration, that is, on the values a and b.

When $a = b$ or $a > b$, Eq. (48) still holds since the definitions and developments of Sec. 19 were carried out without explicit reference to the dummy variable x. But in all cases the value of the definite integral depends on the choice of the limits a and b. Hence, for a fixed function f, the value of the integral depends only on the limits.

In particular, we may keep the limit a fixed and replace the limit b by an independent variable x. This defines a function of x, G, whose value at x is

$$G(x) = \int_a^x f = \int_a^x f(x) \, dx = \int_a^x f(u) \, du. \tag{49}$$

In one of these integrals, x is used in two senses, both as a variable limit and as the dummy variable of integration. When we replace the dummy variable x by u, we do not affect the x used as a variable limit.

22—DERIVATIVES OF INTEGRALS

Let us attempt to find the derivative of the function G of Eq. (49). With $\Delta x = h$, we have

$$G(x + h) - G(x) = \int_a^{x+h} f - \int_a^x f$$
$$= \int_a^{x+h} f + \int_x^a f = \int_x^{x+h} f, \tag{50}$$

by Eqs. (32) and (33).

We next assume that f is continuous on $[a,b]$ and that $a < x < b$. Then we may apply the mean-value theorem, Eq. (45), to deduce that

$$\int_x^{x+h} f = \int_x^{x+h} f(u)\, du = h\, f(u^*), \tag{51}$$

for some value u^* between x and $x + h$. That is,

$$\begin{array}{ll} x \leq u^* \leq x + h & \text{if } h > 0, \\ x + h \leq u^* \leq x & \text{if } h < 0. \end{array} \tag{52}$$

It follows from Eqs. (50) and (51) that

$$\frac{\Delta G}{\Delta x} = \frac{G(x + h) - G(x)}{h} = f(u^*). \tag{53}$$

Now let $h = \Delta x \to 0$. Then, by Eq. (52), $u^* \to x$. And $f(u^*) \to f(x)$, since f is continuous at x. This proves that

$$G'(x) = f(x) \qquad \text{or} \qquad D_x \int_a^x f(u)\, du = f(x) \tag{54}$$

for x on (a,b).

This argument also proves that G has a right-hand derivative equal to $f(a)$ at a and a left-hand derivative equal to $f(b)$ at b. Hence G is continuous on the closed interval $[a,b]$. These restricted derivatives at a and b are the only type which can be taken using values of G on $[a,b]$. Let us use $G'(a)$ and $G'(b)$ to denote these one-sided derivatives. Then

$G' = f$ on $[a,b]$, or for $a \leq x \leq b$.

We call any function F an *antiderivative* of f if $F' = f$. More precisely, F is an antiderivative of f on (a,b) if $F' = f$ for all x on (a,b). If in addition F has a right-hand derivative $f(a)$ at a and a left-hand derivative $f(b)$ at b, we call F an antiderivative of f on $[a,b]$.

Thus we have just proved that G is an antiderivative of f on $[a,b]$. For any constant c, $F = G + c$ is also an antiderivative of f. But the possibility of constructing G shows that antiderivatives always exist for any continuous function f.

We may formulate this result as a theorem:

If the function f is continuous on the closed interval $[a,b]$, then there exists an antiderivative of this function on $[a,b]$.

23—FUNDAMENTAL THEOREM OF THE INTEGRAL CALCULUS

This theorem enables us to evaluate the indefinite integral of a continuous function f whenever we can find an antiderivative of f, or function F such that $F' = f$. We may formulate the theorem as follows:

Let the function f be continuous on the closed interval $[a,b]$. And let F be any antiderivative of f, so that, on $[a,b]$, $F' = f$. Then

$$\int_a^b f(x) \; dx = F(b) - F(a). \tag{55}$$

PROOF. If $G(x)$ is defined by Eq. (49), then $G' = f$ on $[a,b]$ by the remarks following Eq. (54). Let F be any antiderivative of f on $[a,b]$. Then $F' = f$ on $[a,b]$. Hence $(G - F)' = f - f = 0$. Since the derivative of $G - F$ is zero, this function must be a constant C (in Sec. 61 we shall give a proof of this intuitively obvious fact); that is, we have $G(x) - F(x) = C$, or $G(x) = F(x) + C$ on the *open* interval (a,b). But since F

and G are each continuous at the end points a and b, this relation must also hold for these values, so that

$$G(a) = F(a) + C \qquad G(b) = F(b) + C. \tag{56}$$

But, by Eq. (49), we have

$$G(a) = \int_a^a f = 0 \qquad G(b) = \int_a^b f = \int_a^b f(x) \, dx. \tag{57}$$

It follows from Eqs. (56) and (57) that $C = -F(a)$ and that

$$\int_a^b f(x) \, dx = G(b) = F(b) - F(a). \tag{58}$$

This is Eq. (55). ∎

In applying this theorem, it is sometimes convenient to write $[F(x)]_a^b$ or $F(x)|_a^b$ as an abbreviation for $F(b) - F(a)$.

It follows from Probs. 21 and 35 that if $f(x) = x^r$, then for r any positive integer, and also for $r = -\frac{1}{2}, -\frac{3}{2}, -2$, $F(x) = \dfrac{x^{r+1}}{r+1}$ defines an F which is an antiderivative of f. Later we shall show that this holds for any r except $r = -1$. For this value see Prob. 38.

24—SUMS AND INTEGRALS

It follows from Secs. 16 and 23 that

$$\lim_{\delta_M \to 0} \sum_{i=1}^{n} f(\xi_i) \, \Delta x_i = \int_a^b f(x) \, dx$$
$$= F(b) - F(a) \tag{59}$$

As we shall illustrate in the example below, this may sometimes be used to evaluate certain limits of sums.

Its real importance, however, lies in the possibility of defining many geometric and physical concepts in terms of integrals by setting up limits of appropriate sums. This will be illustrated for area in Sec. 26.

In some applications we are led to sums with a product $f_1(\xi_i')f_2(\xi_i'')$, or more generally with an expression $f_3(\xi_i', \xi_i'')$ in place of $f(\xi_i)$. Here ξ_i' and ξ_i'' may be different intermediate points between x_{i-1} and x_i. For any case in which the function f_3 is a continuous function of both variables, it may be deduced from the uniform continuity in a closed two-dimensional region that

$$\lim_{\delta_M \to 0} \sum_{i=1}^{n} f_3(\xi_i', \xi_i'') \, \Delta x_i = \int_a^b f_3(x,x) \, dx. \qquad (60)$$

We shall refer to this extension, which holds for any number of variables, as the Duhamel-Bliss theorem, after J. M. C. Duhamel (1797–1872, French) and G. A. Bliss (1876–1951, American).

EXAMPLE.   Find $\lim\limits_{n \to \infty} T_n$, where

$$T_n = \frac{1}{n^{3/2}} (\sqrt{1} + \sqrt{2} + \sqrt{3} + \cdots + \sqrt{n}).$$

SOLUTION.   The expression can be written as

$$T_n = \sum_{i=1}^{n} \left(\frac{i}{n}\right)^{1/2} \frac{1}{n}.$$

With $f(x) = x^{1/2}$, $\Delta x_i = 1/n$, $x_i = i/n$, we have $x_0 = a = 0$, $x_n = b = 1$, and the sum is $\sum\limits_{i=1}^{n} f(x_i) \, \Delta x_i$. As $n \to \infty$, $1/n \to 0$.
Hence the limit of T_n is

$$\int_0^1 x^{1/2} \, dx = \left[\frac{x^{3/2}}{\frac{3}{2}}\right]_0^1 = \tfrac{2}{3}(1 - 0) = \tfrac{2}{3}.$$

25—IMPROPER INTEGRALS

Let the function f be discontinuous at b. But suppose that it would become continuous on $[a,b]$ if we used a value of $f(b-) = \lim\limits_{x \to b-} f(x)$

at b and would become continuous on $[b,c]$ if we used a suitable value $f(b+) = \lim\limits_{x \to b+} f(x)$ at b. Then we may use Eq. (33) as the definition

of the integral from a to c. We might proceed similarly for any finite number of abutting intervals.

For a semi-infinite integral, we define

$$\int_a^\infty f(x) \, dx = \lim_{b \to \infty} \int_a^b f(x) \, dx, \qquad (61)$$

if the limit exists. We proceed similarly for a limit $-\infty$.

Next suppose that f is continuous at a and in (a,b), but that $f(x) \to \infty$ as $x \to b$ or fails to approach a finite limit equal to $f(b)$ as $x \to b-$. Then we define

$$\int_a^b f(x)\, dx = \lim_{x \to b-} \int_a^x f(x)\, dx, \tag{62}$$

if the limit exists. We proceed similarly if f is continuous at b and in (a,b) but $f(x) \to \infty$ as $x \to a+$ or $f(x)$ is discontinuous in some other way at $x = a$.

The integrals in Eqs. (61) and (62) are called *improper* integrals. We use Eq. (33), and its extension to several intervals, to define the integral from a to c whenever the integrals over the subintervals are defined as proper or as improper integrals.

EXAMPLE 1.   Evaluate $\int_1^\infty (dx/x^2)$.

SOLUTION.   We have

$$\int_1^\infty \frac{dx}{x^2} = \lim_{b \to \infty} \int_1^b x^{-2}\, dx = \lim \left[\frac{x^{-1}}{-1} \right]_1^b$$
$$= \lim \left(-\frac{1}{b} + 1 \right) = 1.$$

EXAMPLE 2.   Evaluate $\int_0^1 (dx/\sqrt{x})$.

SOLUTION.   We have

$$\int_0^1 \frac{dx}{\sqrt{x}} = \lim_{a \to 0+} \int_a^1 x^{-1/2}\, dx = \lim \left[\frac{x^{1/2}}{\frac{1}{2}} \right]_a^1$$
$$= \lim (2 - 2\sqrt{a}) = 2.$$

26—GENERAL DEFINITION OF AREA IN THE PLANE

Let S be a portion of the plane bounded by curved arcs, some of which may be segments of straight lines. Let E be the area of any exterior polygon containing S in its interior, and I be the area of any interior polygon contained in S. Since each polygon E or I

may be decomposed into triangles, its area may be found by elementary geometry.

Suppose that there exists a sequence of exterior areas E_n and a sequence of interior areas I_n such that, as $n \to \infty$,

$$\lim E_n = A \qquad \text{and} \qquad \lim I_n = A. \tag{63}$$

Then the common limit A is called the *area* of S.

The value of A is independent of the choice of the exterior and interior figures. These may be any figures, polygonal or not, whose areas are known, as we shall now show.

Let E'_m and I'_m be a second set of exterior and interior areas for S, with a common limit as $m \to \infty$,

$$\lim E'_m = A' \qquad \text{and} \qquad \lim I'_m = A'. \tag{64}$$

First suppose that $A' \neq A$ and choose the notation so that $A > A'$ and hence $A - A' = p > 0$.

For straight-line figures—and therefore, by our extended definition for other figures—it is true that if S_2 contains S_1, then $A_2 \geq A_1$. This implies that

$$E_n \geq A \qquad I'_m \leq A' \qquad E'_m \geq I_n. \tag{65}$$

Hence $E_n - I'_m \geq A - A' = p$, $E'_m - I_n \geq 0$, so that

$$(E_n - I_n) + (E'_m - I'_m) = (E_n - I'_m) + (E'_m - I_n) \geq p. \tag{66}$$

This leads to a contradiction, since

$$\lim (E_n - I_n) = 0 \qquad \lim (E'_m - I'_m) = 0 \qquad \text{but } p > 0. \tag{67}$$

Since $A' \neq A$ is impossible, we must have $A' = A$.

27—THE AREA UNDER A CURVE

Consider the part of the plane $S = abBA$ (Fig. 9) bounded by portions of the lines Ox (ab), $x = a$ (aA), $x = b$ (bB), and a curved arc AB which is the graph of a continuous function f, with $f(x) \geq 0$. As in Sec. 15, select $n - 1$ values x_i, which satisfy Eq. (4), and draw the ordinates which form part of the lines $x = x_i$. Also, on each interval $[x_{i-1}, x_i]$ of length Δx_i as a base, construct two rec-

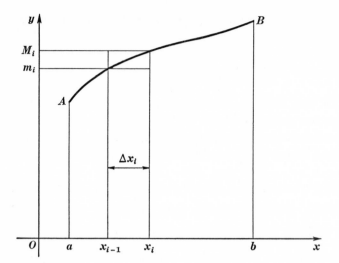

FIGURE 9

tangles whose heights are $m_i = f(u_i)$ and $M_i = f(v_i)$, respectively the length of the least ordinate of the curve and the length of the greatest ordinate of the curve in the interval $[x_{i-1}, x_i]$.

Then (Fig. 10) the rectangles with ordinates m_i constitute a rectilinear figure I which is contained in S and whose area is

$$I = \sum_{i=1}^{n} m_i \, \Delta x_i = \sum_{i=1}^{n} f(u_i) \, \Delta x_i. \tag{68}$$

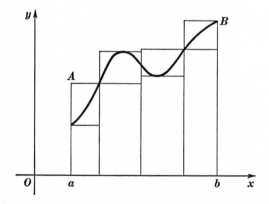

FIGURE 10

And the rectangles with ordinates M_i constitute a rectilinear figure E which contains S and whose area is

$$E = \sum_{i=1}^{n} M_i \, \Delta x_i = \sum_{i=1}^{n} J(v_i) \, \Delta x_i. \qquad (69)$$

The u_i and v_i may each be considered a special choice of the ξ_i in Eq. (7), and f is continuous. For any two sequences E_t and I_t with $\delta_M = \max (\Delta x_i)$ tending to zero as in Eqs. (8) and (9), it follows from Sec. 18 that

$$\lim E_t = \lim I_t = \int_a^b f = \int_a^b f(x) \, dx. \qquad (70)$$

By the definition of area in Sec. 26, this shows that $A_a{}^b$, the area under a curve which is the graph of $y = f(x)$ from a to b, is given by

$$A_a{}^b = \int_a^b f(x) \, dx. \qquad (71)$$

We note (Fig. 11) that any portion of the plane with sufficiently simple boundary of the type discussed in Sec. 26 could be decomposed into a rectilinear figure and additional figures each of the type considered in this section. The conclusion drawn in Sec. 16 from Eq. (67) shows that all such decompositions, with the parts referred to any coordinate axes, must give the same measure for the area.

EXAMPLE 1.   Find the area bounded by Ox and the curve which is the graph of $y = 4 - x^2$.

SOLUTION.   The curve crosses the x axis, where $y = 0$, at points for which $4 - x^2 = 0$; that is, at $x = -2$ and 2. And $4 -$

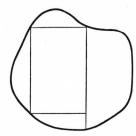

FIGURE 11

$x^2 = -(x + 2)(x - 2)$ is positive on $(-2,2)$. Hence the area is

$$A_{-2^2} = \int_{-2}^{2} (4 - x^2)\, dx$$

$$= \left[4x - \frac{x^3}{3}\right]_{-2}^{2} = (8 - \tfrac{8}{3}) - (-8 + \tfrac{8}{3}) = \tfrac{32}{3} = 10\tfrac{2}{3}.$$

EXAMPLE 2.   Find $\lim\limits_{n \to \infty} T_n$, where

$$T_n = \frac{1}{n}\left(\frac{1}{\sqrt{1}} + \frac{1}{\sqrt{2}} + \frac{1}{\sqrt{3}} + \cdots + \frac{1}{\sqrt{n}}\right).$$

SOLUTION.   The expression T_n can be written as

$$T_n = \sum_{i=1}^{n} \left(\frac{i}{n}\right)^{-1/2} \frac{1}{n}.$$

With $f(x) = x^{-1/2}$, $\Delta x_i = 1/n$, $x_i = i/n$, the sum is $\sum\limits_{i=1}^{n} f(x_i)\, \Delta x_i$. As the x_i here are the u_i, the sum cannot exceed the area whose measure is the *improper* integral $\int_0^1 (dx/\sqrt{x})$. But it may be made arbitrarily close to this integral, so that the required limit of T_n is

$$\lim_{a \to 0} \int_a^1 x^{-1/2}\, dx = \lim \left[\frac{x^{1/2}}{\frac{1}{2}}\right]_a^1 = \lim 2(1 - \sqrt{a}) = 2.$$

28—THE TRAPEZOIDAL RULE

Suppose that f is an increasing function of x in the interval $[a,b]$. That is, if $a \le x_1 < x_2 \le b$, then $f(x_1) < f(x_2)$. Then, for the subinterval $[x_{i-1}, x_i]$ of Sec. 27, we shall have $u_i = x_{i-1}$ and $v_i = x_i$. Then the sum $\Sigma f(x_i)(x_i - x_{i-1})$ exceeds the integral, while the sum $\Sigma f(x_{i-1})(x_i - x_{i-1})$ is less than the integral.

Let us take each of the n subintervals equal in length, so that for any i,

$$x_i - x_{i-1} = \frac{b - a}{n} = h. \tag{72}$$

Let $y_i = f(x_i)$, so that $y_0 = f(a)$ and $y_n = f(b)$.   Then

$$h \sum_{i=1}^{n} y_{i-1} < \int_a^b f(x) \, dx < h \sum_{i=1}^{n} y_i. \tag{73}$$

For a sufficiently large n, or small h, each of the extreme terms will be a good approximation to the integral.   But Eq. (73) suggests that for a moderate value of n, the average of these extremes will be better than either.   This gives

$$T = \frac{h}{2} \sum_{i=1}^{n} (y_{i-1} + y_i)$$

$$= \frac{h}{2} (y_0 + 2y_1 + 2y_2 + \cdots + 2y_{n-1} + y_n), \tag{74}$$

with $h = (b - a)/n$, as the *trapezoidal* approximation to $\int_a^b f(x) \, dx$.

For the area S_i bounded by $y = 0$ and $y = f(x)$ which lies between $x = x_{i-1}$ and $x = x_i$, the terms hy_{i-1} and hy_i are the areas of rectangles approximating S_i from below and from above, while $(h/2)(y_{i-1} + y_i)$ is the area of a trapezoid one of whose sides is a chord of the curve which is the graph of $y = f(x)$.

29—SIMPSON'S RULE

In place of using a straight line, or locus of $y = bx + c$, through two points, we may use a parabola, or locus of $y = ax^2 + bx + c$ through three points.   Let the three points be $(-h, y_0)$, $(0, y_1)$, (h, y_2).   Then the area under the parabola between $x = -h$ and $x = h$ is

$$A_1 = \int_{-h}^{h} (ax^2 + bx + c) \, dx = \left[\frac{ax^3}{3} + \frac{bx^2}{2} + cx \right]_{-h}^{h}$$

$$= \frac{h}{3} (2ah^2 + 6c). \tag{75}$$

But $y_0 = ah^2 - bh + c$, $y_1 = c$, $y_2 = ah^2 + bh + c$, so that $y_0 + y_2 = 2ah^2 + 2c$, and $y_0 + 4y_1 + y_2 = 2ah^2 + 6c$.   Hence

$$A_1 = \frac{h}{3} (y_0 + 4y_1 + y_2). \tag{76}$$

Now let the n in Eq. (72) be *even*. Then, for any curve which is the graph of $y = f(x)$, so that $y_i = f(x_i)$, we may use a series of parabolas. The first, with ordinates y_0, y_1, y_2, has area A_1 as in Eq. (76). A second, with ordinates y_2, y_3, y_4, has area A_2. And so on, ending with a parabola with ordinates y_{n-2}, y_{n-1}, y_n, which has area $A_{n/2}$. By analogy with Eq. (76), we have

$$A_2 = \frac{h}{3}(y_2 + 4y_3 + y_4), \ldots, A_{n/2} = \frac{h}{3}(y_{n-2} + 4y_{n-1} + y_n).$$
(77)

Summing the areas of these parabolas gives

$$S = \frac{h}{3}(y_0 + 4y_1 + 2y_2 + 4y_3 + 2y_4 + \cdots + 4y_{n-1} + y_n), \quad (78)$$

where n is *even* and $h = (b - a)/n$. This is *Simpson's parabolic approximation* to $\int_a^b f(x) \, dx$ (T. Simpson, 1710–1761, English).

EXAMPLE. Using six intervals, find an upper limit, a lower limit, and the trapezoidal and Simpson's rule approximation to $\int_1^2 (dx/x)$.

SOLUTION. Here $n = 6$, $h = (2 - 1)/6 = \frac{1}{6}$. We tabulate

i	0	1	2	3	4	5	6
x_i	1	1.1667	1.3333	1.5	1.6667	1.8333	2.
y_i	1	0.8571	0.75	0.6667	0.6	0.5455	0.5

From these we may calculate $y_0 + y_6 = 1.5$, $A = y_1 + y_3 + y_5 = 2.0693$, $B = y_2 + y_4 = 1.35$. Then the extreme sums in Eq. (73) have the values $h(y_0 + \cdots + y_5) = (1 + A + B)/6 = 0.737$, an upper limit, and $h(y_1 + \cdots + y_6) = (A + B + 0.5)/6 = 0.653$, a lower limit. The inequalities in Eq. (73) are reversed here, since the integrand *decreases* as x increases.

The trapezoidal rule gives $T = (h/2)(y_0 + 2y_1 + \cdots + 2y_5 + y_6) = (1.5 + 2A + 2B)/12 = 0.695$.

Simpson's rule gives $S = (h/3)(y_0 + 4y_1 + 2y_2 + \cdots + y_6) = (1.5 + 4A + 2B)/18 = 0.6932$.

By Prob. 38, below, the value of the integral is $\ln 2 = 0.69315$ to five decimal places.

PROBLEMS

Section 13

1. Let f be defined by $f(x) = 2x + 1$. Verify that if $a < b$, then on $[a,b]$ we have $M = 2b + 1$, $m = 2a + 1$, the oscillation $M - m = 2(b - a)$. Also show that we may take $\epsilon/2$ as the $\delta(\epsilon)$ of uniform continuity.

2. Let f be defined by $f(x) = x^2$. Noting that $f(x_1 + h) - f(x_1) = h(2x_1 + h)$, deduce that in $[0,2]$ we may take $\epsilon/6$ as the $\delta(\epsilon)$ of uniform continuity.

Section 14

3. By the definition of a sequence approaching a limit, if $\lim\limits_{t \to \infty} a_t = L$, for any ϵ there exists a $T(\epsilon)$ such that $|a_t - L| \leq \epsilon$ if $t > T(\epsilon)$. Deduce that if $t_1 > T(\epsilon)$, $t_2 > T(\epsilon)$, then $|a_{t_1} - a_{t_2}| \leq 2\epsilon$, so that Eq. (3) holds with $t_\eta = T(\eta/2)$. This proves that the criterion of Cauchy is a *necessary* condition.

Section 16

4. Let f be the constant function defined by $f(x) = k$. Verify that in this case any sum from Eq. (7) equals $k(b - a)$. This proves that $\int_a^b k\, dx = k(b - a)$.

5. Let f be defined by $f(x) = 2x$. For any partition of $[a,b]$ into n subintervals by points x_i, let $\xi_i = (x_{i-1} + x_i)/2$. Verify that this makes $f(\xi_i)\, \Delta x_i = x_i^2 - x_{i-1}^2$, so that $S = b^2 - a^2$. Hence, for any sequence of this type, with $\delta_M \to 0$, $S \to b^2 - a^2$.

Section 17

Use mathematical induction to prove the validity of each of the following equations:

6. $1 + 2 + 3 + \cdots + n = \dfrac{n(n+1)}{2}$.

7. $1^3 + 2^3 + 3^3 + \cdots + n^3 = \dfrac{n^2(n+1)^2}{4}$.

8. $1 + 3 + 6 + \cdots + \dfrac{n(n+1)}{2!} = \dfrac{n(n+1)(n+2)}{3!}$.

9. $\sin 2A + \sin 4A + \sin 6A + \cdots + \sin 2nA$
$= \dfrac{\cos A - \cos (2n+1)A}{2 \sin A}$.

10. $\cos 2A + \cos 4A + \cos 6A + \cdots + \cos 2nA$
$= \dfrac{\sin (2n+1)A - \sin A}{2 \sin A}$.

11. $\displaystyle\sum_{i=1}^{n} i^r = \dfrac{n^{r+1}}{r+1} + P_r(n),$

where $P_r(n)$ is a polynomial in n of the rth degree. *Hint:* Use mathematical induction on r. For $r = 1$ the result follows from Prob. 6. Define $s_r = \displaystyle\sum_{i=1}^{n} i^r$, and note that

$$n^{r+1} = \sum_{i=1}^{n} i^{r+1} - (i-1)^{r+1} = (r+1)s_r - A_2 s_{r-1} + \cdots,$$

so that

$$s_r = \frac{n^{r+1}}{r+1} + \frac{A_2}{r+1} s_{r-1} - \cdots.$$

This relation may be used to derive, successively, formulas like those of Example 1 and Prob. 7.

Section 18

12. From Prob. 5, deduce that $\displaystyle\int_a^b 2x \, dx = b^2 - a^2$.

13. Let r be a positive integer, and let $b > 0$. Form sums for x^r for the interval $[0,b]$, with $\xi_i = x_i = ib/n$. Thus, from Prob. 11,

$$S = \sum \frac{b}{n}\left(i\frac{b}{n}\right)^r = \frac{b^{r+1}}{n^{r+1}} s_r = \frac{b^{r+1}}{r+1}\left(1 + \frac{B_2}{n} + \cdots\right).$$

As $n \to \infty$, $S \to b^{r+1}/(r+1)$. Deduce that $\displaystyle\int_0^b x^r \, dr = b^{r+1}/(r+1)$.

14. Check Prob. 13 by taking $\xi_i = x_{i-1} = (i-1)b/n$. Here

$$S = \sum \frac{b}{n} \frac{(i-1)b^r}{n} = \frac{b^{r+1}}{r+1} \frac{(n-1)^{r+1} + B_2(n-1)^r + \cdots}{n^{r+1}}.$$

15. Form sums for $f(x) = 1/\sqrt{x}$ in the interval $[1,b]$ with $\xi_i = [\frac{1}{2}(\sqrt{x_i} + \sqrt{x_{i-1}})]^2$. Show that for any n, each sum equals $\Sigma 2(\sqrt{x_i} - \sqrt{x_{i-1}}) = 2(\sqrt{b} - 1)$. Thus $\int_1^b dx/\sqrt{x} = 2\sqrt{b} - 2$.

16. Form sums for $\sin x$ in the interval $[0,b]$ with $\xi_i = x_i = ib/n$. Deduce from Prob. 9 that

$$S = [\cos (b/2n) - \cos (2n+1)(b/2n)] \frac{b/2n}{\sin (b/2n)}.$$

Using the fact that

$$\lim_{x \to 0} \frac{\sin x}{x} = 1,$$

which is proved in Sec. 43, deduce that for this sequence $S \to 1 - \cos b$, so that $\int_0^b \sin x \, dx = 1 - \cos b$.

17. Form sums for $\cos x$ in the interval $[0,b]$ with $\xi_i = x_i = ib/n$. Deduce from Prob. 10 that

$$S = \left[\sin (2n+1) \frac{b}{2n} - \sin \frac{b}{2n} \right] \frac{b/2n}{\sin (b/2n)}.$$

By reasoning as in Prob. 16, deduce that for this sequence $S \to \sin b$ and $\int_0^b \cos x \, dx = \sin b$.

Section 19

18. We might have defined $\int_a^b f$ for $a > b$ by carrying out the procedure of Secs. 15 and 16 with the inequalities in Eqs. (4) to (6) reversed. To each sum S_1 for $\int_b^a f$ would correspond a sum S_2 for $\int_a^b f$, with the same subintervals and intermediate values but taken in reverse order. By comparing a typical term of S_1, $f(\xi)$ $(x'' - x')$, with the term of S_2, $f(\xi)$ $(x' - x'')$, deduce that $S_2 = -S_1$, and—by taking limits—that $\int_a^b f = -\int_b^a f$ as in Eq. (31).

19. Verify that with the definition of Prob. 18, the reasoning of Probs. 13, 16, and 17 applies when $b < 0$.

20. From Probs. 13 and 19 deduce that, for any positive integer r,

$$\int_a^b x^r \, dr = \frac{1}{r+1} \, (b^{r+1} - a^{r+1}).$$

21. From Prob. 20 deduce that for r a positive integer and k a constant,

$$\int_0^b k x^r \, dr = \frac{k}{r+1} \, b^{r+1}.$$

22. From Probs. 16 and 19 deduce that

$$\int_a^b \sin x \, dx = \cos a - \cos b.$$

23. From Probs. 17 and 19 deduce that

$$\int_a^b \cos x \, dx = \sin b - \sin a.$$

24. From Probs. 21 and 4 deduce that

$$\int_0^b (Ax^3 + Bx^2 + Cx + D) \, dx = \frac{A}{4} \, b^4 + \frac{B}{3} \, b^3 + \frac{C}{2} \, b^2 + Db.$$

Section 20

25. For the integral in Prob. 21,

$$\int_0^b k x^r \, dr = \frac{k}{r+1} \, b^{r+1},$$

deduce that, in Eqs. (43) and (45),

$$K = \frac{k}{r+1} \, b^r \quad \text{and} \quad x^* = b(r+1)^{-1/r}.$$

26. Let f be a function which is continuous for all x, with the property that $\int_0^3 f = 2$ and $\int_0^5 f = -2$. Show that $f(x_3) = -\frac{3}{2}$ for some x_3 in the interval $[0,5]$. *Hint:* First show that $f(x_1) = \frac{2}{3}$ for some x_1 on $[0,3]$ and that $f(x_2) = -2$ for some x_2 on $[3,5]$.

Section 21

27. Verify that

$$\int_0^x (Au^3 + Bu^2 + Cu + D)\, du = \frac{A}{4}\, x^4 + \frac{B}{3}\, x^3 + \frac{C}{2}\, x^2 + Dx,$$

using Prob. 24.

28. Verify that $\int_{\pi/2}^x \sin u\, du = -\cos x$, using Prob. 22.

29. Verify that $\int_0^x \cos u\, du = \sin x$, using Prob. 23.

Section 22

30. From the results of this section, deduce that $D_x(ax^4 + bx^3 + cx^2 + dx) = 4ax^3 + 3bx^2 + 2cx + d$, using Prob. 27 with a changed notation.

31. From Prob. 29, deduce that $D_x \sin x = \cos x$.

32. From Prob. 28, deduce that $D_x \cos x = -\sin x$.

Section 23

33. From Prob. 42 of Chap. 1, deduce that

$$\int_0^b (3Au^2 + 2Bu + C)\, du = Ab^3 + Bb^2 + Cb.$$

Check by using Prob. 24 with a change in notation.

34. From Prob. 41 of Chap. 1, deduce that

$$\int_0^b x^r\, dx = \frac{1}{r+1}\, b^{r+1} \qquad \text{for } r = 1, 2,$$

and check by using Prob. 21.

35. From Prob. 41 of Chap. 1, deduce that

$$\int_1^b x^{-r}\, dx = \frac{1}{1-r}\, (b^{1-r} - 1) \qquad \text{for } r = \tfrac{1}{2}, \tfrac{3}{2}, 2.$$

36. Two functions s and c satisfy the relations $\int_0^x s(x)\, dx = 1 - c(x)$ and $\int_0^x c(x)\, dx = s(x)$. Prove that $[s(x)]^2 + [c(x)]^2 = 1$. *Hint:* Show that $D_x\{[s(x)]^2 + [c(x)]^2\} = 0$, and use $s(0) = 0$, $c(0) = 1$. Note that

$$D_x[s(x)]^2 = \lim_{h \to 0} \frac{[s(x+h)]^2 - [s(x)]^2}{h}$$

$$= \lim_{h \to 0} \frac{s(x+h) - s(x)}{h} [s(x+h) + s(x)] = 2s(x) D_x[s(x)]$$

and similarly,

$$D_x[c(x)]^2 = 2c(x) D_x[c(x)].$$

37. Form sums with

$$\xi_i = x_i = 1 + \frac{i(x-1)}{n} \qquad \text{for } \int_1^x \frac{du}{u}$$

and with

$$\xi_i = x_i = y \left[1 + \frac{i(x-1)}{n} \right] \qquad \text{for } \int_y^{xy} \frac{du}{u} \, .$$

Show that in each case

$$S = \sum \frac{x-1}{n + i(x-1)} \, .$$

Deduce that, for $x > 0$ and $y > 0$, $\int_1^x (du/u) = \int_y^{xy} (du/u)$. See Prob. 18 for $x < 1$.

38. Let a function $\ln x$ be defined by $\ln x = \int_1^x (du/u)$ for $x > 0$.
Deduce that $\ln xy = \int_1^{xy} (du/u) = \int_1^y (du/u) + \int_y^{xy} (du/u) = \int_1^y (du/u) + \int_1^x (du/u)$ by Prob. 37, so that $\ln xy = \ln x + \ln y$.
It follows from this that $\ln x^n = n \ln x$, $\ln x^{1/m} = (1/m) \ln x$.
By taking rational sequences approaching any irrational number s, we have $\ln x^s = s \ln x$. Finally, by Prob. 49, there is a number e, approximately 2.718, such that $\ln e = 1$. Thus $\ln e^s = s$, and $\ln x$ is the logarithm of x to the base e. The value $\ln x = \log_e x$ is called the *natural logarithm* of x. From $\ln x = \int_1^x (du/u)$, it follows that $D_x \ln x = 1/x$.

Section 24

39. Find

$$\lim_{n \to \infty} \frac{1}{n^4} (1^3 + 2^3 + 3^3 + \cdots + n^3).$$

Ans.: $\int_0^1 x^3 \, dx = \frac{1}{4}$.

40. Find

$$\lim_{n \to \infty} \left(\frac{1}{n+1} + \frac{1}{n+2} + \frac{1}{n+3} + \cdots + \frac{1}{n+n} \right).$$

Hint: See Prob. 37 with $x = 2$ and Prob. 38.   Ans.: ln 2.

Section 27

In each problem, find the area bounded by the x axis, the graph of the given equation $y = f(x)$, and the two given vertical lines.

41. $y = 6x^2 + 1$, $x = 1$, $x = 3$.

42. $y = 4x$, $x = 2$, $x = 4$.

43. $y = 1/x^2$, $x = 1$, $x = 5$.

44. $y = 1/\sqrt{x}$, $x = 0$, $x = 2$.

45. $y = \sin x$, $x = 0$, $x = \pi$. *Hint:* See Prob. 32 or 22.

Sections 28 and 29

46. Using six intervals, find the trapezoidal and Simpson's rule approximation to $\int_0^\pi \sin x \, dx$, and compare with the exact value 2, found in Prob. 45.

47. Using four intervals, find the trapezoidal and Simpson's rule approximation to $\int_0^4 x^2 \, dx$. Note that Simpson's rule gives the exact value.

48. Using two intervals, find the Simpson's rule approximation to $\int_0^4 x^3 \, dx$. Note that it gives the exact value.

49. In the example of Sec. 29, we found that $0.65 < \int_1^2 (du/u) < 0.74$. By Prob. 38, the integral is ln 2. Thus $\ln 2 < 0.74 < 1$. And $\ln 4 = 2 \ln 2 > 1.3 > 1$. Since $\ln x$ is continuous, by the intermediate-value theorem there must be a number e, with $2 < e < 4$, for which $\ln e = 1$. Determine e more accurately by assuming that the value $\ln 2 = 0.6932$ is correct to four places. *Hint:* If $0.6932 = \log_e 2$, then $e^{0.6932} = 2$, $0.6932 \log_{10} e = \log_{10} 2$, and $\log_{10} e = 0.3010/0.6932 = 0.4342$ and $e = 2.718$.

3

DIFFERENTIATION OF ALGEBRAIC FUNCTIONS AND LOGARITHMS

The use of derivatives in applications is facilitated by a few special rules or formulas. These enable one to write down the derivatives of many functions of simple form by inspection, instead of having to evaluate laboriously the limit which defines the derivative in each instance. In this chapter we shall prove enough theorems or rules for differentiation to determine the derivative of any of the functions encountered in elementary algebra. In most of our work, we represent the independent variable by x, and we write D for D_x.

30—FORMULAS FOR DIFFERENTIATION

We first state six rules which enable us to differentiate any polynomial function:

1. The derivative of a constant function is the zero function:

If $f(x) = c$, then $f'(x) = 0$ $Dc = 0$.

2. The derivative of the identity function is the unit function:

If $f(x) = x$, then $f'(x) = 1$ $Dx = 1$.

3. The derivative of a constant times a function is the constant times the derivative of the function:

$(cf)' = cf'$ $D[c\,f(x)] = c\,D\,f(x)$ $D\,(cu) = c\,Du$.

4. The derivative of the sum of two functions is the sum of their derivatives:

$(f + g)' = f' + g'$ $D[f(x) + g(x)] = D\,f(x) + D\,g(x)$
$$D\,(u + v) = Du + Dv.$$

5. The derivative of the product of two functions is the first times the derivative of the second plus the second times the derivative of the first:

$(fg)' = fg' + gf'$ $D\,f(x)\,g(x) = f(x)\,D\,g(x) + g(x)\,D\,f(x)$
$$D(uv) = u\,Dv + v\,Du.$$

6. The derivative of the power function defined by $f(x) = x^n$, with n a positive integer, is $f'(x) = nx^{n-1}$:

$(x^n)' = nx^{n-1}$ $D\,x^n = nx^{n-1}$.

31—TYPICAL PROOFS

The first four rules are immediate consequences of the definition of a derivative in Sec. 9 and the properties of limits stated in Sec. 11.

To prove rule 5, we write $u = f(x)$, $v = g(x)$, and put $\Delta x = h$ as in Sec. 9. Then $u + \Delta u = f(x + h)$ and $v + \Delta v = g(x + h)$. Also $uv + \Delta uv = f(x + h)\, g(x + h) = (u + \Delta u)(v + \Delta v)$, so that

$$\Delta(uv) = (u + \Delta u)(v + \Delta v) - uv$$
$$= u\, \Delta v + v\, \Delta u + \Delta u\, \Delta v. \tag{1}$$

And from this we have

$$\frac{\Delta(uv)}{h} = u\frac{\Delta v}{h} + v\frac{\Delta u}{h} + \left(\frac{\Delta u}{h}\right)\left(\frac{\Delta v}{h}\right) h. \tag{2}$$

Since $f'(x)$ and $g'(x)$ exist for the value considered,

$$\lim_{h \to 0} \frac{\Delta u}{h} = Du = f(x) \qquad \lim_{h \to 0} \frac{\Delta v}{h} = Dv = g(x). \tag{3}$$

As $h \to 0$, the limit of the right-hand member of Eq. (2) is $u\, Dv + v\, Du + (Du)(Dv) \cdot 0$. Hence the limit of the left-hand member must exist and give the value of $D(uv)$, so that

$$D(uv) = u\, Dv + v\, Du. \tag{4}$$

This is one form of rule 5. ∎

Rule 6 may be proved by the method of mathematical induction described in Sec. 17.

(a) Since $x^0 = 1$, for $n = 1$, rule 6 becomes $D\,x = 1$, which is true by rule 2.

(b) Assume that rule 6 holds for $n = k - 1$, $D\,x^{k-1} = (k - 1)x^{k-2}$. Then use this and rule 5 to find the derivative of $(x)(x^{k-1})$:

$$D\,x^k = D[(x)(x^{k-1})] = x(k - 1)x^{k-2} + x^{k-1} \cdot 1 = kx^{k-1}. \tag{5}$$

This is rule 6 for $n = k$. ∎

EXAMPLE 1.   Find Dy if $y = ax^4 + bx^3 + cx^2 + dx + e$.

SOLUTION.   By rule 4 we may consider the terms separately. From rule 3 we may factor out the constants. Then from rule 1 for e, rule 2 for x, and rule 6 for $n = 2, 3, 4$, we find

$$Dy = 4ax^3 + 3bx^2 + 2cx + d.$$

EXAMPLE 2.   Find Dy if $y = (2x^2 + 3)(3x^2 - 2)$.

SOLUTION.   If $f(x) = 2x^2 + 3$ and $g(x) = 3x^2 - 2$, we find that $f'(x) = 4x$ and $g'(x) = 6x$ by reasoning as in Example 1.   Then from rule 5 we have $Dy = (2x^2 + 3)6x + (3x^2 - 2)4x = 24x^3 + 10x$.   Alternatively, since on multiplying out we have $y = 6x^4 + 5x^2 - 6$, we find as in Example 1 that $Dy = 24x^3 + 10x$.

32—QUOTIENTS

For a quotient, we have the following rule:

7. The derivative of the quotient of two functions is the *denominator* times the derivative of the numerator *minus* the numerator times the derivative of the denominator, all divided by the square of the denominator.

$$\left(\frac{f}{g}\right) = \frac{gf' - fg'}{g^2} \qquad D\frac{f(x)}{g(x)} = \frac{g(x)\, D\, f(x) - f(x)\, D\, g(x)}{g(x)^2}$$

$$D\left(\frac{u}{v}\right) = \frac{v\, Du - u\, Dv}{v^2}.$$

To prove this, we use the notation of Eq. (1) and find

$$\Delta \frac{u}{v} = \frac{u + \Delta u}{v + \Delta v} - \frac{u}{v} = \frac{v\, \Delta u - u\, \Delta v}{(v + \Delta v)v}. \tag{6}$$

And from this we have

$$\frac{\Delta(u/v)}{h} = \frac{v(\Delta u/h) - u(\Delta v/h)}{(v + \Delta v)v}. \tag{7}$$

As $h \to 0$, $\Delta v = (\Delta v/h)h \to g'(x) \cdot 0$, or 0, by Eq. (3).   Hence the limit of the right-hand member of Eq. (7) is $(v\, Du - u\, Dv)/v^2$.   Thus the limit of the left-hand member must exist and give the value of $D(u/v)$, so that

$$D\left(\frac{u}{v}\right) = \frac{v\, Du - u\, Dv}{v^2}. \tag{8}$$

This is one form of rule 7.   ■

EXAMPLE.   Find Dy if $y = x^{-m}$, with m a positive integer and $x \neq 0$.

SOLUTION.   Since $y = 1/x^m$, we find from the quotient rule that

$$Dy = \frac{x^m \, D1 - 1 \cdot D \, x^m}{(x^m)^2} = \frac{x^m \cdot 0 - mx^{m-1}}{x^{2m}} = -mx^{-m-1} \qquad (9)$$

The example shows that $D \, x^{-m} = -mx^{-m-1}$, or, with $-m = n$, $D \, x^n = nx^{n-1}$. This proves that rule 6 may be applied when the exponent is a negative integer.

33—THE CHAIN RULE

For a composite function we have this rule:

8. The derivative of $f(g)$, defined by the relations $y = f(u)$ and $u = g(x)$, is the derivative of f with respect to u times the derivative of g with respect to x:

$$[f(g)]' = f'(g) \, g' \qquad D_x y = D_u y \, D_x u = f'(u) \, D_x u.$$

This applies only at a point where $g'(x)$ and $f'(u)$ exist.

To prove this, we first note that since $u = g(x)$ and $g'(x)$ exists, we have

$$\lim_{\Delta u \to 0} \frac{\Delta u}{\Delta x} = D_x u = g'(x). \qquad (10)$$

Also since $y = f(u)$ and $f'(u)$ exists for $u = g(x)$, we have

$$\lim_{\Delta u \to 0} \frac{\Delta y}{\Delta u} = D_u y = f'(u). \qquad (11)$$

Let us assume that $D_x u \neq 0$. (This restriction will be removed in Sec. 34.) Then, for sufficiently small values of Δx, Δu will not be zero. Hence, if we confine our attention to such values of Δx, any sequence with $\Delta x \to 0$ will correspond to a sequence of values of $\Delta u \to 0$. That is, Δu tends to, but never equals, zero. And, using such values, we may conclude that

$$\lim_{\Delta x \to 0} \frac{\Delta y}{\Delta x} = \lim_{\Delta x \to 0} \frac{\Delta y}{\Delta u} \frac{\Delta u}{\Delta x}$$

$$= \lim_{\Delta x \to 0} \frac{\Delta y}{\Delta u} \lim_{\Delta x \to 0} \frac{\Delta u}{\Delta x}$$

$$= \lim_{\Delta u \to 0} \frac{\Delta y}{\Delta u} \lim_{\Delta x \to 0} \frac{\Delta u}{\Delta x} = D_u y \, D_x u. \qquad (12)$$

Hence the limit in the left-hand member exists and gives the value of $D_x y$, so that

$$D_x y = D_u y \, D_x u. \tag{13}$$

This is one form of rule 8. ∎

In the language of rates, the chain rule states that the rate of change of y with respect to x equals the rate of change of y with respect to u times the rate of change of u with respect to x. Thus the relation which is obvious for average rates of change continues to hold for true rates of change.

EXAMPLE. Find Dy if

$$y = \left(\frac{1 - 2x}{1 + 2x}\right)^2.$$

SOLUTION. If $g(x) = (1 - 2x)/(1 + 2x)$, we find from the quotient rule that

$$g'(x) = \frac{(1 + 2x) \, D(1 - 2x) - (1 - 2x) \, D(1 + 2x)}{(1 + 2x)^2}$$

$$= \frac{(1 + 2x)(-2) - (1 - 2x)(2)}{(1 + 2x)^2} = \frac{-4}{(1 + 2x)^2}.$$

And if $u = g(x)$, then

$$y = u^2 \qquad D_u y = 2u = 2\left(\frac{1 - 2x}{1 + 2x}\right).$$

Hence, finally, we have

$$Dy = D_x y = D_u y \, D_x u = 2\left(\frac{1 - 2x}{1 + 2x}\right)\frac{-4}{(1 + 2x)^2} = \frac{8(2x - 1)}{(2x + 1)^3}.$$

34—GENERAL PROOF OF THE CHAIN RULE

To prove that the chain rule holds in all cases, including that in which $\Delta u = 0$ for some arbitrarily small values of Δx, we may proceed as follows. For the fixed value of x under consideration, let $u = g(x)$. Define a function $F : [\Delta u, F(\Delta u)]$ by

$$F(\Delta u) = \frac{f(u + \Delta u) - f(u)}{\Delta u} \qquad \text{if } \Delta u \neq 0, F(0) = f'(u). \qquad (14)$$

The domain of this function is the set of all numbers Δu such that $u + \Delta u$ is in the domain of f. Then this function is continuous at $\Delta u = 0$, since $f'(u)$ exists. Take any $\Delta x \neq 0$, and corresponding Δu, for which $x + \Delta x$ is in the domain of g and $u + \Delta u$ is in the domain of f. Then, since $y = f(u)$,

$$\Delta y = f(u + \Delta u) - f(u) = \Delta u \, F(\Delta u), \qquad (15)$$

where the last form follows from Eq. (14), whether $\Delta u \neq 0$ or $\Delta u = 0$. On dividing by Δx and letting $\Delta x \to 0$, which makes the corresponding values of Δu approach zero (possibly including some values equal to zero), we obtain

$$\lim_{\Delta x \to 0} \frac{\Delta y}{\Delta x} = \lim_{\Delta x \to 0} \frac{\Delta u}{\Delta x} F(0) = D_x u \, f \,(u). \qquad (16)$$

This shows that the limit on the left exists and that

$$D_x y = D_x u \, f'(u) = D_u y \, D_x u. \qquad (17)$$

This establishes the chain rule for all cases. ∎

35—IMPLICIT DIFFERENTIATION

Suppose that a relation is defined by an equation involving x and y, such as

$$x^2 + y^2 = 1. \qquad (18)$$

There are many ways of defining unrestricted functions whose graphs will consist entirely of points satisfying the relation just written. For example, we might take $y = \sqrt{1 - x^2}$, when x is a rational number with $|x| \leq 1$, and $y = -\sqrt{1 - x^2}$, when x is an irrational number with $|x| < 1$. If, however, we take a particular point, as $(0,1)$ on the graph of the relation (18), and insist that in some interval including the x of this point, such as $-h < x < h$, with $|h| < 1$, the function must be continuous, then we must use $y = \sqrt{1 - x^2}$ throughout this interval. Thus, for each point satisfying Eq. (18), with $y > 0$, this equation *implicitly* defines the continuous function explicitly defined by

$$y = \sqrt{1 - x^2}. \tag{19}$$

For $-1 < x < 1$, this function is differentiable. In fact, if $u = 1 - x^2$, then $D_x u = -2x$. And for $y = \sqrt{u}$, by the example in Sec. 9, $D_u y = 1/2\sqrt{u}$. Hence, by the chain rule,

$$D_x y = D_u y\, D_x u = \frac{1}{2\sqrt{1 - x^2}}(-2x) = -\frac{x}{\sqrt{1 - x^2}}. \tag{20}$$

If we had known that the function was differentiable, we could have obtained its derivative more simply, directly from Eq. (18), by a process known as *implicit differentiation*. For, with y a differentiable function of x, the left-hand member of Eq. (18) defines a function which has as its derivative $2x + 2y\, D_x y$. Here we have used the chain rule to differentiate y^2 with respect to x. This must equal 0, the derivative of the function defined by the right-hand member 1. Thus we have

$$2x + 2y\, D_x y = 0 \qquad D_x y = -\frac{x}{y}. \tag{21}$$

In view of Eq. (19), this agrees with Eq. (20). Note that, for a point on the lower half of the circle, y would be negative, and the expression would give the correct derivative for the function $y = -\sqrt{1 - x^2}$.

If $P_0(x_0, y_0)$ is any point on the circle which is the locus of Eq. (18), then $x_0^2 + y_0^2 = 1$. And from the value of the slope at P_0, $m_0 = -x_0/y_0$, we should find, for the equation of the tangent line,

$$y - y_0 = -\frac{x_0}{y_0}(x - x_0) \qquad \text{or } xx_0 + yy_0 = x_0^2 + y_0^2 = 1. \tag{22}$$

As we should guess from continuity considerations, the second form is valid for the tangent at *any* point of the circle, including the points where $y_0 = 0$ and Eq. (21) is not applicable.

In general, for a relation of the form $G(x,y) = 0$, the above process would lead to an equation of the form $M(x,y) + N(x,y)\, D_x y = 0$; whence $D_x y = -M(x,y)/N(x,y)$.

Let $P_0(x_0,y_0)$ be any point on the graph of this relation, so that $G(x_0,y_0) = 0$. And let each of the functions G, M, N defined by $G(x,y)$, $M(x,y)$, $N(x,y)$ be a continuous function of two variables in some two-dimensional neighborhood of (x_0,y_0). Further, suppose that $N(x_0,y_0) \neq 0$. Then for x in some neighborhood of x_0, there is a unique continuous function $F:(x,y)$, with $y = F(x)$, such that $y_0 = F(x_0)$, $G[x_0, F(x_0)] = 0$. The function F is then differentiable at $x = x_0$, with $F'(x) = -M(x_0,y_0)/N(x_0,y_0)$.

We omit the proof of this *implicit-function* theorem.

EXAMPLE.   Find an equation for the line tangent to the locus of the equation $x^3 - x^2y - y^5 = 3$ at the point $(2,1)$.

SOLUTION.   For Dy, the derivative of the implicitly defined F, with $y = F(x)$, we have the relation

$3x^2 - 2xy - x^2\, Dy - 5y^4\, Dy = 0.$

Hence

$$Dy = \frac{3x^2 - 2xy}{x^2 + 5y^4} = \frac{3 \cdot 2^2 - 2 \cdot 2 \cdot 1}{2^2 + 5 \cdot 1^4} = \frac{8}{9} \qquad \text{at } (2,1).$$

The equation of the tangent line is

$$y - 1 = \tfrac{8}{9}(x - 2) \qquad \text{or } 8x - 9y = 7.$$

36—INVERSE FUNCTIONS

Consider the differentiable function f defined by $y = f(x)$. By interchanging variables we obtain the relation

$$x = f(y). \tag{23}$$

For a particular y_0, let $x_0 = f(y_0)$ and assume that $f'(y_0) \neq 0$. Then, by applying the implicit-function theorem to the relation (23), or $f(y) - x = 0$, we know that there is a function $y = F(x)$ defined in some neighborhood of x_0 whose derivative is given by

$$1 = f'(y)\, Dy \qquad \text{or} \qquad F'(x) = Dy = \frac{1}{f'(y)}. \tag{24}$$

This function F is called the *inverse* of the function f and is denoted by f^{-1}. Thus

$$x = f[f^{-1}(x)] \qquad D[f^{-1}(x)] = \frac{1}{f'[f^{-1}(x)]} \, . \tag{25}$$

Since interchanging x and y in the relation $y = f^{-1}(x)$ or $x = f(y)$ would lead us back to the relation defining the original function, f is the inverse of f^{-1}, and

$$x = f^{-1}[f(x)] \qquad D[f(x)] = \frac{1}{(f^{-1})'[f(x)]} \, . \tag{26}$$

EXAMPLE. Let $f(x) = x^p$, with p a positive integer and $x > 0$. Find $D f^{-1}(x) = D \, x^{1/p}$.

SOLUTION. We have $f'(x) = px^{p-1} \neq 0$. The relation defining the inverse function is $x = y^p$, so that $f^{-1}(x) = x^{1/p}$. Its derivative is

$$D \, x^{1/p} = \frac{1}{p(x^{1/p})^{p-1}} = \frac{1}{p} x^{(1/p)-1}.$$

This has the same form as rule 6 with $n = 1/p$.

37—RATIONAL POWERS

We showed that rule 6 holds for negative integral powers in the example of Sec. 32. We may show that it holds for n *any rational number* as follows. Let $n = p/q$, with q a positive integer and p a positive or negative integer. Then from $y = x^{p/q}$, we may derive the equation $y^q = x^p$. Let $x \neq 0$ ($x > 0$ for q an even integer). Then $y \neq 0$ and we may apply the implicit-function theorem to deduce that

$$qy^{q-1} \, Dy = px^{p-1} \qquad Dy = \frac{px^{p-1}}{qy^{q-1}} = \frac{p}{q} x^{p-1} y^{1-q}. \tag{27}$$

Since $y = x^{p/q}$, this becomes

$$D \, x^{p/q} = \frac{p}{q} x^{p-1} (x^{p/q})^{1-q} = \frac{p}{q} x^{(p/q)-1}. \tag{28}$$

This proves rule 6 for $n = p/q$. ■

38—LOGARITHMS

We recall that for any base $a > 1$, we may define logarithms to the base a by the equivalence

$$\log_a u = b \qquad a^b = u, u > 0. \tag{29}$$

The basic properties of logarithms, corresponding to the laws for exponents, are

$$\log_a u + \log_a v = \log_a (uv) \qquad \log_a u - \log_a v = \log_a \frac{u}{v}$$

$$s \log_a u = \log_a (u^s). \tag{30}$$

Let us find the derivative of the function defined by the equation $y = \log_a x$ for any value $x > 0$ in its domain. With $\Delta x = h$, we have $y + \Delta y = \log_a (x + h)$ so that

$$\Delta y = \log_a (x + h) - \log_a x$$

$$= \log_a \frac{x + h}{x} = \log_a \left(1 + \frac{h}{x}\right). \tag{31}$$

Whence

$$\frac{\Delta y}{\Delta x} = \frac{1}{h} \log_a \left(1 + \frac{h}{x}\right) = \frac{1}{x} \log_a \left(1 + \frac{h}{x}\right)^{x/h}. \tag{32}$$

As we shall discuss more fully in the next section,

$$\lim_{h \to 0} \left(1 + \frac{h}{x}\right)^{x/h} = e = 2.71828 \cdots . \tag{33}$$

Since the function $\log_a$ is continuous, it follows from the last two equations that

$$Dy = D \log_a x = \frac{1}{x} \log_a e. \tag{34}$$

39—THE NUMBER e

We may evaluate $A(h/x) = (1 + h/x)^{x/h}$ by using logarithms to the base 10. For fixed positive x, when $h \to 0$, so does h/x. Let us take $h/x = 10^{-3}$. From a 5-place table of logarithms, we find that $\log_{10} 1.001 = 0.00043$. Hence $\log_{10} A(10^{-3}) = 0.43$, and to two figures

$A(10^{-3}) = 2.7$. This same value would result for any smaller value of h/x, since we should obtain the logarithm for $\theta/1{,}000$ with $0 < \theta < 1$ by interpolation as $\theta(0.00043)$, which, multiplied by $1{,}000/\theta$, again gives 0.43. A 6-place table gives $0.434 = \log_{10} 2.72$ for $h/x < 10^{-4}$. And a 12-place table gives $0.434294 = \log_{10} 2.71828$ for $h/x < 10^{-6}$. This makes Eq. (33) plausible.

If $h/x \to 0$, $x/h \to \infty$. In fact, if $x/h = n$, the equation

$$\lim_{|n| \to \infty} \left(1 + \frac{1}{n}\right)^n = e \tag{35}$$

is equivalent to Eq. (33). Without attempting a complete and rigorous proof of this, let us restrict our attention to positive integral values of n and note that, by the binomial theorem,

$$\left(1 + \frac{1}{n}\right)^n = 1 + n\left(\frac{1}{n}\right) + \frac{n(n-1)}{1 \cdot 2}\left(\frac{1}{n}\right)^2 + \cdots$$
$$= 1 + 1 + \frac{1}{2!}\left(1 - \frac{1}{n}\right)$$
$$+ \frac{1}{3!}\left(1 - \frac{1}{n}\right)\left(1 - \frac{2}{n}\right) + \cdots . \tag{36}$$

For n large, $1/n$ is small and the individual terms approximate those of an infinite series, suggesting that

$$e = 1 + 1 + \frac{1}{2!} + \frac{1}{3!} + \cdots + \frac{1}{k!} + \cdots . \tag{37}$$

By Prob. 29, the sum of $(k + 1)$ terms of this series increases with k, but never exceeds 3. Further, this positive series is convergent, that is, the sequence of partial sums $1, 1 + 1, 1 + 1 + \frac{1}{2!}, \ldots$, approaches a definite limit, so that

$$e = \lim_{k \to \infty} \left(1 + 1 + \frac{1}{2!} + \cdots + \frac{1}{k!}\right). \tag{38}$$

This may be used to find e to any desired accuracy. In fact, the first 10 terms show that $e = 2.71828$, to five decimal places.

40—NATURAL LOGARITHMS

Logarithms to the base e are called *natural* logarithms. We write ln in place of $\log_e$. Thus we write

$$\ln u = b \qquad e^b = u, \, u > 0. \tag{39}$$

In particular, since $u = e$ when $b = 1$, $\ln e = \log_e e = 1$. Hence, when we use natural logarithms, Eq. (34) takes the simplified form

$$D (\ln x) = \frac{1}{x} \cdot \tag{40}$$

Because of this simplification, natural logarithms are used almost exclusively in the calculus. Tables of them are found in most mathematical handbooks. For other bases, we should write

$$\log_a u = \frac{\ln u}{\ln a} \qquad \text{obtained from } u = a^{\log_a u} \tag{41}$$

by taking natural logarithms on both sides.

By Sec. 23, the two properties $D \ln x = 1/x$ and $\ln 1 = 0$ are equivalent to $\ln x = \int_1^x (du/u)$. The development of the theory of natural logarithms from this integral, taken as the basic definition, was sketched in Prob. 38 of Chap. 2.

From Eq. (40) and the chain rule we formulate the following rule:

$$[\ln f(x)]' = \frac{f'(x)}{f(x)} \qquad D_x (\ln u) = \frac{1}{u} D_x u. \tag{42}$$

9. The derivative of the (natural) logarithm of a function is the derivative of the function, divided by the value of the function.

EXAMPLE 1.   Show that

$$D_x (\ln |u|) = \frac{1}{u} D_x u \qquad \text{for } u \neq 0. \tag{43}$$

SOLUTION.   Let g be defined by $g(x) = |x|$. For $x > 0$, we have $g(x) = x$ and $g'(x) = 1 = |x|/x$. For $x < 0$, however, $g(x) = -x$ and $g'(x) = -1 = |x|/x$. Hence, for $x \neq 0$, $g'(x) = |x|/x$, so that

$$D_x \left(\ln |x| \right) = D_x \ln \left[g(x) \right] = \frac{g'(x)}{g(x)} = \frac{|x|/x}{|x|} = \frac{1}{x} \cdot$$

With the chain rule this gives

$$D_x \left(\ln |u| \right) = D_u \left(\ln |u| \right) D_x u = \frac{1}{u} D_x u \qquad \text{for } u \neq 0.$$

Let $|u| = |v| \neq 0$. Then the equation

$$\frac{1}{u} D_x u = \frac{1}{v} D_x v \tag{44}$$

follows from Eq. (43). The procedure of taking logarithms (of absolute values) before differentiating is known as *logarithmic differentiation*. It sometimes simplifies the calculation of derivatives.

EXAMPLE 2.   Find Dy if

$$y = \left[\frac{x^2 (4 - x^2)}{1 - 2x} \right]^{2/3} \cdot$$

SOLUTION.   By logarithmic differentiation we find that

$$\frac{1}{y} Dy = \frac{2}{3} \left(\frac{2}{x} - \frac{2x}{4 - x^2} + \frac{2}{1 - 2x} \right),$$

so that, if $x \neq 2, -2$, or $\frac{1}{2}$,

$$Dy = \frac{4}{3} \left(1 - \frac{2x^2}{4 - x^2} + \frac{2x}{1 - 2x} \right) x^{1/3} (4 - x^2)^{2/3} (1 - 2x)^{-2/3}.$$

EXAMPLE 3.   Show that $D x^c = c x^{c-1}$.

SOLUTION.   By logarithmic differentiation, from $y = x^c$, $\ln |y| = c \ln |x|$, we find that

$$\frac{1}{y} Dy = \frac{c}{x};$$

whence

$$Dy = \frac{c}{x} y = \frac{c}{x} x^c = c x^{c-1}.$$

This proves that rule 6 may be applied when the exponent is any real number and $x > 0$. If c is rational and $c = p/q$ with

q an odd integer, it also applies with $x < 0$, as well as $x = 0$ if $c \geq 1$. At $x = 0$, for all values of $c > 1$, rule 6 gives zero, which is the correct value of the right-hand derivative. With the chain rule, this leads to rule $6a$:

$$D_x(u^c) = cu^{c-1} D_x u. \tag{45}$$

EXAMPLE 4.   Show that for $a > 0$

$$D \, a^x = (\ln a) \, a^x. \tag{46}$$

SOLUTION.   From $y = a^x$, we have $\ln y = x \ln a$; whence $(1/y) Dy = \ln a$ and $Dy = (\ln a)a^x$.

EXAMPLE 5.   Show that for $u > 0$,

$$D_x(u^v) = v \, u^{v-1} D_x u + (\ln u) \, u^v \, D_x v. \tag{47}$$

SOLUTION.   From $y = u^v$, we have $\ln y = v \ln u$; whence

$$\frac{1}{y} D_x y = v \frac{1}{u} D_x u + (\ln u) \, D_x v$$

and

$$D_x y = u^v \left[\frac{v}{u} D_x u + (\ln u) \, D_x v \right] = v \, u^{v-1} D_x u + (\ln u) u^v \, D_x v.$$

41—THE EXPONENTIAL FUNCTION

The *exponential function* exp is defined by the equation

$$y = \exp x = e^x. \tag{48}$$

Since this implies that $x = \ln y$, the functions ln and exp are inverse in the sense of Sec. 36. As in Eq. (24), from $x = \ln y$ we obtain $1 = (1/y) Dy$, whence $Dy = y$, so that

$$D \, e^x = e^x. \tag{49}$$

This also follows from Eq. (46). With the chain rule, from Eq. (49) we may derive the following rule:

10. The exponential of a function has as its derivative the exponential times the derivative of the function:

$$[\exp f(x)]' = [\exp f(x)] f'(x) \qquad D_x e^u = e^u D_x u. \qquad (50)$$

For other bases we may use Eq. (46) and the chain rule. Or we may write $a^u = e^{u \ln a}$ and deduce from rule 10 that

$$D_x a^u = e^{u \ln a} (\ln a) D_x u = (\ln a) a^u D_x u. \qquad (51)$$

PROBLEMS

Section 31

Let $y = f(x)$. Find $Dy = f'(x)$ for each given $f(x)$.

1. $2x^8 + 3x^5 + 7$.
2. $(4x + 5)(6x - 4)$.
3. $\frac{1}{4}x^4 - \frac{2}{3}x^3 + \frac{1}{2}x^2 - \frac{1}{3}$.
4. $2(x^5 + x)(x^5 - x)$.
5. Use mathematical induction (Sec. 17) to prove that $a^n - b^n = (a - b)(a^{n-1} + a^{n-2}b + a^{n-3}b^2 + \cdots + b^{n-1})$. Note that $a^k - b^k = a(a^{k-1} - b^{k-1}) + (a - b)b^{k-1}$.

   From this and the form of the derivative given in Eq. (26) of Sec. 8, give an alternative proof of rule 6.
6. For $x > 0$, let $f(x) = x^{p/q}$, with p and q positive integers. Then

   $$f'(x) = \lim_{x_2 \to x} \frac{x_2^{p/q} - x^{p/q}}{x_2 - x}.$$

   If $t = x^{1/q}$, then

   $$f'(x) = \lim_{t_2 \to t} \frac{t_2^p - t^p}{t_2^q - t^q}.$$

   From this and the identity of Prob. 5 deduce that

   $$f'(x) = \frac{p}{q} t^{p-q} = \frac{p}{q} x^{(p/q)-1}.$$

Section 32

Let $y = f(x)$. Find $Dy = f'(x)$ for each given $f(x)$.

7. $\dfrac{5x + 3}{3x + 2}$.
8. $\dfrac{2}{x} + \dfrac{3}{x^2} + \dfrac{1}{x^3}$.

9. $\dfrac{x^2}{1 - x^2}$.

10. $\dfrac{2x^3 + 3}{3x^3 + 2}$.

11. Prove that for $x > 0$, rule 6 holds for n any positive or negative rational number. *Hint:* Use Prob. 6 for $n = p/q > 0$. And use Eq. (9) with $m = p/q$ for $n = -p/q$.

Section 33

Let $y = f(x)$. Find $Dy = f'(x)$ for each given $f(x)$.

12. $(x^3 + 2)^5$.

13. $(x + 2)^2(3x - 1)^3$.

14. $\dfrac{1}{(3x^2 + x)^2}$.

15. $(x + 1/x)^3$.

Section 34

16. Let $f(u) = u^2$ and $g(x) = 1$. Verify that if $G = G(f)$, then $G(x) = 1$ and the chain rule holds in this case since $G'(x) = f'(u) \, g'(x)$ becomes $0 = 2u \cdot 0$. Note that if $u = g(x) = 1$, then $\Delta u = 0$ for any Δx. Thus Eq. (12) may not be used here. But the reasoning of Sec. 34 applies, with $\Delta y = 0$, $\Delta u = 0$, and $F(\Delta u) = F(0) = f'(u) = 2u$ for any Δx.

17. Let $u = g(x)$, and for any fixed x under consideration, assume that $\Delta u = 0$ for some arbitrarily small values of Δx. From

$$g'(x) = \lim_{\Delta x \to 0} \frac{\Delta u}{\Delta x},$$

deduce that if $g'(x)$ exists, then $g'(x) = 0$, and hence, by the chain rule, $D_x f[g(x)] = 0$ for the particular fixed x.

Section 35

In Probs. 18 to 21, find the slope of each curve whose equation is given at the indicated point or points:

18. $y^3 - 3xy = -10$ at the point where $y = 2$.

19. $xy^2 + y = 6$ at the point where $y = 1$.

20. $x^2y^3 = 4x + 2y$ at the points where $y = 2$.

21. $x^3 + 3xy + y^3 = 0$ at any point (x,y) on the curve.

22. Show that an equation for the line tangent to the hyperbola with equation $xy = a^2$, at (x_0,y_0), where $x_0y_0 = a^2 \neq 0$, is $xy_0 + yx_0 = 2a^2$.

Section 36

23. From Prob. 38 of Chap. 2, if $f(y) = \ln y$, then $f'(y) = 1/y$. But from $x = \ln y = \log_e y$, $y = e^x$ defines the inverse function $f^{-1}(x)$. Show that $De^x = e^x$.

Section 37

Let $y = f(x)$. Find $Dy = f'(x)$ for each given $f(x)$.

24. $x^{3/2} + x^{5/3}$.

25. $(x^3 + a^3)^{2/3}$.

26. $(x + 1)/x\sqrt{x}$.

27. $x/\sqrt{a^2 - x^2}$.

Section 39

28. Verify that each term of S, the series in Eq. (37), is less than or equal to the corresponding term of the series S': $1 + 1 + \frac{1}{2} + \cdots + 1/2^{k-1} + \cdots$.   Note that $k! = 2 \cdot 3 \cdot 4 \cdot k \geq 2^{k-1}$.

Let S'_t denote the sum of the first k terms of S'. Verify that $S'_{k+1} = 3 - 1/2^{k-1}$. Deduce that $\lim_{t \to \infty} S'_t = 3$ and that, by the Cauchy necessary condition of Sec. 14, for any positive η, there is a t_η such that $0 \leq S'_{t_2} - S'_{t_1} \leq \eta$ if $t_2 \geq t_1 > t_\eta$.

Let S_t denote the sum of the first k terms of S. From $0 \leq S_{t_2} - S_{t_1} \leq S'_{t_2} - S'_{t_1} \leq \eta$, and the Cauchy sufficient condition of Sec. 14, deduce that $\lim_{t \to \infty} S_t = L$.

For $t > 3$, show that $2.5 < S_t \leq S'_t < 3$, and hence that $2.5 \leq L \leq 3$.

Section 40

In Probs. 29 to 32, let $y = f(x)$. Find $Dy = f'(x)$ for each given $f(x)$.

29. $\ln (4x - 5)$.

30. $x \ln x - x$.

31. $(\ln x)^3$.

32. $\ln \sqrt{\dfrac{x-1}{x+1}}$.

Section 41

In Probs. 33 to 36, let $y = f(x)$. Find $Dy = f'(x)$ for each given $f(x)$.

33. $(x-1)e^x$.

34. $\ln (1 + e^{3x})$.

35. e^{2x^2}.

36. x^x.

Let $y = F(x)$ be implicitly defined by the given equation and a particular (x,y) satisfying this equation. In each of Probs. 37 to 40 find Dy in terms of x and y.

37. $\ln (xy) = x + y$.

38. $e^x + e^y = xy$.

39. $\ln (x + y) = 2x + 3y$.

40. $e^{x-y} = \ln (y/x)$.

4

TRIGONOMETRIC AND HYPERBOLIC
FUNCTIONS,
DIFFERENTIALS

We shall now prove those additional rules of differentiation which are necessary for the treatment of the remaining elementary transcendental functions. We also introduce differentials and the notation associated with them.

42—THE SINE FUNCTION

We briefly recall the definition of the radian measure of an angle. Let AOB (Fig. 12) be a central angle in a circle of center O and radius $1 = OA = OB$. Then the *radian measure* of angle AOB is the distance θ traveled on the unit circle as OA rotates to OB to generate the angle AOB. The number θ is positive for a clockwise rotation and negative for a counterclockwise rotation.

If D is the degree measure of an angle and θ is its radian measure, the ratio of the angle to a straight angle is $D/180 = \theta/\pi$, so that $\theta = (\pi/180)D$ and $D = (180/\pi)\theta$. In particular, the radian measures of angles of $90°$, $45°$, $1°$ are $\pi/2$, $\pi/4$, $\pi/180$, respectively.

For any number x, the value $y = \sin x$ may be found either by applying the geometric definition of the sine to an angle of x radians or by calculating $D = (180/\pi)x$ and using the tables of sines of angles in degrees to find the sine of $D°$.

Let the function sin be defined by the equation $y = \sin x$, where x is measured in radians. To find the derivative of this function, with $\Delta x = h$, we have $y + \Delta y = \sin (x + h)$, so that

$$\Delta y = \sin (x + h) - \sin x. \tag{1}$$

Let us recall the trigonometric identity

$$\sin A - \sin B = 2 \cos \frac{A + B}{2} \sin \frac{A - B}{2}, \tag{2}$$

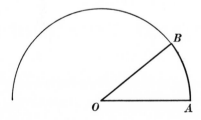

$$O \qquad A \qquad \textbf{FIGURE 12}$$

and in it take $A = x + h$, $B = x$. Then, from Eq. (1), we find

$$\frac{\Delta y}{\Delta x} = \frac{1}{h} 2 \cos\left(x + \frac{h}{2}\right) \sin\frac{h}{2} = \cos\left(x + \frac{h}{2}\right) \frac{\sin{(h/2)}}{h/2}. \qquad (3)$$

In Prob. 1 of Chap. 4, it is shown that

$$\lim_{h\to 0} \frac{\sin{(h/2)}}{h/2} = 1. \qquad (4)$$

It follows from the last two equations that

$$D_x y = D_x (\sin x) = \cos x. \qquad (5)$$

43—SMOOTH ARCS

Let each of the functions f and g be defined on the interval $[a,b]$. Then the graph of the *parametric equations*

$$x = f(t) \qquad y = g(t) \qquad \text{for } a \le t \le b \qquad (6)$$

with parameter t is the set of all points (x,y) satisfying Eq. (6): that is, all points $P(t) = [f(t), g(t)]$ obtained by using values of t in $[a,b]$.

Let $P(t_0) = (x_0,y_0)$. Suppose that there is a derivative $f'(t_0) \ne 0$. Then, by Sec. 36, in some neighborhood of x_0, there is an inverse function f^{-1} such that $t = f^{-1}(x)$ is implied by $x = f(t)$. In this neighborhood of x_0, the graph is that of $y = g[f^{-1}(x)]$, and so is a curve. By Eq. (25) of Sec. 36, at x_0 we have

$$D_x t = D_x f^{-1}(x) = \frac{1}{f'[f^{-1}(x)]} = \frac{1}{f'(t)}. \qquad (7)$$

Suppose that there is also a derivative $g'(t_0)$. Then at x_0,

$$D_x y = D_t y\, D_x t = g'(t) \frac{1}{f'(t)} = \frac{g'(t)}{f'(t)} = \frac{D_t y}{D_t x}. \qquad (8)$$

Thus the curve has a tangent at x_0.

Now assume that each of the derivatives f' and g' is a continuous function of t for $a \le t \le b$. Also assume that $f'(t)$ and $g'(t)$ are never both zero for the same value of t in $[a,b]$. If $f'(t) = 0$, then $g'(t) \neq 0$ and we may interchange the roles of x and y in Eq. (8).   Then the graph of Eq. (6) will be a curve with a continuously turning tangent. We call it a *smooth arc AB*, where $A = P(a)$ and $B = P(b)$.

For any two points of a smooth arc, $P_1(t_1)$ and $P_2(t_2)$, the length of arc P_1P_2 is a well-defined number.   (Compare Sec. 80.)   And for a sequence of arcs obtained by letting $t_2 \to t_1$, we have

$$\lim_{P_2 \to P_1} \frac{\text{chord } P_1P_2}{\text{arc } P_1P_2} = 1. \tag{9}$$

Here, for brevity, we have written "chord P_1P_2" for the length of this chord, and similarly for "arc P_1P_2". We omit the proof of this *property of smooth arcs*.

In particular, consider the parametric equations

$$x = \sqrt{1 - t^2} \qquad y = t \qquad \text{for } -0.8 \leq t \leq 0.8. \tag{10}$$

These show that the quadrant of the unit circle $x^2 + y^2 = 1$, centered on $P_1 = (1,0)$, is a smooth arc.   Let $0 < u < \pi/8$.   If $t = \sin 2u$, then $\sqrt{1 - t^2} = \cos 2u$. Let $P_2 = (\cos 2u, \sin 2u)$.   Then arc $P_1P_2 = 2u$, and by Eq. (6) of Sec. 2,

$$\begin{aligned}
\text{chord } P_1P_2 &= \sqrt{(1 - \cos 2u)^2 + \sin^2 2u} \\
&= \sqrt{2 - 2\cos 2u} = \sqrt{2 - 2(\cos^2 u - \sin^2 u)} \\
&= 2 \sin u. \tag{11}
\end{aligned}$$

This is also evident from the geometric fact that in a unit circle, $\sin u$ is half the chord of an arc of length $2u$.   Thus we have

$$\frac{\text{chord } P_1P_2}{\text{arc } P_1P_2} = \frac{2 \sin u}{2u} = \frac{\sin u}{u}. \tag{12}$$

Now let u tend to zero through positive values.   Then $P_2 \to P_1$, and from Eqs. (9) and (12) we have $(\sin u)/u \to 1$ for $u \to 0+$.

For negative values of u, put $u = -w$, with w positive.   Then $(\sin u)/u = (\sin -w)/-w = (\sin w)/w$. Since $w \to 0+$ when $u \to 0-$, $(\sin u)/u$ for $u \to 0-$ tends to $\lim (\sin w)/w$ for $w \to 0+$, or **1**. Hence

$$\lim_{u \to 0} \frac{\sin u}{u} = 1 \tag{13}$$

holds without regard to the sign of u.

If we put $u = h/2$, this establishes Eq. (4) by a method alternative to that of Prob. 1 of Chap. 4.

44—TRIGONOMETRIC FUNCTIONS

For differentiating the six trigonometric functions, we formulate rules 11 to 16.

11. $\sin' = \cos$, $D_x \sin u = \cos u\ D_x u$.

12. $\cos' = -\sin$, $D_x \cos u = -\sin u\ D_x u$.

13. $\tan' = \sec^2$, $D_x \tan u = \sec^2 u\ D_x u$.

14. $\cot' = -\csc^2$, $D_x \cot u = -\csc^2 u\ D_x u$.

15. $\sec' = \sec\tan$, $D_x \sec u = \sec u \tan u\ D_x u$.

16. $\csc' = -\csc\cot$, $D_x \csc u = -\csc u \cot u\ D_x u$.

Rule 11 follows from Eq. (5). To prove the first form of rule 12 we write $\cos x = \sin(\pi/2 - x)$, so that

$$D_x \cos x = D_x \sin\left(\frac{\pi}{2} - x\right) = \cos\left(\frac{\pi}{2} - x\right) D_x\left(\frac{\pi}{2} - x\right)$$
$$= (\sin x)(-1) = -\sin x. \tag{14}$$

As in all six rules, the second form follows from the first by an application of the chain rule.

Rules 12 to 16 may be proved by expressing the appropriate function of x in terms of $\sin x$ and $\cos x$.

In remembering rules 11 to 16, it is helpful to notice that there are three pairs. Either member of a pair may be obtained from the other by changing each function to its cofunction and inserting one minus sign. This is not an accident, but results from the procedure of Eq. (14).

EXAMPLE 1.   Find Dy if $y = 2\cos^4(x^2/3)$.

SOLUTION.   Let $x^2/3 = u$, $v = \cos x^2/3$. Then

$$Dv = D_x \cos u = -\sin u\ Du = -\left(\sin\frac{x^2}{3}\right)\left(\frac{2x}{3}\right).$$

And

$$y = 2v^4 \qquad D_x y = 8v^3\ D_x v.$$

Hence

$$Dy = 8 \cos^3 \frac{x^2}{3} \left(-\sin \frac{x^2}{3}\right)\left(\frac{2x}{3}\right) = -\frac{16x}{3} \cos^3 \frac{x^2}{3} \sin \frac{x^2}{3}$$

EXAMPLE 2.   Find $D_x y$ if $x = \cos t$, $y = \sin t$.

SOLUTION.   From Eq. (8) we have

$$D_x y = \frac{D_t y}{D_t x} = \frac{\cos t}{-\sin t} = -\cot t.$$

The parametrization of the unit circle in Example 2 shows that any arc of the circle is smooth. But we could not use this argument before showing that sin and cos were differentiable functions.

45—INVERSE TRIGONOMETRIC FUNCTIONS

Let us apply the procedure of Sec. 36 to the function sin. Let y_0 be any value in the open interval $(-\pi/2, \pi/2)$ so that $-\pi/2 < y_0 < \pi/2$. Let $x_0 = \sin y_0$. Thus x_0 is in the open interval $(-1,1)$ and $-1 < x_0 < 1$. Then, for $f(y) = \sin y$, $f'(y) = \cos y \neq 0$ in the interval $(-\pi/2, \pi/2)$. Thus, for the neighborhood $(-1,1)$ of x_0, $-1 < x < 1$, there is an inverse function f^{-1} or $\sin^{-1}$ whose derivative is

$$D \sin^{-1} x = \frac{1}{f'(y)} = \frac{1}{\cos y}. \tag{15}$$

In the interval considered, $\cos y$ is positive, and from $\sin^2 y + \cos^2 y = 1$ and $x = \cos y$, we find $\sin y = \sqrt{1 - x^2}$.

Thus we have

$$D \sin^{-1} x = \frac{1}{\sqrt{1 - x^2}} \qquad \text{for } -\frac{\pi}{2} < \sin^{-1} x < \frac{\pi}{2}. \tag{16}$$

The relation $y = \sin^{-1} x$ is sometimes understood to be merely equivalent to $x = \sin y$. In this book, unless otherwise explicitly indicated, we shall assume that $y = \sin^{-1} x$ means the *principal value*, or unique value with $-\pi/2 < y < \pi/2$ such that $x = \sin y$, and so defines a function for the domain $-1 < x < 1$. By conti-

$$\sinh (x + y) = \sinh x \cosh y + \cosh x \sinh y, \tag{21}$$
$$\cosh (x + y) = \cosh x \cosh y + \sinh x \sinh y, \tag{22}$$

by replacing each value of a hyperbolic function by its expression in terms of exponential functions.

The corresponding formulas for differences follow from these and

$$\sinh (-x) = -\sinh x \qquad \cosh (-x) = \cosh x. \tag{23}$$

Numerical values, graphs, and other identities involving hyperbolic functions may be found in most handbooks of mathematical tables.

We see from Eq. (18) that

$$D \sinh x = \cosh x \qquad D \cosh x = \sinh x. \tag{24}$$

For differentiating the six hyperbolic functions, we formulate rules 23 to 28.

23. $D_x \sinh u = \cosh u \, D_x u.$
24. $D_x \cosh u = \sinh u \, D_x u.$
25. $D_x \tanh u = \operatorname{sech}^2 u \, D_x u.$
26. $D_x \coth u = -\operatorname{csch}^2 u \, D_x u.$
27. $D_x \operatorname{sech} u = -\operatorname{sech} u \tanh u \, D_x u.$
28. $D_x \operatorname{csch} u = -\operatorname{csch} u \coth u \, D_x u.$

Rules 23 and 24 follow from Eq. (24) and the chain rule. Rules 25 to 28 may be proved by expressing the appropriate function of x in terms of $\sinh x$ and $\cosh x$.

47—INVERSE HYPERBOLIC FUNCTIONS

Let us apply the procedure of Sec. 36 to the function sinh. Let y_0 be any number, $-\infty < y_0 < \infty$. Let $x_0 = \sinh y_0$, so that $-\infty < x_0 < \infty$. If $f(y) = \sinh y$, then $f'(y) = \cosh y \neq 0$. Thus, for the neighborhood of x_0, $-\infty < x < \infty$, which is the range of sinh, there is an inverse function f^{-1} or $\sinh^{-1}$ whose derivative is

$$D \sinh^{-1} x = \frac{1}{f'(y)} = \frac{1}{\cosh y}. \tag{25}$$

Since $\cosh^2 y - \sinh^2 y = 1$, $x = \sinh y$, and $\cosh y$ is positive, we find $\cosh y = \sqrt{1 + x^2}$. Thus we have

$$D \sinh^{-1} x = \frac{1}{\sqrt{1 + x^2}}. \tag{26}$$

Similar considerations may be applied to $\operatorname{csch}^{-1} x = \sinh^{-1} (1/x)$. Its domain is all $x \neq 0$, which is the range of csch. For $\tanh^{-1}$ and $\coth^{-1}$ the domain is $(-1,1)$.

For $\cosh^{-1}$ we take the *positive* value in $(0, \infty)$, for x in $(1, \infty)$. We define $\cosh^{-1} 1 = 0$. But $\cosh^{-1}$ is not differentiable for $x = 1$. Also for $\operatorname{sech}^{-1} x = \cosh^{-1} (1/x)$, we take the *positive* value in $(0, \infty)$ for x in $(0,1)$.

For differentiating the six inverse hyperbolic functions, we formulate rules 29 to 34:

29. $D_x \sinh^{-1} u = \dfrac{D_x u}{\sqrt{1 + u^2}}.$

30. $D_x \cosh^{-1} u = \dfrac{D_x u}{\sqrt{u^2 - 1}}, \ u > 1.$

31. $D_x \tanh^{-1} u = \dfrac{D_x u}{\sqrt{1 - u^2}}, \ |u| < 1.$

32. $D_x \coth^{-1} u = \dfrac{D_x u}{\sqrt{1 - u^2}}, \ |u| > 1.$

33. $D_x \operatorname{sech}^{-1} u = \dfrac{D_x u}{u\sqrt{1 - u^2}}, \ 0 < u < 1.$

34. $D_x \operatorname{csch}^{-1} u = \dfrac{-D_x u}{u\sqrt{1 + u^2}}, \ u \neq 0.$

It is sometimes convenient to express the inverse hyperbolic functions in terms of logarithms by such formulas as

$$\sinh^{-1} x = \ln (x + \sqrt{x^2 + 1}) \qquad -\infty < x < \infty, \tag{27}$$
$$\cosh^{-1} x = \ln (x + \sqrt{x^2 - 1}) \qquad x \geq 1, \tag{28}$$
$$\tanh^{-1} x = \tfrac{1}{2} \ln \frac{1 + x}{1 - x} \qquad |x| < 1, \tag{29}$$
$$\coth^{-1} x = \tfrac{1}{2} \ln \frac{x + 1}{x - 1} = \tanh^{-1} \frac{1}{x} \qquad |x| > 1, \tag{30}$$
$$\operatorname{sech}^{-1} x = \ln \frac{1 + \sqrt{1 - x^2}}{x} = \cosh^{-1} \frac{1}{x} \qquad 0 < x \leq 1, \tag{31}$$
$$\operatorname{csch}^{-1} x = \ln \left(\frac{1}{x} + \frac{\sqrt{1 + x^2}}{x} \right) = \sinh^{-1} \frac{1}{x} \qquad x \neq 0. \tag{32}$$

To prove any one of these we use the relation $x = f(y)$, which is satisfied by $y = f^{-1}(x)$. We express $f(y)$ in terms of exponential functions by means of Eqs. (18), (19), or the similar ones.   The result may then be written as a first- or second-degree equation in e^y.   We solve for e^y, taking the appropriate sign of the radical in the case of a quadratic, and then write $y = \ln e^y$.

For example, if $y = \sinh^{-1} x$, then $x = \sinh y = (e^y - e^{-y})/2$. And $(e^y)^2 - 2x(e^y) - 1 = 0$.   The solution of this quadratic equation is $e^y = x + \sqrt{x^2 + 1}$, with the plus sign to make $e^y > 0$.   This leads to Eq. (27).

48—DIFFERENTIALS

Let the function f be defined by $y = f(x)$.   And let us consider a particular value of x at which there is a derivative $f'(x)$.   Then the *differential* of the *independent* variable, dx, is any number selected arbitrarily.   It is often taken as fixed, or constant, during the discussion.   But sometimes dx is itself regarded as an additional independent variable.   The *differential* of the *dependent* variable is then defined by the equation

$$dy = f'(x)\, dx. \tag{33}$$

Let $f(g)$ be a composite function defined by the relations $y = f(u)$ and $u = g(x)$, as in Sec. 33.   Then, by the definition just given and rule 8 of Sec. 33, we have

$$du = g'(x)\, dx \qquad dy = f'(u)\, g'(x)\, dx. \tag{34}$$

It follows that

$$dy = f'(u)\, du. \tag{35}$$

Thus this relation holds regardless of whether u is the independent variable, or u and y are each dependent variables.   If $du \neq 0$ in Eq. (35), $f'(u) = dy/du$.

If $dx \neq 0$ in Eq. (33), we may write

$$f'(x) = \frac{dy}{dx}. \tag{36}$$

We also write $dy/dx = (d/dx)(y) = (d/dx)\, f(x)$, so that d/dx is an alternative to D_x.

This notation was used as early as 1677 by Leibniz. The definition of differential given here, due to C. J. de la Vallée Poussin (1866– , Belgian), became known through his textbook on analysis of 1912.

If $dx \neq 0$ and $du \neq 0$ in Eq. (34), we have

$$g'(x) = \frac{du}{dx} \qquad f'(u) = \frac{dy}{du} \qquad [f(g)]'(x) = \frac{dy}{dx} \, . \tag{37}$$

Thus the chain rule takes the form of an algebraic identity

$$\frac{dy}{dx} = \frac{dy}{du}\frac{du}{dx} \, . \tag{38}$$

This fact sometimes simplifies the technique of differentiation if differentials are used.

Again, in Eq. (8) of Sec. 43, we found that the slope of a curve given by the parametric equations $x = f(t)$, $y = g(t)$ was given by $D_x y = g'(t)/f'(t)$. With the differential notation, this is obtained by division from

$$dx = f'(t)\, dt \qquad dy = g'(t)\, dt \tag{39}$$

by canceling dt. Thus

$$\frac{dy}{dx} = \frac{g\ (t)\ dt}{f'(t)\ dt} = \frac{g'(t)}{f'(t)} \, . \tag{40}$$

Again, consider Eq. (26) of Sec. 36. Here $y = f(x)$, $D_x f(x) = dy/dx$. And $x = f^{-1}(y)$, so that $(f^{-1})'(y) = dx/dy$. Thus Eq. (26) of Sec. 36 becomes

$$\frac{dy}{dx} = \frac{1}{dx/dy} \, . \tag{41}$$

We show in Example 3, below, how the method of implicit differentiation becomes more symmetric when differentials are used.

EXAMPLE 1.   Find dy if $y = x^4 - \sin x$.

SOLUTION.   We have $f'(x) = Dy = 4x^3 - \cos x$. Hence $dy = f'(x)\, dx = (4x^3 - \cos x)\, dx$.

EXAMPLE 2.   Find dy if $y = uv$, with $u = f(x)$, $v = g(x)$.

SOLUTION.   By rule 5 of Sec. 30, we have $Dy = u\, Dv + v\, Du$, or $dy/dx = u\ (dv/dx) + v\ (du/dx)$. Hence $dy = u\, dv + v\, du$.

EXAMPLE 3. Find $D_x y$ in terms of x and y if $2x^3 + 3y^2 = 5$.

SOLUTION. Taking differentials of each side of the given equation leads to $6x^2\,dx + 6y\,dy = 0$, $y\,dy = -x^2\,dx$, and $D_x y = dy/dx = -x^2/y$.

49—FORMULAS FOR DIFFERENTIALS

If $y = f(x)$, the differential dy may be found by first calculating $f'(x) = D_x y = dy/dx$ and multiplying this by dx. Hence any rule for finding derivatives may be converted into a rule for finding differentials through multiplying, by dx, both sides of the equation expressing the rule. This was illustrated for the product rule in Example 2 of Sec. 48. By this procedure we may deduce from the rules derived in Chap. 3 the following rules for differentials:

1. $dc = 0$.
3. $d(cu) = c\,du$.
4. $d(u + v) = du + dv$.
5. $d(uv) = u\,dv + v\,du$.
6a. $d\,u^c = cu^{c-1}\,du$.
7. $d\,(u/v) = (v\,du - u\,dv)/v^2$.
9. $d\,(\ln u) = du/u$.
10. $d\,e^u = e^u\,du$.

The analogues of rule 2 $(dx = dx)$ and of rule 8 $\left(\dfrac{dy}{dx} = \dfrac{dy}{du}\dfrac{du}{dx}\right)$ are omitted since they are formally identities and so do not have to be used explicitly. Further, we have taken rule 6a as superseding rule 6.

Corresponding analogues of rules 11 to 34 could be written, such as $d\,(\sin u) = \cos u\,du$ or $d\,(\sinh^{-1} u) = du/\sqrt{1 + u^2}$. After the student has derived a few of these for himself, he will be able to read them from the formulas for derivatives in this chapter by mentally substituting d for D_x throughout.

EXAMPLE 1. Find dy if $y = x^2 \cos (x^2 - 2x)$.

SOLUTION. From rule 5, $dy = x^2\,d \cos (x^2 - 2x) + \cos (x^2 - 2x)\,d\,(x^2) = x^2[-\sin (x^2 - 2x)](2x - 2)\,dx + \cos (x^2 - 2x)2x\,dx$. Thus $dy = 2x[x(1 - x) \sin (x^2 - 2x) + \cos (x^2 - 2x)]\,dx$.

EXAMPLE 2.   Find dy if $y = x/\sqrt{4 - x^2}$.

SOLUTION.   Using logarithmic differentiation as in Sec. 40, we find

$$\frac{dy}{y} = \frac{dx}{x} - \frac{1}{2}\frac{-2x\,dx}{4 - x^2} = \frac{4 - x^2 + x^2}{x(4 - x^2)}\,dx = \frac{4\,dx}{x(4 - x^2)}.$$

Hence

$$dy = y\,\frac{4\,dx}{x(4 - x^2)} = \frac{4\,dx}{(4 - x^2)^{3/2}}.$$

EXAMPLE 3.   For a small value of $dx = \Delta x$, dy is approximately equal to Δy. Use this fact to find an approximation to $\sqrt[3]{1.06}$.

SOLUTION.   Let $f(x) = x^{1/3}$. For $x = 1$, $dx = \Delta x = 0.06$, $y + dy$ will be close to $y + \Delta y = f(1.06) = \sqrt[3]{1.06}$. Since $y = f(1) = 1$ and $dy = f'(x)\,dx = \frac{1}{3}x^{-2/3}\,dx = 0.02$, 1.02 is the desired approximation.

50—DERIVATIVES OF HIGHER ORDER

The derivative f' of the function f is the *first* derivative of f. The derivative of f', designated by f'', is the *second* derivative of f. Similarly, the derivative of f'', designated by f''', is the third derivative of f. And we may continue, with $f^{(n)}$ denoting the nth derivative of f. In $f^{(4)}$ or $f^{(n)}$ we use the parentheses about 4 or n to distinguish the derivative from the corresponding power. The other notations for the value of higher derivatives at x are

$$\frac{d^2y}{dx^2} = y'' = D_x^2 y = \left(\frac{d}{dx}\right)^2 f(x) = f''(x), \tag{42}$$

$$\frac{d^n y}{dx^n} = y^{(n)} = D_x^n y = \left(\frac{d}{dx}\right)^n f(x) = f^{(n)}(x). \tag{43}$$

The reader should note carefully the placing of the index n in $d^n y/dx^n$. This is suggested by the form in terms of the operator (d/dx) involving $(d/dx)^n$. It is best to think of the expression $d^n y/dx^n$ as a single symbol, rather than a quotient. This symbol is more widely used than any of the other expressions in Eq. (43). The evaluation of d^2y/dx^2 by thinking of it as $(d/dx)(d/dx)$ is illustrated in the examples that follow.

In Sec. 35 we stated a theorem on implicit functions and described a procedure for finding their first derivatives. It is a corollary of that theorem that the process may be repeated to give higher derivatives and will always give correct results if all the functions of x and y met are continuous and we encounter no zero denominators. As in Example 2, it will always turn out that the denominator for d^2y/dx^2, or for any higher derivative, will necessarily be $\neq 0$ if that for $dy/dx \neq 0$.

EXAMPLE 1.   Find d^ny/dx^n if $y = 2x/(2 - x)$.

SOLUTION.   We have

$$\frac{dy}{dx} = 2\,\frac{(2 - x) \cdot 1 - x(-1)}{(2 - x)^2} = \frac{4}{(2 - x)^2} = 4(2 - x)^{-2}.$$

$$\frac{d^2y}{dx^2} = \frac{d}{dx}\,4(2 - x)^{-2} = 4(-2)(2 - x)^{-3}(-1)$$
$$= 4 \cdot 2\,(2 - x)^{-3}.$$

Similarly,

$$\frac{d^3y}{dx^3} = 4 \cdot 3 \cdot 2\,(2 - x)^{-4}.$$

This suggests that

$$\frac{d^ny}{dx^n} = \frac{4(n!)}{(2 - x)^{n+1}},$$

which is easily verified by mathematical induction (Sec. 17).

EXAMPLE 2.   Find d^2y/dx^2 if $x^2 - y^2 = 1$.

SOLUTION.   By implicit differentiation, $2x\,dx - 2y\,dy = 0$, $dy/dx = x/y$. Further,

$$d\left(\frac{dy}{dx}\right) = \frac{y\,dx - x\,dy}{y^2},$$

so that

$$\frac{d^2y}{dx^2} = \frac{d(dy/dx)}{dx} = \frac{y - x(dy/dx)}{y^2}.$$

On replacing dy/dx by its value x/y, we find that

$$\frac{d^2y}{dx^2} = \frac{y - x(x/y)}{x^2} = \frac{y^2 - x^2}{y^3} = \frac{-1}{y^3},$$

since $x^2 - y^2 = 1$. Thus $d^2y/dx^2 = -1/y^3$.

EXAMPLE 3.   Find d^2y/dx^2 if $x = \cosh t$, $y = \sinh t$.

SOLUTION.   We have $dx = \sinh t\ dt$, $dy = \cosh t\ dt$, so that $dy/dx = (\cosh t\ dt)/(\sinh t\ dt) = \coth t$. Hence $d\ (dy/dx) = -\operatorname{csch}^2 t\ dt$. On dividing this by $dx = \sinh t\ dt$, we find $d^2y/dx^2 = -\operatorname{csch}^3 t$.

As we remarked after Eq. (20), the graph of Example 3 is the right-hand half of that in Example 2. And from Example 2, $d^2y/dx^2 = -1/y^3 = -1/\sinh^3 t = -\operatorname{csch}^3 t$, which checks Example 3.

EXAMPLE 4.   Find the acceleration $a = dv/dt = d^2s/dt^2$ if $s = b \sinh \omega t + c \cosh \omega t$.

SOLUTION.   We have

$$\frac{ds}{dt} = b\omega \cosh \omega t + c\omega \sinh \omega t,$$

and

$$\frac{d^2s}{dt^2} = \frac{d}{dt}\left(\frac{ds}{dt}\right) = b\omega^2 \sinh \omega t + c\omega^2 \cosh \omega t.$$

Hence $a = \omega^2(b \sinh \omega t + c \cosh \omega t)$. We note that $a = \omega^2 s$.

PROBLEMS

Section 42

1. Let OP_1 be a radius of the unit circle and P_1P_2 be an arc equal to u, so that the central angle $P_1OP_2 = u$. Let the line tangent to the circle at P_1 cut OP_2 produced at P_3. And let Q be the foot of the perpendicular from P_2 to OP_1. Verify that $OQ = \cos u$, $QP_2 = \sin u$, $OP_1 = 1$, $P_1P_3 = \tan u$. Note that triangle OP_1P_3

contains sector OP_1P_2, which contains triangle OQP_2. As in Sec. 26, deduce that

area $OP_2 \leq$ area sector $OP_1P_2 \leq$ area OP_1P_3.

Or $\frac{1}{2} \cos u \sin u \leq \frac{1}{2} u \leq \frac{1}{2} \tan u$, so that $\cos u \leq u/\sin u \leq 1/\cos u$. Taking limits gives $u/\sin u \to 1$ as $u \to 0+$, and hence a proof that $\sin u/u \to 1$ for $u \to 0+$. If $u = |h|/2$, this establishes Eq. (4).

Section 43

2. Prove that

$$\lim_{x \to 0} \frac{1 - \cos x}{x^2} = \frac{1}{2}.$$

Hint: $1 - \cos x = 2 \sin^2 (x/2)$.

Evaluate each of the following limits:

3. $\lim_{x \to 0} \dfrac{\tan 2x}{4x}$.

4. $\lim_{x \to 0} \dfrac{\sin 3x}{\tan 5x}$.

5. $\lim_{x \to 0} \dfrac{1 - \cos x}{\sin^2 x}$.

Hint: Use Prob. 2.

6. $\lim_{x \to \pi} \dfrac{\sin 3x}{\pi - x}$.

Hint: Put $\pi - x = v$.

Section 44

Find $f'(x)$ for each given $f(x)$ in Probs. 7 to 12.

7. $2 \cos 4x + 3 \sin 2x$.

8. $\tan 3x + \cot 3x$.

9. $\sec 2x \csc 2x$.

10. $x^3 \tan x$.

11. $e^x \sin 3x$.

12. $x^2 \sin (1/x)$.

Find $D_x y$ in terms of x and y for each given equation in Probs. 13 to 20.

13. $\sin xy = 2x + 3y$.

14 $\cos (x + y) = x \sin y$.

Section 45

15. $\tan^{-1} \sqrt{x}$.

16. $x \sin^{-1} x$.

17. $2 \sec^{-1} 3x$.

18. $\cos^{-1} (1 - x)$.

19. $\sin^{-1} e^x$.

20. $\cos^{-1} (\ln x)$.

21. Check rule 22 by noting that $\csc^{-1} x = \sin^{-1} (1/x)$ for $x > 0$, but $\csc^{-1} x = -\sin^{-1} (1/x)$ for $x < 0$.

Section 46

Find $f'(x)$ for each given $f(x)$:

22. $\sinh 5x$.

23. $\cosh 4x$.

24. $\tanh 6x$.

25. $\operatorname{sech}^2 3x$.

26. $\sinh^3 x$.

27. $\cosh^2 3x$.

Section 47

Find $f'(x)$ for each given $f(x)$:

28. $\sinh^{-1} 2x$.

29. $\cosh^{-1} 3x$.

30. $\tanh^{-1} \sqrt{x}$.

31. $\coth^{-1} \sqrt{x}$.

Section 48

Find dy/dx for each of the following relations:

32. $x^4 + y^4 = 1$.

33. $x = 4 \sin 2t, y = \cos 2t$.

34. $2e^x + e^{2y} = 3$.

35. $x = 2 \sinh t, y = 6 \cosh t$.

36. $x = t^2, y = \ln t$.

37. $x = t^2 + 1, y = t^4$.

Section 49

If $y = f(x)$, find dy for each given $f(x)$:

38. $\sin 3x \sin 5x$.

39. $e^x \sec x$.

40. $(\cos 3x)/(\cos 2x)$.

41. $(\sinh 2x)/(\cosh 3x)$.

Find dy/dx for each given equation:

42. $x^2 y = x + 2$.

43. $x^2 + 3xy = 5$.

44. $x \, e^y = y \sin x$.

45. $\ln (x + 2y) = 3xy$.

Find a reasonable approximation to each of the following:

46. $\sqrt{171.6}$.

47. $\sqrt[4]{81.8}$.

48. $\sqrt[3]{28.2}$.

49. $\sqrt[5]{33}$.

Section 50

50. If $y = \ln x$, verify that $\dfrac{d^n y}{dx^n} = (-1)^{n-1} \dfrac{(n-1)!}{x^n}$.

51. If $y = \dfrac{1}{1 - 2x}$, verify that $\dfrac{d^n y}{dx^n} = \dfrac{2^n \, n!}{(1 - 2x)^{n+1}}$.

52. If $y = a \, e^{bx}$, verify that $\dfrac{d^n y}{dx^n} = ab^n \, e^{bx}$.

Find $d^2 y/dx^2$ for each of the following relations:

53. $x^2 + 4y^2 = 1$.

54. $x = 2 \cos t, \; y = \sin t$.

55. $xy = 1$.

56. $x = 1/t, \; y = t$.

Find the acceleration for the motions given by each of the following equations:

57. $s = \sqrt{t^2 + 1}$.

58. $s = a \cos \omega t + b \sin \omega t$.

59. $s = t^2/(1 + t)$.

60. $s = 4e^{2t} + 6e^{-2t}$.

5

APPLICATIONS OF DIFFERENTIATION

We are now in a position to apply the technique of differentiation to questions concerning rates, maxima and minima, and curve tracing.

51—INCREASING AND DECREASING FUNCTIONS

Let the function f, defined by $y = f(x)$, be such that dy/dx is positive when $x = x_0$. Then near (x_0, y_0) the graph of $y = f(x)$ rises upward to the right and falls downward to the left. To see this, let $f'(x_0) = p > 0$. Then since $\Delta y/\Delta x \to p$, for sufficiently small Δx the ratio is within $p/2$ of the limit, and so is $> p/2 > 0$. Thus Δy has the same sign as Δx. We say that f is *increasing* at x_0, meaning that as x increases through x_0, $f(x)$ increases.

A similar discussion may be made when $f'(x_0) < 0$. This proves the theorem:

The function f is *increasing* at any value where $f'(x)$ is *positive*. And f is *decreasing* at any value x where $f'(x)$ is *negative*.

EXAMPLE.   At noon one ship A is steaming east at the rate of 10 mph. A second ship B is 6 miles north of A at noon and steaming southeast at the rate of $8\sqrt{2}$ mph. How fast are the ships separating or approaching each other after t hr?

SOLUTION.   Let the origin be at the position of ship A at noon, the x axis to the east and the y axis to the north. Then after t hr, the position of A is $(10t, 0)$. And the position of B is $(8t, 6 - 8t)$. If s is the distance between the ships at time t, then $s^2 = (10t - 8t)^2 + (0 - 6 + 8t)^2 = (2t)^2 + (8t - 6)^2$. From this equation it follows that $2s\, ds = 4 \cdot 2t\, dt + 2(8t - 6)8\, dt = 8(17t - 12)$. Thus

$$\frac{ds}{dt} = \frac{8(17t - 12)}{2s} = \frac{8(17t - 12)}{4\sqrt{t^2 + (4t - 3)^2}} = \frac{2(17t - 12)}{\sqrt{17t^2 - 24t + 9}} .$$

The ships are approaching for $0 < t < 12/17$ when $ds/dt < 0$, and separating for $t > 12/17$ when $ds/dt > 0$.

52—RELATED RATES

Many problems involve time rates of change of several variables, each of which is a differentiable function of the time. The rates of some are given, and the rates of others are to be found. This is accomplished by writing down the equations which the variables must satisfy and differentiating each of these with respect to the time or forming the corresponding differentials. The resulting relations will determine the unknown rates in terms of the known rates. During this procedure care must be taken not to substitute values of the variables given for a particular time before differentiating.

EXAMPLE 1.   At a particular time, the sides of a right triangle are $x = 3, y = 4, z = 5$. If at this time $dy/dt = 2$ and $dz/dt = -2$, find dx/dt.

SOLUTION.   At any time, $z^2 = x^2 + y^2$. From this, $2z\,dz = 2x\,dx + 2y\,dy$. Dividing by $2\,dt$ gives $z\,(dz/dt) = x\,(dx/dt) + y\,(dy/dt)$. Inserting the given values, we find $5(-2) = 3\,(dx/dt) + 4(2)$, so that $dx/dt = \dfrac{-10 - 8}{3} = -6$.

EXAMPLE 2.   The sides of a rectangle are x in. and y in. The area of the rectangle is constantly equal to 18 in.^{2} At time t_0, x is decreasing twice as fast as y is increasing. Find x and y at this time t_0.

SOLUTION.   At any time, we have $xy = 18$. Thus $x\,dy + y\,dx = 0$ and $dy/dx = -y/x$. At time t_0, $dx/dt = -2\,(dy/dt)$. Hence

$$\frac{dy}{dx} = \frac{dy/dt}{dx/dt} = -\frac{1}{2} = -\frac{y}{x} \qquad \text{and} \qquad x = 2y \text{ at } t_0.$$

Since $xy = 18$, we have $2y^2 = 18$, $y^2 = 9$, and therefore $y = 3$, since -3 is not admissible as the measure of a side. Hence $x = 18/y = 6$. Thus at t_0, $x = 6$ and $y = 3$.

53—TANGENT AND NORMAL LINES

Let $P_1(x_1, y_1)$ be a point on the curve C which is the graph of the equation $y = f(x)$. Then $f'(x_1)$ is the slope of T, the straight line *tangent* to C at P_1. And from Eq. (11) of Sec. 4, one form of the equation of T is

$$y - y_1 = f'(x_1)\,(x - x_1). \tag{1}$$

This may also be written

$$y - y_1 = \left(\frac{dy}{dx}\right)_1 (x - x_1). \tag{2}$$

Here the subscript 1 means that dy/dx is evaluated for $x = x_1$.

If the locus is given by an equation in x and y as in Sec. 35, we may find dy/dx in terms of x and y by the implicit-differentiation method of that section. And if the curve C is given by parametric equations, we may find dy/dx from Eq. (40) of Sec. 48.

The line N, drawn through P_1 *perpendicular* to the tangent line, is called the *normal* to the curve C at P_1. If ϕ_t is the inclination of the tangent line to the x axis, and ϕ_n is the inclination of the normal, we have

$$\tan \phi_n = \tan \left(\phi_t \pm \frac{\pi}{2}\right) = -\cot \phi_t = -\frac{1}{\tan \phi_t}. \tag{3}$$

Hence one form of the equation of the normal N is

$$y - y_1 = \frac{-1}{(dy/dx)_1} (x - x_1). \tag{4}$$

The angle between two curves which intersect at a point P_0 is defined as the angle between their tangent lines at P_0. Let these tangent lines L_1 and L_2 have inclinations to the x axis ϕ_1 and ϕ_2, respectively. Then one angle from L_1 to L_2 is $\alpha = \phi_2 - \phi_1$, so that

$$\tan \alpha = \frac{\tan \phi_2 - \tan \phi_1}{1 + \tan \phi_1 \tan \phi_2} = \frac{m_2 - m_1}{1 + m_1 m_2}, \tag{5}$$

where $\tan \phi_1 = m_1$, $\tan \phi_2 = m_2$.

54—APPROXIMATE VALUE OF
SMALL INCREMENTS

Let the increment Δy correspond to Δx for $y = f(x)$, so that

$$\Delta y = f(x_1 + \Delta x) - f(x_1). \tag{6}$$

Let ϵ be defined in terms of x_1 and Δx by

$$\epsilon = \frac{\Delta y}{\Delta x} - f'(x_1) \text{ if } \Delta x \neq 0 \qquad \epsilon = 0 \text{ if } \Delta x = 0. \tag{7}$$

When $\Delta x \to 0$, $\Delta y/\Delta x \to f'(x_1)$, so that $\epsilon \to 0$. Hence ϵ is a continuous function of Δx at $\Delta x = 0$. Also, for all values of Δx, we have

$$\Delta y = f'(x_1)\,\Delta x + \epsilon\,\Delta x. \tag{8}$$

Let y_{tan} denote the y on the tangent line. Then it follows from Eq. (1) that

$$y_{\text{tan}} - y_1 = f'(x_1)(x - x_1) \qquad \text{or } \Delta y_{\text{tan}} = f'(x_1)\,\Delta x. \tag{9}$$

From Eq. (33) of Sec. 48, $\Delta y_{\text{tan}} = dy$ if $dx = \Delta x$. Thus Eq. (8) may be written

$$\Delta y = \Delta y_{\text{tan}} + \epsilon\,\Delta x = dy + \epsilon\,\Delta x. \tag{10}$$

When $\Delta x \to 0$, $\epsilon \to 0$. Hence, for sufficiently small Δx, $\Delta y - dy$ is a small fraction of Δx. And if $f'(x_1) \neq 0$, it is a small fraction of dy or Δy. Hence dy is a good approximation to Δy. We used this fact in Example 3 of Sec. 49.

EXAMPLE 1.   Use differentials to approximate the value of tan 59°.

SOLUTION.   Let $y = \tan x$. Then $dy = \sec^2 x\,dx$. If $x_1 = \pi/3$ radians (60°), then $y_1 = \sqrt{3} = 1.732$. And $\sec^2(\pi/3) = 4$. Let $dx = \Delta x = -0.01745$ radian (−1°). Then $dy = 4(-0.0175) = -0.070$. Hence $\tan 59° = y_1 + \Delta y \sim y_1 + dy = 1.732 - 0.070 = 1.662$.

EXAMPLE 2.   For a simple pendulum of length L, the period T is given by $T = 2\pi\sqrt{L/g}$. Find an approximation to the largest possible percentage error in the calculated value of T if the error in L is at most 2 per cent and that in g is at most 1 per cent.

SOLUTION.   From $T = 2\pi\sqrt{L/g}$, by logarithmic differentiation we have $dT/T = \frac{1}{2}(dL/L) - \frac{1}{2}(dg/g)$. With $dL/L = 0.02$ and $dg/g = -0.01$, we have $dT/T = 0.01 + 0.005 = 0.015$. Hence the largest possible relative error in T is approximately 1.5 per cent.

55—SKETCHING GRAPHS

In plotting the graph of the function f defined by $y = f(x)$, a knowledge of the behavior of $f'(x)$ and $f''(x)$ is helpful. Suppose that $f'(x) > 0$ throughout some open interval. Then, by Sec. 51, the graph is rising to the right in that interval. And if $f'(x) < 0$ throughout some interval, the graph is falling to the right in that interval.

At an isolated point separating two such intervals of opposite type (Fig. 13) we shall often find $f'(x) = 0$. But such a point (Fig. 14) may be one at which $f'(x)$ fails to exist.

Let f be continuous at x_1. And, for some $h > 0$, let the graph be rising in the left-hand interval $(x_1 - h, x_1)$ and falling in the right-hand interval $(x_1, x_1 + h)$. These conditions are sufficient for f to have a *relative* or *local maximum* at $x = x_1$ (Figs. 13 and 14).

Next, for some $h > 0$, let the graph be falling in the left-hand interval $(x_2 - h, x_2)$ and rising in the right-hand interval $(x_2, x_2 + h)$. These conditions are sufficient for f to have a *relative* or *local minimum* at x_2 (Fig. 15).

For brevity, it is convenient to use the term *extremum*, or *extreme value*, to mean either a maximum or a minimum.

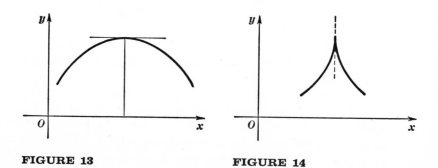

FIGURE 13   FIGURE 14

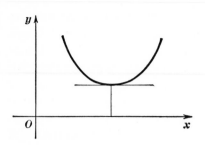

FIGURE 15

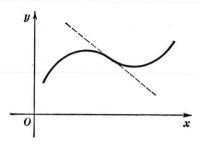

FIGURE 16

The second derivative, which was defined in Sec. 50,

$$f''(x) = \frac{d^2y}{dx^2} = \frac{d}{dx}\left(\frac{dy}{dx}\right),$$ (11)

is the derivative of the slope function. If $d^2y/dx^2 > 0$ throughout an open interval, the slope increases there. Thus the inclination of the tangent increases, and the curve is *concave upward* in the interval.

Similarly, if $d^2y/dx^2 < 0$ throughout an open interval, the curve is *concave downward* in the interval.

A point (Fig. 16) separating an arc which is concave upward from an arc which is concave downward is called a *point of inflection*. At such a point, we often have $f''(x) = 0$. But such a point may be one at which $f''(x)$ fails to exist.

EXAMPLE. Sketch the graph of $y = x^3/(x^2 - 1)$.

SOLUTION. We have

$$\frac{dy}{dx} = \frac{x^2(x^2 - 3)}{(x^2 - 1)^2} \qquad \frac{d^2y}{dx^2} = \frac{2x(x^2 + 3)}{(x^2 - 1)^3} \qquad \text{(Fig. 17)}.$$

The lines $x = 1$, $x = -1$ are vertical asymptotes, since parts of the locus with large $|y|$ closely approximate these lines. Also, $y \to +\infty$ as $x \to -1+$ or $x \to 1+$, but $y \to -\infty$ as $x \to -1-$ or $x \to 1-$. The graph is rising in the intervals $(-\infty, -\sqrt{3})$ and $(\sqrt{3}, \infty)$, where $dy/dx > 0$. The graph is falling in the intervals $(-\sqrt{3}, -1)$, $(-1, 0)$, $(0, 1)$, $(1, \sqrt{3})$, where $dy/dx < 0$. Hence $(-\sqrt{3}, -3\sqrt{3}/2)$ is a maximum point, and $(\sqrt{3}, 3\sqrt{3}/2)$ is a minimum point, on the graph. The graph is concave upward in the intervals $(-1,0)$, $(1, \infty)$, where $d^2y/dx^2 > 0$, and concave downward in the intervals $(-\infty, -1)$, $(0,1)$, where $d^2y/dx^2 < 0$. Hence $(0,0)$ is a point of inflection.

Since $y = x + x/(x^2 - 1)$ and the last fraction $\to 0$ when $x \to \infty$, it follows that $y = x$ is an oblique asymptote, the curve being above this for x large and positive and below this for x large numerically but negative. Hence the graph is as shown in Fig. 17.

This example shows that we may have $dy/dx = 0$ without having a maximum or a minimum, and also that the value of y at a relative minimum may be greater than that at a relative maximum.

We might have noticed that for this $f(x)$, $f(-x) = -f(x)$. This shows that if (x,y) is on the graph, so is $(-x, -y)$. Thus the origin is a center of symmetry, each chord through it being bisected by the origin. This is best used as a check, but might have been used to construct the graph for $(-\infty, 0)$ from that for $(0, \infty)$.

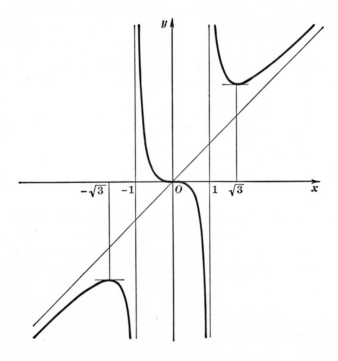

FIGURE 17

56—ABSOLUTE MAXIMUM AND MINIMUM

Let the function f be defined at each point of some set E, which may be part or all of its domain. Suppose that v is a point of E such that $f(v) \geq f(x)$ for any x in E. Then $f(v)$ is called the (*absolute*[1]) *maximum* value of f on the set E. Similarly, if u is a point of E such that $f(u) \leq f(x)$ for any x in E, then $f(u)$ is called the (*absolute*) *minimum* value of f on E.

For example, let f be the identity function, defined by $f(x) = x$. Then, if E is the closed interval $-h \leq x \leq h$, the maximum is $f(h) = h$ and the minimum is $f(-h) = -h$. This illustrates the *extreme-value theorem* which we stated in Sec. 13. We restate it in terms of the definitions of this section:

If the function f is continuous on a closed interval $a \leq x \leq b$, then there exists at least one number u and one number v (but perhaps more than one) such that $f(u) = m$ is the absolute minimum of f and $f(v) = M$ is the absolute maximum of f on the closed interval $[a,b]$. Thus $m \leq f(x) \leq M$ for all x in $[a,b]$.

As an illustration of more than one value, we may consider the function $\sin$ on the interval $-2\pi \leq x \leq 2\pi$. Here the maximum is $1 = f(\pi/2) = f(-3\pi/2)$. And the minimum is $-1 = f(-\pi/2) = f(3\pi/2)$. For an open interval, we may not have any values u and v. For example, consider $f(x) = x$ on the open interval $(-1,1)$, or $-1 < x < 1$. There is no maximum or minimum assumed on this open interval.

If a function has a relative maximum (or minimum) at x_1 of the type considered in Sec. 55, then there is some neighborhood of x_1, $x_1 - h < x < x_1 + h$ in which $f(x_1)$ is the absolute maximum (or minimum).

Let f have a derivative f', and let $f'(x) > 0$ throughout the closed interval $[a,b]$. Then f is increasing in this interval, $f(a)$ is the minimum, and $f(b)$ is the maximum on the interval.

---

[1] Some writers who use the term *local* extremum in preference to *relative* extremum, in contradistinction use *global* extremum in place of *absolute* extremum.

Similarly, if $f'(x) < 0$ on $[a,b]$, $f(a)$ is the maximum and $f(b)$ is the minimum on the interval.

Among the interior points of a closed interval, possible maximum or minimum points may be found by considering the derivative.

57—CRITICAL VALUES

Let the function f be continuous on the open interval (a,b). And let $f'(x)$ exist for each point of the interval, with the exception of certain isolated points. Then any point x of the interval at which $f'(x) = 0$, or $f'(x)$ fails to exist, is called a *critical value* for f.

Suppose that f assumes an absolute maximum on (a,b) at some interior point x_0, $a < x_0 < b$. Then x_0 must be a critical point for f. To prove this, let us first assume that $f'(x_0)$ is positive, $f'(x_0) > 0$. Then, by Sec. 51, for each sufficiently small positive value of h, we have $\Delta y = f(x_0 + h) - f(x_0) > 0$, and $f(x_0) < f(x_0 + h)$. With an h such that $x_0 + h < b$, this contradicts the assumption that $f(x_0)$ is the absolute maximum of f on (a,b).

Similar reasoning shows that for some h with $a < x_0 - h$, we have $f(x_0) < f(x_0 - h)$ if $f'(x_0) < 0$. This also contradicts the assumption that $f(x_0)$ is a maximum.

Since $f'(x_0)$ cannot be positive and cannot be negative, it either exists and is zero or fails to exist. In either case, x_0 is a critical point of f and we have proved the theorem:

If a function f which is continuous on the open interval (a,b) assumes its absolute maximum (or minimum) at a point x_0 with $a < x_0 < b$, then x_0 is a critical point for f.

The part about the minimum may be proved either by using similar reasoning or by noting that if $f(x_0)$ is a minimum of f, then $-f(x_0)$ is a maximum of $-f$.

58—TESTS FOR RELATIVE MAXIMA OR MINIMA

Let f have a relative maximum or minimum at x_0. Then, since this is an absolute maximum or minimum for some interval containing x_0, by the theorem just proved, x_0 will be a critical point for f.

Let f be continuous and differentiable in some neighborhood of x_0, with the possible exception of x_0 itself. Then:

If $f'(x)$ changes from positive to negative as x increases through x_0, the function f has a relative maximum at $x = x_0$.

If $f'(x)$ changes from negative to positive as x increases through x_0, the function f has a relative minimum at $x = x_0$.

If $f'(x)$ has the same sign on both sides of $x = x_0$, the function has neither a maximum nor a minimum at $x = x_0$.

These theorems all follow by the relation of a positive (negative) sign of the derivative to the increasing (decreasing) character of a function, discussed in Sec. 51.

Occasionally, as with polynomials, it is simpler to consider the sign of the second derivative instead of examining the sign changes. In order to have a second derivative at x_0, the first derivative must exist, so that if x_0 is a critical point, we must have $f'(x_0) = 0$. If $f''(x_0) > 0$, $f'(x)$ must increase through zero and so change from negative to positive, giving a minimum. Similarly, $f''(x_0) < 0$ means that $f'(x)$ decreases through zero from plus to minus, and so gives a maximum. This proves the theorem:

If $f'(x_0) = 0$ and $f''(x_0) < 0$, then $f(x_0)$ is a relative maximum value of f. If $f'(x_0) = 0$ and $f''(x_0) > 0$, then $f(x_0)$ is a relative minimum value of f.

EXAMPLE 1.   Find the absolute maximum and minimum values of f, defined by $f(x) = x^3 - 3x$, on the interval $-a \leq x \leq a$.

SOLUTION.   We have $y = x^3 - 3x$, $dy/dx = 3x^2 - 3$, $d^2y/dx^2 = 6x$. Now $3(x + 1)(x - 1) = 0$ when $x = 1$ or -1, the critical points. Either from the change in sign of $x - 1$ from $-$ to $+$ or from the positive value of $6(1)$, we see that $x = 1$ gives a relative minimum. Similarly, from either the change of sign of $-(x + 1)$ from $+$ to $-$ or the negative value of $6(-1)$, we see that $x = -1$ gives a relative minimum. Since $f(x)$ increases in $(-\infty, -1)$ and $(1, \infty)$ and decreases in $(-1,1)$, it follows that if $a \leq 1$, then $f(-a)$ is a maximum and $f(a)$ is a minimum. For $a = 2$, $f(2) = f(-1) = 2$ is a maximum and $f(-2) = f(1) = -2$ is a minimum. Hence, for $1 < a < 2$, $f(-1) = 2$ is a maximum and $f(1) = 2$ is a minimum. For $a > 2$, $f(a)$ is a maximum and $f(-a)$ is a minimum.

EXAMPLE 2.   Find the absolute maximum value of f, defined by $f(x) = 2 - x^{2/3}$.

SOLUTION.   We have $y = 2 - x^{2/3}$, $dy/dx = -\frac{2}{3}x^{-1/3}$. This becomes infinite for $x = 0$, the only critical value. The sign change of $f'(x)$ from $+$ to $-$ shows that this gives a maximum. Hence $f(0) = 2$ is the absolute maximum. There is no minimum, since y decreases to $-\infty$ as $x \to \infty$ or as $x \to -\infty$.

59—APPLIED PROBLEMS IN MAXIMA AND MINIMA

Many problems are concerned with finding the greatest or least value of some magnitude which varies continuously subject to certain restrictions. We use the given conditions to express the numerical measure of the magnitude as a function of a single variable in some interval. The absolute maximum or minimum of the function in this interval may be found as illustrated in Sec. 58.

EXAMPLE 1.   Find the box of largest volume which can be made from a sheet of aluminum in the form of a square b in. on a side by cutting out and discarding equal square pieces at the corners and bending up the projecting rectangles thus formed.

SOLUTION.   Let x, necessarily with $0 < x < b/2$, be the height of the box. Then the side of the square base of the box is $b - 2x$, so that the volume of the box is $V = x(b - 2x)^2$. Whence $dV/dx = (b - 2x)^2 - 4x(b - 2x) = 12(x - b/6)(x - b/2)$. Thus V has critical values $x = b/6$, a relative maximum since dV/dx changes from $+$ to $-$, and $x = b/2$, a relative minimum since dV/dx changes from $-$ to $+$. On the interval $[0, b/2]$ the minimum value of V is 0. This is assumed at the end points $x = 0$ (no height) and $x = b/2$ (no base). Thus, for an actual box, or the open interval $(0, b/2)$, there is no minimum. The maximum value of V, $2b^3/27$ in.³, is assumed at $x = b/6$ in.

EXAMPLE 2.   Find the volume of the right circular cylinder of largest volume that can be inscribed in a sphere of radius R.

SOLUTION.   Let a meridian section of the sphere be the circle with equation $x^2 + y^2 = R^2$. Then the corresponding section of the cylinder will be a rectangle, with one corner (x,y) on this circle. If the radius of base of the cylinder is x, then the height of the cylinder is $2y$, so that its volume is $V = 2\pi x^2 y$. From this and $x^2 + y^2 = R^2$, it is best to eliminate x and so find $V = 2\pi y(R^2 - y^2)$. Thus $dV/dy = 2\pi(R^2 - 3y^2)$. This is zero for $y = R/\sqrt{3}$, and $y = -R/\sqrt{3}$, the critical values for unrestricted y. As $0 < y < R$, we consider $y = R/\sqrt{3}$. For this, dV/dy changes from $+$ to $-$, so that it gives a maximum. Correspondingly, $x^2 = R^2 - y^2 = 2R^2/3$, $x = \sqrt{2}R/\sqrt{3}$. Thus the greatest volume is $(4\pi\sqrt{3}/9)\ R^3$.

60—ROLLE'S THEOREM

Suppose that a smooth curve which is the graph of $y = f(x)$ crosses the x axis at $x = a$ and at $x = b$. Then it is intuitively plausible that there is at least one point (x_0, y_0) with $a < x < b$ at which the tangent line is horizontal, or parallel to the x axis. That is, $f'(x_0) = 0$. This fact was observed in 1690 by M. Rolle (1652–1719, French). A present-day formulation is the following:

Rolle's Theorem.   Let the function f, defined by $y = f(x)$, be continuous in the closed interval $a \leq x \leq b$. And suppose that its derivative f' exists throughout the open interval $a < x < b$. Furthermore, let $f(a) = f(b) = 0$. Then there is at least one x_0 in the open interval where $f'(x_0) = 0$:

$$f'(x_0) = 0 \text{ for some } x_0 \text{ with } a < x_0 < b. \tag{12}$$

To prove this, we consider the maximum $f(v)$ and the minimum $f(u)$ of f on $[a,b]$, where u and v are known to exist by the extreme-value theorem of Sec. 56.   If $f(u) = f(v) = 0$, then $f(x) = 0$, and $f'(x) = 0$, throughout (a,b).   Hence x_0 may be any value on (a,b).

If $f(u)$, or $f(v)$, $\neq 0$, then u, or v, cannot equal a or b.   Hence we may take this u or v as the x_0 of the theorem in Sec. 57 and conclude that x_0 is a critical point of f.   Since $f'(x_0)$ is assumed to exist, it follows that $f'(x_0) = 0$, and the theorem is proved.   ■

61—THE MEAN-VALUE THEOREM

Let the portion of the graph of $y = f(x)$ between the points $[a, f(a)]$ and $[b, f(b)]$ be a smooth arc.   Then it is intuitively plausible that there is at least one point x_0, with $a < x_0 < b$, at which the tangent line is parallel to the chord.   Precisely, we have the following result:

Mean-value Theorem.   Let the function f, defined by $y = f(x)$, be continuous in the closed interval $a \leq x \leq b$.   And suppose that its derivative f' exists throughout the open interval $a < x < b$.   Then there is at least one point x_0 in the open interval such that $f(b) - f(a) = (b - a) f'(x_0)$:

$$\frac{f(b) - f(a)}{b - a} = f'(x_0) \text{ for some } x_0 \text{ with } a < x_0 < b. \tag{13}$$

To prove this, we form the function F defined by

$$F(x) = (b - a)[f(x) - f(a)] - (x - a)[f(b) - f(a)]. \tag{14}$$

Substitution shows that $F(a) = 0$ and $F(b) = 0$.   Also, from the assumptions made on f, the function F is continuous in the closed interval $[a,b]$ and differentiable in the open interval (a,b).   Hence we may apply Rolle's theorem to F, and so deduce that there is at least one x_0 in (a,b) such that

$$0 = F'(x_0) = (b - a) f'(x_0) - [f(b) - f(a)]. \tag{15}$$

When solved for $f'(x_0)$, this is Eq. (13).   ■

EXAMPLE. Let the functions F and G have the same derivative on an open interval (a,b). Prove that on this interval, $G(x) - F(x) = C$, or

$$G(x) = F(x) + C \qquad \text{where } C \text{ is a constant.} \tag{16}$$

SOLUTION. Let $H = G - F$. Then, since $F' = G'$, we have $H' = G' - F' = 0$. And $H'(x_0) = 0$ throughout (a,b). Since H' exists, H is continuous in (a,b). Select any two values x_1, x_2 such that $a < x_1 < x_2 < b$, and apply the mean-value theorem to the function H in $[x_1,x_2]$. This shows that there is an x_0, with $x_1 < x_0 < x_2$, such that $H(x_2) - H(x_1) = (x_2 - x_1)H'(x_0)$. Since $H'(x_0) = 0$, it follows that $H(x_2) - H(x_1) = 0$ or $H(x_2) = H(x_1)$ for $a < x_1 < x_2 < b$. Thus $H(x)$ is the same for any two values in (a,b), so that $H(x) = C$ on (a,b). That is, $G(x) - F(x) = C$.

62—CAUCHY'S MEAN-VALUE THEOREM

Let the portion of the graph of the parametric equations $x = f(t)$, $y = g(t)$ between $f(a)$, $g(a)$ and $f(b)$, $g(b)$ be a smooth arc as in Sec. 43. Then it is intuitively plausible that there is at least one value of the parameter $t = t_0$, with $a < t_0 < b$, at which the tangent line is parallel to the chord. This suggests a more general mean-value theorem, due to Cauchy. A present-day formulation is the following:

Cauchy's Mean-value Theorem. Let each of the two functions f, defined by $y = f(x)$, and g, defined by $y = g(x)$, be continuous in the closed interval $a \le x \le b$. And suppose that each of the derivatives f' and g' exists throughout the open interval $a < x < b$. Also assume that $g'(x) \ne 0$ in (a,b). Then there is at least one value x_0 in the open interval such that

$$\frac{f(b) - f(a)}{g(b) - g(a)} = \frac{f'(x_0)}{g'(x_0)} \qquad \textit{for some } x_0 \textit{ with } a < x_0 < b. \tag{17}$$

To prove this, we form the function F defined by

$$F(x) = [f(b) - f(a)][g(x) - g(a)] - [g(b) - g(a)][f(x) - f(a)]. \tag{18}$$

Substitution shows that $F(a) = 0$ and $F(b) = 0$. Also, from the assumptions on f and g, the function F is continuous in the closed interval $[a,b]$ and differentiable in the open interval (a,b). Hence we may apply Rolle's theorem to F, and so deduce that there is at least one x_0 in (a,b) such that

$$0 = [f(b) - f(a)] \, g'(x_0) - [g(b) - g(a)] \, f'(x_0). \tag{19}$$

Since $g'(x) \neq 0$ in (a,b), it follows from the mean-value theorem that $[g(b) - g(a)] \neq 0$. Hence we may divide by this difference times $g'(x_0) \neq 0$, and so deduce Eq. (17). ∎

63—INDETERMINATE FORMS

Let each of the functions f and g be continuous at $x = a$. Then, if $g(a) \neq 0$,

$$\lim_{x \to a} \frac{f(x)}{g(x)} = \frac{f(a)}{g(a)}. \tag{20}$$

If $f(a) = 0$ and $g(a) = 0$, the attempt to apply this equation leads to the meaningless expression $0/0$. We speak of the *indeterminate form* $0/0$ to mean that we are concerned with $\lim f(x)/g(x)$ as $x \to a$, and that $\lim f(x) = 0$, $\lim g(x) = 0$ as $x \to a$. A method of evaluating such limits by using derivatives was found by G. F. Marquis de L'Hôpital (1661–1704, French). We may state the basic theorem as follows:

L'Hôpital's Rule. Let each of the functions f and g be differentiable in some open right-hand interval $(a, a + h)$, with $g'(x) \neq 0$ there. If $\lim f(x) = 0$ and $\lim g(x) = 0$ as $x \to a+$, then

$$\lim_{x \to a+} \frac{f(x)}{g(x)} = \lim_{x \to a+} \frac{f'(x)}{g'(x)}, \tag{21}$$

provided that this latter expression approaches a limit or becomes infinite.

To prove this, let us define, or redefine, the functions f and g at a so that $f(a) = 0$ and $g(a) = 0$. Let x be any value such that $a <$

$x < a + h$. Then, in the closed interval $[a,x]$, all the conditions of Cauchy's mean-value theorem are satisfied, so that

$$\frac{f(x)}{g(x)} = \frac{f(x) - f(a)}{g(x) - g(a)} = \frac{f'(x_0)}{g'(x_0)} \qquad a < x_0 < x. \tag{22}$$

When $x \to a+$, necessarily $x_0 \to a+$, which proves the rule. ∎

A similar argument applies when $x \to a-$ or $x \to a$ without regard to a restriction in sign. And it may be proved by changing variables from x to $u = 1/x$ with $u \to 0$ as $x \to \infty$ that the rule holds if $x \to \infty$ instead of $x \to a$.

If $\lim f(x) = \infty$ and $\lim g(x) = \infty$, the rule also holds. We omit the more involved proof for this case.

If the expression $f'(x)/g'(x)$ at $x = a$ is again an indeterminate form $0/0$ or ∞ / ∞, we may repeat the rule, either directly or after making an algebraic simplification. Such a simplification is nearly always necessary at some stage for the form ∞ / ∞.

EXAMPLE 1.   Evaluate

$$\lim_{x \to 1} \frac{x^2 - 1}{x - 1}.$$

SOLUTION.   By L'Hôpital's rule, this is $\lim_{x \to 1} (2x/1) = 2$. This checks Eq. (52) of Sec. 12.

EXAMPLE 2.   Find

$$\lim_{x \to 0} \frac{\sin x}{x}.$$

SOLUTION.   This equals

$$\lim_{x \to 0} \frac{\cos x}{1} = 1.$$

This checks Eq. (13) of Sec. 43.

EXAMPLE 3.   Find $\lim_{x \to \infty} (1 + 1/x)^x$.

SOLUTION.   Let $u = (1 + 1/x)^x$. Then $\ln u = x \ln (1 + 1/x)$. This is the indeterminate form $\infty \cdot 0$. We may write it as a quotient

$$\ln \left(1 + \frac{1}{x}\right) \Big/ \frac{1}{x} \cdot$$

By L'Hôpital's rule, this has the same limit as

$$\frac{1}{(1 + 1/x)} \left(\frac{-1}{x^2}\right) \Big/ \frac{-1}{x^2} \quad \text{or} \quad \frac{1}{1 + 1/x},$$

which $\to 1$ as $x \to \infty$.

Since $\ln u \to 1$, $u \to e^1 = e$. This checks Eq. (35) of Sec. 39.

EXAMPLE 4. Find $\lim_{x \to 0} (\csc x)(\cot x - \csc x)$.

SOLUTION. We have $(\csc x)(\cot x - \csc x) = (\cos x - 1)/\sin^2 x$. The limit as $x \to 0$ has the form $0/0$, and so is equal to the limit of $(-\sin x)/(2 \sin x \cos x)$, or $-1/(2 \cos x)$, which $\to -\frac{1}{2}$, the desired limit.

PROBLEMS

Section 51

Two objects A and B are moving away from the point O along two straight lines through O. At the instant t_0, $OA = a$, $OB = b$, the speed of A is a_1 and the speed of B is b_1. How fast are they separating at time t_0 if

1. The lines are perpendicular? *Hint:* If $OA = x$; $OB = y$; $s^2 = x^2 + y^2$, $s \, (ds/dt) = x \, (dx/dt) + y \, (dy/dt)$. And at t_0,

$$\sqrt{a^2 + b^2} \, \frac{ds}{dt} = aa_1 + bb_1.$$

2. Angle $AOB = \omega$? *Hint:* $s^2 = x^2 + y^2 - 2xy \cos \omega$.

Section 52

A right triangle has sides x and y and hypothenuse z.

3. Let $y = b$ and $dx/dt = a$. Find dz/dt when $x = x_1$.
4. Let $z = c$ and $dx/dt = a$. Find dy/dt when $x = x_1$.
5. Let $dx/dt = a$ and $dy/dt = b$. Find dz/dt when $x = x_1$, $y = y_1$.

The radius of an expanding sphere is r in. at time t sec. Find dr/dt at the instant t_1 when $r = r_1$ if:

6. $dS/dt = b$ in.^{2}/sec, where $S = 4\pi r^2$ is the surface of the sphere.

7. $dV/dt = c$ in.^{3}/sec, where $V = \frac{4}{3}\pi r^3$ is the volume of the sphere.

8. The volume of a cone is increasing at the rate of c in.^{3}/sec. Find the rate of increase of the radius r, if at all times the altitude $h = 3r$ so that $V = \frac{1}{3}\pi r^2 h = \pi r^3$.

Section 53

Find an equation for the tangent line T and for the normal line N to each given curve at the indicated point:

9. $y = \ln x$, $x = e$.

10. $y = \sin x$, $x = \pi/2$.

11. $y = xe^x$, $x = 1$.

12. $y = \tan x$, $x = \pi/4$.

13. $x^2 y^2 = x + 2y$, $(2,1)$.

14. $x^3 + y^3 = 2xy$, $(1,1)$.

For each given pair of curves, find the angle at which they meet at each intersection:

15. $y = x^2$, $y^2 = 3y + 2x$.

16. $y = x^2$, $xy = 1$.

Section 54

Use differentials to approximate each quantity:

17. $\sin 45.5°$.

18. $\csc 31°$.

19. $\sqrt[3]{63}$.

20. $\ln (1.04)$.

The error in x is at most p per cent, and the error in y is at most q per cent. In each case verify that r is the largest possible resulting percentage error in z:

21. $z = xy$ or y/x $r = p + q$.

22. $z = x^a y^b$ $r = |a|\, p + |b|\, q$.

23. Verify the following alternative proof of the chain rule for $D_x u$ when $y = f(u)$ and $u = g(x)$ [Eq. (17) of Sec. 34]. From Eq. (8), $\Delta y = f'(u_1)\, \Delta u + \epsilon\, \Delta u$. Divide by Δx and take the limit as $\Delta x \to 0$. Thus $D_x y = f'(u_1)\, D_x u = D_u y\, D_x u$.

Section 55

Sketch the graph of each given equation:

24. $y = 5x^3 - 3x^5$.

25. $y = x^3 - 12x + 1$.

26. $y = xe^x$.

27. $y = 2 \sin (3x - 6)$.

28. $y = e^{-x^2}$.

29. $y = 3 \tan x/2$.

30. $y^2 = x^3 + x^2$.

31. $y^2 = x^3 - x$.

32. $y = (x^2 + 1)/x$.

33. $y = (x^3 - 2)/x$.

Sections 56 to 58

For the f defined by each given $f(x)$ on the indicated closed interval, find the absolute maximum M and the absolute minimum m. Also find all values of u and v on the interval such that $f(u) = m$ and $f(v) = M$:

34. $2x^{3/2} - 3$, $[0,2]$.

35. $x^{2/3}$, $[-1,2]$.

36. $\sqrt{4 - x^2}$, $[-1,2]$.

37. $x^{1/3}$, $[-2,1]$.

38. $(\ln x)/x$, $[1,3]$.

39. xe^{-x}, $[0,2]$.

40. $x - 2 \sin x$, $[0, \pi/2]$.

41. $x + 2 \cos x$, $[0, \pi/2]$.

42. $\sin x + \cos x$, $[0,1]$.

43. $\cos x \cos (x - 1)$, $[0,1]$.

Section 59

Show that the rectangle having greatest area:

44. Which has a given perimeter is a square.

45. Which is inscribable in a circle is a square.

46. Which is inscribable in a triangle has an area equal to half the area of the triangle.

Let c, m, n be positive. Show that for $x \geq 0$, $y \geq 0$, and $x + y = c$:

47. $x^m y^n$ is maximum for $x = mc/(m + n)$, minimum for $x = 0$ or c.

48. $x^{m+1} + n^m y^{m+1}$ is minimum for $x = \dfrac{nc}{(1+n)}$ and is maximum for $x = 0$ if $n^m \geq 1$, but for $x = c$ if $n^m \leq 1$.

49. Show that the point on the curve $y^2 = 4x + a$ which is nearest to the origin is $(-2, \pm\sqrt{a-8})$ if $a > 8$, but is $(-a/4, 0)$ if $a \leq 8$.

50. A man in a rowboat at a point A which is a miles from a straight shore wishes to go to a point B which is b miles up the beach from a point C opposite A. If he can row r mph and walk w mph and aims for a point x miles up the beach from C, verify that he takes T hr to go from A to B, where $T = (1/r)\sqrt{x^2 + a^2} + (1/w)|b - x|$. Deduce that T is a minimum for $x = (r/w)\sqrt{a^2 + b^2}$ if $w > (r/b)\sqrt{a^2 + b^2}$, but for $x = b$ if $w \leq (r/b)\sqrt{a^2 + b^2}$.

51. A and B are points on the same side of a plane mirror. A ray of light passes from A to B by way of a point C on the mirror. Show that the length of path $AC + CB$ will be least when the lines CA, CB make equal angles with the mirror.

52. Let the velocity of light be V_a in air and V_w in water. The path of a ray of light from a point A in the air to a point B below the surface is bent at C, where it enters the water. If θ_a and θ_w are the angles that CA and CB make with the perpendicular to the surface, show that the time required for light to pass from A to B will be least if B is so placed that $(\sin \theta_a)/(\sin \theta_w) = V_a/V_w$.

53. A manufacturer can sell x articles per week at d dollars each, where $d = a - bx$. The cost of producing the articles is $c = e + fx$. Show that the profit $P = x(a - bx) - (e + fx)$ is greatest when $x = (a - f)/2b$ and hence $d = (a + f)/2$. Assume that $a > f$.

54. If, in Prob. 53, a unit tax of t dollars is imposed on each article, then $d + t = a - bx$. Deduce that the profit $P = x(a - bx - t) - (e + fx)$ is a maximum when $x = (a - f - t)/2b$ and hence $d + t = (a + f + t)/2$. Assume that $t < a - f$.

55. Show that in Prob. 54 the total tax collected is greatest when t is set at $t = (a - f)/2$, assuming that the manufacturer will maximize his profit for any t set.

56. If, in Prob. 53, a tax proportional to the price is imposed, pd, then $(1 + p)d = a - bx$. Deduce that the profit

$$P = x \frac{a - bx}{1 + p} - (e + fx)$$

is a maximum when

$$x = \frac{a - f - pf}{2b} \quad \text{and} \quad (1 + p)d = \frac{a + f + pf}{2}.$$

Assume that $p < a/f - 1$.

57. Show that $(\ln x)/x^2$ is a maximum when $x = \sqrt{e}$.

58. Show that the rectangle of maximum area with one side on the x axis and inscribed in the curve $y = e^{-x^2}$ has two of its vertices at the inflection points $(\pm 1/\sqrt{2}, e^{-1/2})$.

59. For a, b, p, q positive, show that $ae^{px} + be^{-qx}$ assumes its minimum value when

$$x = \frac{1}{p + q} \ln \frac{bq}{ap}.$$

60. A tablet a ft high is placed on a wall with its base b ft above the observer's eye. Show that the angle of vision is greatest when the eye of the observer is $x = \sqrt{ab + b^2}$ from the wall. *Hint:* For any x, the angle is given by $\theta = \cot^{-1}[x/(a + b)] - \cot^{-1}(x/b)$.

61. A corridor a^3 ft wide runs at right angles to a passageway b^3 ft wide. A thin pole is to be carried in a horizontal position from the corridor into the passageway. Show that for any inclination θ to the first corridor, a length $x = a^3 \csc \theta + b^3 \sec \theta$ will just clear the corner. Deduce that the maximum length of the pole which will just clear in all positions is the minimum of x, $m = (a^2 + b^2)^{3/2}$.

Section 60

For the function f defined by each given $f(x)$ on the specified interval, verify that the hypothesis of Rolle's theorem is satisfied. Also verify that the x_0 are values in the open interval and that $f'(x_0) = 0$:

62. $x^2 - x$, $[-2,2]$, $x_0 = 0$.

63. $x^3 - 3x$, $[-\sqrt{3},\sqrt{3}]$, $x_0 = 1, -1$.

64. $\sqrt{4x - x^2}$, $[0,4]$, $x_0 = 2$.

65. $\pi \tan x - 4x$, $[-\pi/4, \pi/4]$, $x_0 = \pm\cos^{-1}(\sqrt{\pi}/2)$.

66. $\sin x$, $[0,3\pi]$, $x_0 = \pi/2, 3\pi/2, 5\pi/2$.

67. Let $a < b < c$. Let f be differentiable on $[a,c]$, and let $f(a) = 0$, $f(b) = 0$, $f(c) = 0$. Prove that there is at least one x_3 in (a,c) such that $f''(x_3) = 0$.

68. Let f be differentiable on $[a,b]$. Let $f(x) > 0$ on (a,b), and let $f(a) = 0$, $f(b) = 0$. Prove that if there is exactly one critical point x_0 on (a,b), then $f(x_0) = M$, the maximum value of f on $[a,b]$.

69. Let f be differentiable, with $f'(x) \neq 0$, on $[a,b]$. Prove that if $f(a)$ and $f(b)$ have opposite signs, then there is one and only one real root of the equation $f(x) = 0$ on (a,b).

Solution: By Sec. 12, f is continuous on $[a,b]$. Hence, by the intermediate-value property of Sec. 13, there is a c_1 on (a,b) with $f(c_1) = 0$. If $f(c_2)$ were equal to 0 for a $c_2 > c_1$, then there would be a value x_0 on (c_1,c_2) with $f'(x_0) = 0$, which contradicts the condition that $f'(x) \neq 0$.

Use Prob. 69 to show that each given $f(x)$ is zero at exactly one point in the specified open interval:

70. $x^5 + 2x - 1$, $(0,1)$.

71. $6 \sin x - 5x$, $(\pi/4, \pi/2)$.

Section 61

For the function f defined by each given $f(x)$ on the specified interval, verify that the hypothesis of the mean-value theorem is satisfied. Also, verify that the x_0 are values in the open interval and that Eq. (13) is valid:

72. x^n, $n > 1$, $[0,b]$. $x_0 = b\, n^{1/(1-n)}$.

73. $Ax^2 + Bx + C$, $[a,b]$. $x_0 = (a + b)/2$.

74. Let f satisfy the hypothesis of the mean-value theorem on $[0,b]$, and in addition let $f(0) = 0$. Prove that $[f(b)]/b = f'(x_0)$ for some x_0 on $(0,b)$.

For any $b > 0$, deduce from Prob. 74 that, for some x_0 on $(0,b)$,

75. $(\sin b)/b = \cos x_0$.

76. $(\tan b)/b = \sec^2 x_0$.

77. Give an alternative proof of Eq. (45) of Sec. 20 by using the theorem of this section. *Hint:* By Sec. 22, there is an F such that $F' = f$, and by Sec. 23, $\int_a^b f(x)\, dx = (b - a)\, f'(x^*)$ becomes $F(b) - F(a) = (b - a)\, F'(x^*)$, which is essentially Eq. (13).

78. Use the result or method of the example (Sec. 61) to prove that if $f'(x) = 0$ on (a,b), then $f(x)$ is constant on (a,b).

79. Prove that if $f'(x) > 0$ on $[a,b]$, and x_1 and x_2 are such that $a \le x_1 < x_2 \le b$, then $f(x_1) < f(x_2)$, and f is increasing on $[a,b]$. Similarly, show that if $f'(x) < 0$ on $[a,b]$, then f is decreasing on $[a,b]$.

80. From Prob. 79, deduce that if $f(a) = g(a)$, and $f'(x) > g'(x)$ on (a,b), then $f(x) > g(x)$ for x on (a,b).

Use Prob. 80 to prove each of the following inequalities:

81. $1 - 1/x < \ln x < x - 1$, for $x > 1$.
82. $x/(x^2 + 1) < \tan^{-1} x < x$, for $x > 0$.
83. $e^x > 1 + x$ and $e^{-x} > 1 - x$ for $x > 0$.

Use the mean-value theorem to prove the following inequalities:

84. $|\sin x_2 - \sin x_1| \le |x_2 - x_1|$.
85. $|\cos x_2 - \cos x_1| \le |x_2 - x_1|$.

Section 62

For the functions f, g defined by each pair of $f(x)$, $g(x)$ on the specified interval, verify that the hypothesis of the Cauchy mean-value theorem is satisfied. Also verify that the x_0 is a value in the open interval and that Eq. (17) is valid:

86. $f(x) = Ax^2 + Bx + C$, $g(x) = Ex^2 + Fx + G$, $[a,b]$. $x_0 = (a + b)/2$.
87. $f(x) = x^n$, $n > 1$. $g(x) = x^m$, $m > 0$, $[0,b]$. $x_0 = b(m/n)^{1/(n-m)}$.

Section 63

Evaluate each of the following limits:

88. $\displaystyle\lim_{x \to 2} \frac{x^4 - 16}{x - 2}$.

89. $\displaystyle\lim_{x \to 0} \frac{e^{-x} - 1}{x}$.

90. $\displaystyle\lim_{x \to 0} \frac{\ln (1 + x)}{x}$.

91. $\lim\limits_{x \to \pi/4} \dfrac{\tan x - 1}{x - (\pi/4)}$.

92. $\lim\limits_{x \to -1} \dfrac{\sin \pi x}{1 + x}$.

93. $\lim\limits_{x \to \pi/3} \dfrac{\cos x - (1/2)}{x - (\pi/3)}$.

94. $\lim\limits_{x \to 0+} x \ln x$.

95. $\lim\limits_{x \to a} \dfrac{\cos x - \cos a}{\sin x - \sin a}$.

96. $\lim\limits_{x \to 0} \dfrac{\ln \cos x}{x^2}$.

97. $\lim\limits_{x \to a} \dfrac{\sec x - \sec a}{\tan x - \tan a}$.

98. $\lim\limits_{x \to \pi/2} (\sin x)^{\tan x}$.

99. $\lim\limits_{x \to 0} \dfrac{x - \sin x}{x^3}$.

100. Verify that each of the limits in Probs. 88 to 93 may be evaluated by a direct application of the definition of the derivative in the form

$$\lim_{x \to a} \frac{f(x) - f(a)}{x - a} = f'(a).$$

6

INTEGRATION
AS ANTIDIFFERENTIATION

The process of differentiation takes us from a function to its derivative. As we saw in Sec. 23, it is sometimes desirable to reverse this procedure. The reversed process, or antidifferentiation, is called *integration;* it plays a leading role in the branch of our subject known as the integral calculus. In this chapter we define integration and the indefinite integral and introduce appropriate notation.

64—INTEGRATION

Suppose that the derivative of a function F is a known function f, defined by $y = f(x)$. And we wish to find the equation $y = F(x)$ which defines F. This process of finding $F(x)$, such that

$$F'(x) = \frac{dF}{dx} = f(x), \tag{1}$$

is inverse to differentiation. The process is called *antidifferentiation*, or *integration*. The result of the operation is called an *antiderivative*, or an *integral*.

For example, let $f(x) = 3x^2$. Then, by remembering that $(d/dx)\, x^3 = 3x^2$, we see that x^3 is one possible value of $F(x)$. In terms of the values of the functions, we say that x^3 is an integral of $3x^2$ with respect to x. Since

$$\frac{d}{dx}\, x^3 = 3x^2 \qquad \text{and} \qquad d\, x^3 = 3x^2\, dx \tag{2}$$

are equivalent relations, we also say that x^3 is an integral of the differential $3x^2\, dx$. The operation of integration is indicated by writing the *integral sign* $\int$ before the differential. Thus we write $\int 3x^2\, dx = x^3$, read "an integral of $3x^2\, dx$ equals x^3". In the general case we write $\int f(x)\, dx$, read "an integral of $f(x)\, dx$," to mean any $F(x)$ satisfying Eq. (1). In the expression $\int f(x)\, dx$, $f(x)$ is called the *integrand*.

65—CONSTANT OF INTEGRATION

For any constant C, $dC = 0$. Hence, if $d\,F(x) = f(x)\,dx$, we have $d\,[F(x) + C] = f(x)\,dx$. Thus if $F(x)$ is an integral of $f(x)\,dx$, so is $F(x) + C$.

Again, let G be any other function such that $d\,G(x) = f(x)\,dx$ on some open interval (a,b). Then $F'(x) = G'(x)$ on (a,b), and it follows from the example in Sec. 61 that $G(x) = F(x) + C$. Hence, if $F(x)$ is any *particular integral* of $f(x)\,dx$, the *general integral* of $f(x)$ is $F(x) + C$. Since any constant value can be assigned to C, it is called an *arbitrary constant*. As C is independent of the *variable of integration* x, we often call C the *constant of integration*. The expression for the general integral, $F(x) + C$, is known as the *indefinite integral* of $f(x)\,dx$.

EXAMPLE 1.   Find an equation of the curve passing through (2,15) whose slope at (x,y) is $3x^2$.

SOLUTION.   Since $dy/dx = 3x^2$, $y = \int 3x^2\,dx = x^3 + C$. Hence $15 = 2^3 + C$, $C = 7$, and $y = x^3 + 7$.

EXAMPLE 2.   At time t, the velocity of a moving particle is $v = \sin t$. If $s = 0$ when $t = 0$, find the distance s in terms of t.

SOLUTION.   We have $ds/dt = v = \sin t$. Hence $s = \int \sin t\,dt = -\cos t + C$. $0 = -\cos 0 + C$, $C = 1$, and $s = 1 - \cos t$.

66—OPERATIONS ON INTEGRALS

Certain simple rules of operations on integrals are often useful. First we have

$$d \int f(x)\,dx = f(x)\,dx. \tag{3}$$

This follows directly from the definition. It may always be used to check a final evaluation of an indefinite integral obtained by manipulation or taken from a table of integrals.

If k is a constant, then, except for an additive constant,

$$\int k\, f(x)\, dx = k\, \int f(x)\, dx, \tag{4}$$

since each side has the same differential, $k\, f(x)\, dx$. By Eq. (4) it is legitimate to shift a *constant* factor from a position inside to one outside the integral sign. Shifting a factor involving the variable of integration is not allowable. Thus $\int x \cdot x^2\, dx = \int x^3\, dx = x^4/4 + C$. But $x \int x^2\, dx = x(x^3/3 + C) = x^4/3 + Cx$.

If f_1 and f_2 are any two functions, then, except for an additive constant,

$$\int f_1(x)\, dx + \int f_2(x)\, dx = \int [f_1(x) + f_2(x)]\, dx. \tag{5}$$

We may extend this to the sum of any finite number of functions.

We shall continually use the rules of this section without explicit reference to them.

EXAMPLE 1. Verify that $\int x^n\, dx = x^{n+1}/(n+1)$ for $n \neq -1$, but $\int x^{-1}\, dx = \int (dx/x) = \ln |x| + C$.

SOLUTION. We have

$$d \left(\frac{x^{n+1}}{n+1} \right) = x^n\, dx \qquad \text{for } n \neq -1.$$

And by Eq. (43) in Sec. 40, $d\, (\ln |x|) = dx/x$.

EXAMPLE 2. Evaluate $\int (ax^2 + bx + c)\, dx$.

SOLUTION. From Example 1, we find $ax^3/3 + bx^2/2 + cx + C$.

67—SUBSTITUTIONS

As in Sec. 33, let $y = f(u)$ and $u = g(x)$. Then we have

$$\int f(u)\, \frac{du}{dx}\, dx = \int f\, [g(x)]\, g'(x)\, dx = \int f(u)\, du. \tag{6}$$

To prove the second equality, let the last integral equal $F(u) + C = F[g(x)] + C$. Then we have for its differential $dF = f(u)\, du$, so that $dF/du = f(u)$. Hence

$$\frac{dF}{dx} = \frac{dF}{du}\frac{du}{dx} = f(u)\frac{du}{dx} \quad \text{and} \quad dF = f(u)\frac{du}{dx}\,dx.$$

Thus $F[g(x)] + C$ is the evaluation of the first integral in Eq. (6). We state this as a theorem:

Under the integral sign, as elsewhere, when $u = g(x)$, we may replace $(du/dx)\,dx$ by du, and conversely.

An integral $\int f(x)\,dx$ may often be reduced to a more familiar form by expressing x as a function of a new variable t. It follows from the result just stated that if $x = g(t)$, with an inverse $g^{-1}(x)$, where g and g^{-1} are differentiable, the substitution $x = g(t)$, $dx = g'(t)\,dt$ will transform $\int f(x)\,dx$ into an equivalent integral in t, $\int f[g(t)]\,g'(t)\,dt$. If this has $F(t)$ as an integral, then $F[g^{-1}(x)] + C$ is the evaluation of the original integral.

The great advantage of the notation $\int \cdots dx$ for the operation of integration lies in the theorem of this section. That is, if we deal with the values of the functions, the integral of a differential is the same whether we use x or some other variable as the independent variable. The notation by the first form indicates that x is the variable of integration; to make t the variable of integration, we merely transform the differential. For example, consider $\int x^3\,dx = x^4/4 + C$ for $x > 0$. If we let $x = \sqrt{t}$, then we have $dx = \frac{1}{2}t^{-1/2}\,dt$. And the integral becomes $\int t^{3/2}\frac{1}{2}t^{-1/2}\,dt = \int(t/2)\,dt = t^2/4 + C$. Since $t = x^2$, this is $x^4/4 + C$, checking the first evaluation.

By analogy with the notation for the definite integral in Eq. (10) of Sec. 17, we may use $\int f$ to mean an indefinite integral, or any function F for which $F' = f$. With this notation in the example just treated, F would be defined by $F(x) = x^4/4 + C$. And with $x = \sqrt{t}$, we would have to form g defined by $g(t) = f(x)\,(dx/dt) = t^{3/2}\frac{1}{2}t^{-1/2} = t/2$, without its being suggested by the notation. Then $\int g = t^2/4 + C$. And with $t = x^2$ this is again $x^4/4 + C$. The notation $\int f$ has the advantage of compactness and is convenient for theoretic discussions like that of Sec. 19.

EXAMPLE 1.   Evaluate $\int x(ax^2 + b)^n\,dx$, $n \neq -1$, $a \neq 0$.

SOLUTION.   If $u = ax^2 + b$, then $du = 2ax\,dx$, so that $x\,dx = (1/2a)\,du$. Hence the integral is

$$\int \frac{1}{2a} u^n \, du = \frac{1}{2a} \frac{u^{n+1}}{n+1} + C = \frac{(ax^2 + b)^{n+1}}{2a(n+1)} + C.$$

EXAMPLE 2.   Evaluate

$$\int \frac{e^x}{e^x + e^{-x}} \, dx.$$

SOLUTION.   The integrand is

$$\frac{e^x}{e^x + e^{-x}} = \frac{e^{2x}}{e^{2x} + 1}.$$

If $u = e^{2x} + 1$, then $du = 2e^{2x} \, dx$ and the integral is $\int \frac{1}{2} (du/u) = \frac{1}{2} \ln u + C = \frac{1}{2} \ln (e^{2x} + 1) + C$.

EXAMPLE 3.   Evaluate

$$\int \frac{dx}{2 + (x - 5)^{1/3}}.$$

SOLUTION.   Let $t = (x - 5)^{1/3}$.   Then $x = 5 + t^3$, and $dx = 3t^2 \, dt$.

$$\int \frac{dx}{2 + (x - 5)^{1/3}} = \int \frac{3t^2}{2 + t} \, dt = \int 3 \left(t - 2 + \frac{4}{t + 2} \right) dt$$
$$= 3 \left(\frac{t^2}{2} - 2t + 4 \ln |2 + t| \right) + C$$
$$= \tfrac{3}{2} (x - 5)^{2/3} - 4(x - 5)^{1/3}$$
$$+ 4 \ln |2 + (x - 5)^{1/3}| + C.$$

Example 3 illustrates the fact that if $f(x)$ is rational with respect to x and $(ax + b)^{1/n}$, the substitution $t = (ax + b)^{1/n}$ will transform $\int f(x) \, dx$ into an integral with respect to t, whose integrand is rational with respect to t.

68—SEPARABLE DIFFERENTIAL EQUATIONS

An equation of the form $dy/dx = f(x)/g(y)$ is called a *separable differential equation*.   Any function F leads to a solution of this equation if the equation is identically satisfied when we substitute $y = F(x)$, $dy/dx = F'(x)$.   Since the solution makes $f(x) \, dx = g(y) \, dy$, by the first result of Sec. 67 we have $\int f(x)\ dx = \int g(y)\ dy + C$. This gives a new relation which must be satisfied for some value of C by any solution in a range in which f and g are finite.

EXAMPLE 1.   A certain curve (Fig. 18) in the first quadrant is such that if the tangent line at P cuts the positive x axis at A and the positive y axis at B, then $BA = 3PA$. Find an equation for the curve.

SOLUTION.   If $P = (x,y)$, the condition makes $OB = 3y$, $OA = 3(OA - x)$, or $OA = 3x/2$. Hence the slope at P is $-OB/OA = -2y/x$, so that $dy/dx = -2y/x$. Hence $dy/y = -2\ (dx/x)$, or $\ln|y| = -2\ln|x| + C$. $|y| = e^C/x^2$. With $e^C = C_1, C_1 > 0$. Thus we have $y = C_1/x^2$ with $C_1 > 0, x > 0$, $y > 0$ as an equation of the desired curve.

EXAMPLE 2.   Find the distance s in terms of t if the velocity v is given by $v = t/(s + 1)$ and $s = 0$ when $t = 0$.

SOLUTION.   We have $ds/dt = v = t/(s + 1)$, or $(s + 1)\ ds = t\ dt$. Hence $\int (s + 1)\ ds = \int t\ dt$ or $[(s + 1)^2]/2 = t^2/2 + C$. For $s = 0, t = 0$, we have $\frac{1}{2} = 0 + C, C = \frac{1}{2}$. Hence $(s + 1)^2 = t^2 + 1, s = -1 + \sqrt{t^2 + 1}$, since this sign makes $s = 0$ when $t = 1$.

EXAMPLE 3.   If k is a positive constant and the positive quantity x decreases at a time rate which is k times x, find x in terms of t.

SOLUTION.   We have $dx/dt = -kx$, or $dx/x = -k\ dt$. Hence $\int (dx/x) = -kt + C$, $\ln x = -kt + C$, $x = Ce^{-kt}$. Since $x = C$, for $t = 0$, we have $x = x_0 e^{-kt}$ if $x = x_0$ at $t = 0$.

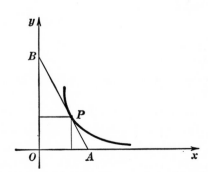

FIGURE 18

69—BASIC INTEGRATION FORMULAS

We list here some of the more important indefinite integrals. In each formula u may represent the variable of integration or some function of that variable. As is customary in tables of integrals, we list one integral in each case. If the general integral is required, a constant of integration C should be added. The student will find it easy to remember the first nine of these by associating them with the corresponding rules of differentiation which he already knows. For many of the latter integrals, it is sufficient to learn what integrands are in the list. When applying them, the student may refer to this or to a larger table of integrals for the detailed evaluation.

1. $\int u^n\, du = \dfrac{u^{n+1}}{n+1},\ n \neq -1.$

2. $\int du/u = \ln |u|.$

3. $\int e^u\, du = e^u.$

4. $\int \sin u\, du = -\cos u.$

5. $\int \cos u\, du = \sin u.$

6. $\int \sec^2 u\, du = \tan u.$

7. $\int \sec u \tan u\, du = \sec u.$

8. $\int \csc^2 u\, du = -\cot u.$

9. $\int \csc u \cot u\, du = -\csc u.$

10. $\int \tan u\, du = -\ln |\cos u|.$

11. $\int \cot u\, du = \ln |\sin u|.$

12. $\int \sec u\, du = \ln |\sec u + \tan u|.$

13. $\int \csc u\, du = -\ln |\csc u + \cot u|.$

14. $\int \sin^2 u\, du = \dfrac{u}{2} - \dfrac{\sin u \cos u}{2}.$

15. $\int \cos^2 u\, du = \dfrac{u}{2} + \dfrac{\sin u \cos u}{2}.$

16. $\displaystyle\int \frac{du}{u^2 + a^2} = \frac{1}{a}\tan^{-1}\frac{u}{a}.$

17. $\displaystyle\int \frac{du}{a^2 - u^2} = \frac{1}{2a}\ln\left|\frac{u - a}{u + a}\right|.$

18. $\displaystyle\int \frac{du}{\sqrt{a^2 - u^2}} = \sin^{-1}\frac{u}{a}\ \text{or}\ -\cos^{-1}\frac{u}{a}.$

19. $\int \dfrac{du}{\sqrt{u^2 \pm a^2}} = \ln |u + \sqrt{u^2 \pm a^2}|.$

20. $\int \sqrt{a^2 - u^2}\, du = \dfrac{u}{2} \sqrt{a^2 - u^2} + \dfrac{a^2}{2} \sin^{-1} \dfrac{u}{a}.$

21. $\int \sqrt{u^2 \pm a^2}\, du = \dfrac{u}{2} \sqrt{u^2 \pm a^2} \pm \dfrac{a^2}{2} \ln |u + \sqrt{u^2 \pm a^2}|.$

Formulas 10 to 18 may be verified by differentiation, as we illustrate in Examples 1 and 2 below. Formula 20 may be derived from 14 by putting $u = a \sin t$. And formula 19 may be derived from 12 by putting $u = a \tan t$ for the plus sign and $u = a \sec t$ for the minus sign. For formula 21, see Example 3. Methods of *deriving* some of these formulas will be given in the following sections.

EXAMPLE 1. Verify formula 12 by differentiation.

SOLUTION. We have

$$d \ln |\sec u + \tan u| = \frac{d(\sec u + \tan u)}{\sec u + \tan u}$$
$$= \frac{(\sec u \tan u + \sec^2 u)\, du}{\sec u + \tan u}$$
$$= \frac{(\tan u + \sec u) \sec u\, du}{\sec u + \tan u} = \sec u\, du.$$

This checks the evaluation.

EXAMPLE 2. Verify formula 14 by differentiation.

SOLUTION. We have

$$d \frac{u - \sin u \cos u}{2} = \tfrac{1}{2}(1 - \cos^2 u + \sin^2 u)\, du.$$

Since $1 - \cos^2 u = \sin^2 u$, this is $\tfrac{1}{2}(2 \sin^2 u)\, du = \sin^2 u\, du$. This checks the evaluation.

EXAMPLE 3. Verify formula 21.

SOLUTION. By formula 19, the differential of the second term in formula 21 is

$$\pm \frac{a^2}{2} \frac{du}{\sqrt{u^2 \pm a^2}}.$$

And we have

$$d\,\frac{u\sqrt{u^2+a^2}}{2} = \tfrac{1}{2}\left(\sqrt{u^2\pm a^2} + \frac{u^2}{\sqrt{u^2\pm a^2}}\right)du.$$

Thus the differential of the right-hand member of formula 21 is

$$\frac{du}{2}\left(\sqrt{u^2\pm a^2} + \frac{u^2\pm a^2}{\sqrt{u^2\pm a^2}}\right) = \sqrt{u^2\pm a^2}\ du,$$

which checks the evaluation.

70—PRODUCTS OF TRIGONOMETRIC FUNCTIONS

An integral of the type $\int \sin^m x \cos^n x\ dx$ may be integrated if n is an odd positive integer. We need merely put $\sin x = t$, $\cos x\ dx = dt$, and the integral becomes $\int t^m(1-t^2)^s\ dt$, where $s = (n-1)/2$, and so is zero or a positive integer.

Similarly, if m is an odd positive integer, we put $\cos x = t$, $\sin x\ dx = -dt$.

If both m and n are even integers, we may use the relations

$$\sin^2 u = \frac{1-\cos 2u}{2} \qquad \cos^2 u = \frac{1+\cos 2u}{2}$$

$$\sin u \cos u = \frac{\sin 2u}{2} \tag{7}$$

to simplify the integral.

Integrals of the form $\int \sin mx \sin nx\ dx$, and similar integrals with one or both sines replaced by cosines, may be simplified by using one of the relations

$$\sin A \sin B = \tfrac{1}{2}\,[\cos (A-B) - \cos (A+B)],$$
$$\sin A \cos B = \tfrac{1}{2}\,[\sin (A-B) + \sin (A+B)], \tag{8}$$
$$\cos A \cos B = \tfrac{1}{2}\,[\cos (A-B) + \cos (A+B)].$$

For an integral of the type $\int \sec^m x \tan^n x\ dx$, with m an even positive integer, we may put $t = \tan x$, $\sec^2 x\ dx = dt$. If n is an odd positive integer, we may put $t = \sec x$, $\sec x \tan x\ dx = dt$. For these integrals, we also use the identity $\tan^2 x + 1 = \sec^2 x$.

Similar remarks apply to $\int \csc^m x \cot^n x\ dx$.

EXAMPLE 1. Evaluate $\int \sin^4 x \cos^2 x \, dx$.

SOLUTION. From Eq. (7),

$$\sin^4 x \cos^2 x = \sin^2 x (\sin x \cos x)^2 = \frac{1 - \cos 2x}{2} \frac{\sin^2 2x}{4}.$$

And

$$\int \tfrac{1}{8}(\sin^2 2x - \sin^2 2x \cos 2x) \, dx$$

$$= \tfrac{1}{16}\left(x - \frac{\sin 2x \cos 2x}{2} - \frac{\sin^3 2x}{3} \right) + C,$$

by formula 14, with $u = 2x$, and formula 1, with $u = \sin 2x$.

EXAMPLE 2. Evaluate $\int \cos 3x \cos 5x \, dx$.

SOLUTION. From Eq. (8), $\cos 5x \cos 3x = \tfrac{1}{2}(\cos 2x + \cos 8x)$. Whence $\int \cos 3x \cos 5x \, dx = \tfrac{1}{4} \sin 2x + \tfrac{1}{16} \sin 8x + C.$

EXAMPLE 3. Evaluate $\int \tan^3 x \sqrt{\sec x} \, dx$.

SOLUTION. Let $t = \sec x$, $\tan x \sec x \, dx = dt$, $\tan^2 x = t^2 - 1$. The integral becomes $\int (t^2 - 1)t^{-1/2} \, dt = \int (t^{3/2} - t^{-1/2}) \, dt = \tfrac{2}{5}t^{5/2} - 2t^{1/2} + C = (\tfrac{2}{5} \sec^2 x - 2) \sqrt{\sec x} + C.$

71—INTEGRATION BY PARTS

The rule for differentiating products, $(fg)' = fg' + gf'$, may be written in the form $fg' = (fg)' - gf'$. This shows that

$$\int f(x) \, g'(x) \, dx = f(x) \, g(x) - \int g(x) \, f'(x) \, dx, \tag{9}$$

with a suitable choice of the additive constant, since both sides of this equation have the same derivatives with respect to x.

If we let $u = f(x)$, $v = g(x)$, Eq. (9) becomes

$$\int u \, dv = uv - \int v \, du. \tag{10}$$

This also follows directly from rule 5 of Sec. 49.

Either Eq. (9) or Eq. (10) is known as the rule for *integration by parts*. Its value in transforming an integral to one which is easier to find is illustrated by the examples.

EXAMPLE 1. Evaluate $\int x^2 \tan^{-1} x \, dx$.

SOLUTION. Let $\tan^{-1} x = u$, $dv = x^2 \, dx$. Then $v = x^3/3$, and $du = dx/(1 + x^2)$. Hence

$$\int x^2 \tan^{-1} x \, dx = x^3/3 \tan^{-1} x - \int \frac{x^3 \, dx}{3(1 + x^2)} \, .$$

Since

$$\frac{x^3}{1 + x^2} = x - \frac{x}{1 + x^2} \, ,$$

the integral is equal to

$$\frac{x^3}{3} \tan^{-1} x - \frac{x^2}{6} + \frac{1}{6} \ln (1 + x^2) + C.$$

EXAMPLE 2. Evaluate $\int \ln x \, dx$.

SOLUTION. Let $\ln x = u$, $dv = dx$. Then $v = x$, and $du = dx/x$. Hence $\int \ln x \, dx = x \ln x - \int x \, (dx/x) = x \ln x - x + C$.

Examples 1 and 2 illustrate that when a logarithm or an inverse trigonometric or hyperbolic function appears by itself or with a simple factor like x^n, integration by parts with this inverse function as u often leads to a simpler integral.

EXAMPLE 3. Evaluate $\int x^2 \sin x \, dx$.

SOLUTION. Let $x^2 = u$, $dv = \sin x \, dx$. Then $v = -\cos x$, and $du = 2x \, dx$. Hence $\int x^2 \sin x \, dx = -x^2 \cos x - \int(-\cos x) \, 2x \, dx = -x^2 \cos x + 2\int x \cos x \, dx$. Next use another integration by parts on $\int x \cos x \, dx$. Let $x = u$, $dv = \cos x \, dx$. Then $v = \sin x$ and $du = dx$. Hence $\int x \cos x \, dx = x \sin x - \int \sin x \, dx = x \sin x + \cos x + C_1$. It follows that, with $C = 2C_1$, $\int x^2 \sin x \, dx = -x^2 \cos x + 2x \sin x + 2 \cos x + C$.

Example 3 illustrates that when one of the functions e^x, $\sin x$, $\cos x$, $\sinh x$, or $\cosh x$ appears multiplied by x^n, with n a positive integer, n integrations by parts with the power of x as u in each case will lead to an evaluation of the integral.

EXAMPLE 4. Evaluate $\int \sqrt{x^2 + A} \, dx$.

SOLUTION. With $u = \sqrt{x^2 + A}$ and $dv = dx$, we find that the integral equals

$$x\sqrt{x^2 + A} - \int \frac{x^2\,dx}{\sqrt{x^2 + A}}\,.$$

Note that

$$\frac{x^2}{\sqrt{x^2 + A}} = \frac{x^2 + A - A}{\sqrt{x^2 + A}} = \sqrt{x^2 + A} - \frac{A}{\sqrt{x^2 + A}}\,.$$

Hence

$$\int\sqrt{x^2 + A}\,dx = x\sqrt{x^2 + A} - \int\sqrt{x^2 + A}\,dx + A\int \frac{dx}{\sqrt{x^2 + A}}\,,$$

so that

$$2\int\sqrt{x^2 + A}\,dx = x\sqrt{x^2 + A} + A\int \frac{dx}{\sqrt{x^2 + A}}\,.$$

It follows from formula 19 that

$$\int\sqrt{x^2 + A}\,dx = \frac{x\sqrt{x^2 + A}}{2} + \frac{A}{2}\ln|x + \sqrt{x^2 + A}| + C.$$

Example 4 illustrates that if one or more integrations by parts lead to the original integral, with a coefficient $\neq 1$, we may solve the equation to obtain the integral. Incidentally, Example 4 provides a *derivation* of formula 21 from formula 19.

EXAMPLE 5.   Derive the reduction formulas

$$\int\cos^n x\,dx = \frac{\cos^{n-1} x \sin x}{n} + \frac{n-1}{n}\int\cos^{n-2} x\,dx,$$

$$\int\sin^n x\,dx = -\frac{\sin^{n-1} x \cos x}{n} + \frac{n-1}{n}\int\sin^{n-2} x\,dx. \qquad (11)$$

SOLUTION.   In $\int\cos^n x\,dx = \int\cos^{n-1} x\,(\cos x)\,dx$, let $u = \cos^{n-1} x$, $dv = \cos x\,dx$. Then $v = \sin x$ and $du = (n-1)\cos^{n-2} x\,(-\sin x\,dx)$. Hence $\int\cos^n x\,dx = \cos^{n-1} x \sin x + (n-1)\int\sin^2 x \cos^{n-2} x\,dx$. On replacing $\sin^2 x$ by $1 - \cos^2 x$, the last term becomes $(n-1)\int\cos^{n-2} x\,dx - (n-1)\int\cos^n x\,dx$. Transposing the second of these terms leads to $n\int\cos^n x\,dx = \cos^{n-1} x \sin x + (n-1)\int\cos^{n-2} x\,dx$. And division by n gives the first part of Eq. (11). The second part follows from the first by replacing x in the first part by $(\pi/2 - x)$.

With $n = 2$, these reduction formulas may be used to give a new derivation of formulas 14 and 15.

EXAMPLE 6.   Use Example 5 to evaluate $\int \sin^4 x\ dx$.

SOLUTION.   With $n = 4$ in the second of Eqs. (11), we have $\int\sin^4 x\ dx = -\frac{1}{4}\sin^3 x \cos x + \frac{3}{4}\int\sin^2 x\ dx$, so that by formula 14, $\int\sin^4 x\ dx = -\frac{1}{4}\sin^3 x \cos x + 3x/8 - \frac{3}{8}\sin x \cos x + C$.

72—QUADRATIC EXPRESSIONS

The quadratic expressions in formulas 16 to 21 contain no first-degree term.   The corresponding integrals with the quadratic expression $ax^2 + bx + c$ can be reduced to this form by completing the square,

$$a\left(x^2 + \frac{bx}{a} + \frac{b^2}{4a^2}\right) + c - \frac{b^2}{4a} = a\left(x + \frac{b}{2a}\right)^2 + \frac{4ac - b^2}{4a}, \quad (12)$$

and taking $x + b/2a = u$ as a new variable.

EXAMPLE 1.   Evaluate

$$\int \frac{dx}{2x^2 - 2x + 1}.$$

SOLUTION.   Here $2x^2 - 2x + 1 = 2(x - \frac{1}{2})^2 + \frac{1}{2}$, and by formula 16 with $u = x - \frac{1}{2}$,

$$\tfrac{1}{2}\int \frac{dx}{(x - \frac{1}{2})^2 + \frac{1}{4}} = \tan^{-1} \frac{x - \frac{1}{2}}{\frac{1}{2}} + C = \tan^{-1}(2x - 1) + C.$$

EXAMPLE 2.   Evaluate

$$\int \frac{5x + 4}{\sqrt{x^2 + 6x}}\ dx.$$

SOLUTION.   Since the numerator contains a term in x, we write

$$\int \frac{5x + 4}{\sqrt{x^2 + 6x}}\ dx = \frac{5}{2} \int \frac{2x + 6}{\sqrt{x^2 + 6x}}\ dx - 11 \int \frac{dx}{\sqrt{x^2 + 6x}}.$$

In the first integral the numerator $(2x + 6)\ dx$ is taken as the differential of $x^2 + 6x$, the 5/2 is inserted to produce the $5x$ term, and the second integral is found by subtraction. From formula 1, with $u = x^2 + 6x$, and formula 19, with $u = x + 3$, $x^2 + 6x = u^2 - 9$, we find that

$$\int \frac{5x + 4}{\sqrt{x^2 + 6x}}\,dx = 5\sqrt{x^2 + 6x} - 11\ln|x + 3 + \sqrt{x^2 + 6x}| + C.$$

EXAMPLE 3.   Evaluate

$$\int \frac{dx}{(x - 2)\sqrt{x^2 - 4x - 5}}.$$

SOLUTION.   Put $t = 1/(x - 2)$. Then $x = 2 + 1/t$ and $dx = -dt/t^2$. Also $x^2 - 4x - 5 = (2 + 1/t)^2 - 4(2 + 1/t) - 5 = 1/t^2 - 9$. Hence the integral equals

$$\int \frac{t(-dt/t^2)}{\sqrt{(1/t^2) - 9}} = -\tfrac{1}{3}\int \frac{dt}{\sqrt{\tfrac{1}{9} - t^2}}.$$

By formula 18 this is $\tfrac{1}{3}\cos^{-1}(t/\tfrac{1}{3}) + C$. Since $\cos^{-1} 3t = \sec^{-1}(1/3t)$ in the first quadrant, the integral has as its value $\tfrac{1}{3}\sec^{-1}[(x - 2)/3] + C$.

Example 3 illustrates that some integrals having a factor $(x - a)$ outside a radical in the denominator are simplified by making the substitution $t = \dfrac{1}{x - a}$.

73—TRIGONOMETRIC SUBSTITUTIONS

If an integrand contains $\sqrt{a^2 - x^2}$ or $\sqrt{x^2 \pm a^2}$, the substitution using a new variable equal to the square root may be effective. Otherwise, we may substitute in accordance with the following table of factors and substitutions:

FACTOR	SUBSTITUTION	
$\sqrt{a^2 - x^2}$	$x = a\sin t,\ \sqrt{a^2 - x^2} = a\cos t$	
$\sqrt{x^2 + a^2}$	$x = a\tan t,\ \sqrt{x^2 + a^2} = a\sec t$	(13)
$\sqrt{x^2 - a^2}$	$x = a\sec t,\ \sqrt{x^2 - a^2} = a\tan t$	

EXAMPLE 1.   Evaluate

$$\int \frac{x^3}{\sqrt{x^2 + a^2}} \, dx.$$

SOLUTION.   Let $t = \sqrt{x^2 + a^2}$, $x^2 = t^2 - a^2$, $x \, dx = t \, dt$.   Hence

$$\int \frac{x^3}{\sqrt{x^2 + a^2}} \, dx = \int \frac{(t^2 - a^2)t \, dt}{t} = \int (t^2 - a^2) \, dt = \frac{t^3}{3} - a^2 t$$

$$+ \, C = (x^2 + a^2)^{1/2} \tfrac{1}{3}(x^2 + a^2 - 3a^2) + C$$

$$= \tfrac{1}{3}\sqrt{x^2 + a^2}(x^2 - 2a^2) + C.$$

EXAMPLE 2.   Evaluate

$$\int \frac{dx}{(x^2 + a^2)^{3/2}}.$$

SOLUTION.   Let $x = a \tan t$, $\sqrt{x^2 + a^2} = a \sec t$, $dx = a \sec^2 t \, dt$.   Hence

$$\int \frac{dx}{(x^2 + a^2)^{3/2}} = \int \frac{a \sec^2 t}{a^3 \sec^3 t} \, dt = \frac{1}{a^2} \int \cos t \, dt = \frac{\sin t}{a^2} + C$$

$$= \frac{x}{a^2 \sqrt{x^2 + a^2}} + C.$$

The methods of this section may be extended to integrands containing $\sqrt{ax^2 + bx + c}$ by completing the square as in Eq. (12) before using the substitutions like those of Eqs. (13).   In particular, we notice that if $x - p = q \tan t$, then

$$\int \frac{dx}{[(x - p)^2 + q^2]^{m/2}} = \frac{1}{q^{m-1}} \int \cos^{m-2} t \, dt. \tag{14}$$

For m a positive integer, this may be evaluated by repeated use of the reduction formula in Eqs. (11).

74—HYPERBOLIC SUBSTITUTIONS

We shall now give an example in which a substitution analogous to those of Eqs. (13) involving the hyperbolic functions of Secs. 46 and 47 is effective.

EXAMPLE.   Derive formula 19 of Sec. 69.

SOLUTION.   For the plus sign, let $u = a \sinh t$, $\sqrt{u^2 + a^2} = a \cosh t$, $du = a \cosh t \, dt$.   Then

$$\int \frac{du}{\sqrt{u^2 + a^2}} = \int \frac{a \cosh t \, dt}{a \cosh t} = \int dt = t + C_1.$$

From Eq. (27) of Sec. 47, with $x = u/a$, we find

$$\sinh^{-1} \frac{u}{a} = \ln (u + \sqrt{u^2 + a^2}) - \ln a. \tag{15}$$

For the minus sign, take $a > 0$. First assume $u \geq a > 0$ and let $u = a \cosh t$, $\sqrt{u^2 - a^2} = \sinh t$, $du = a \sinh t \, dt$. Then

$$\int \frac{du}{\sqrt{u^2 - a^2}} = \int \frac{a \sinh t \, dt}{a \sinh t} = \int dt = t + C_1.$$

From Eq. (28) of Sec. 47, with $x = u/a$, we find

$$\cosh^{-1} \frac{u}{a} = \ln (u + \sqrt{u^2 - a^2}) - \ln a \qquad u \geq a > 0. \tag{16}$$

For the minus sign, we must have $|u| \geq a$ to make $\sqrt{u^2 - a^2}$ real. When $u > 0$, this is $u \geq a$ as we assumed. And when $u < 0$, it is $-u > a > 0$. In the latter case put $u = -a \cosh t$, and

$$\int \frac{du}{\sqrt{u^2 - a^2}} = \int \frac{-a \sinh t \, dt}{a \sinh t} = -\int dt = -t + C_1.$$

Now

$$-\cosh^{-1} \frac{-u}{a} = -\ln (-u + \sqrt{u^2 - a^2}) + \ln a$$
$$= \ln |u + \sqrt{u^2 - a^2}| - \ln a \qquad u \leq -a < 0. \tag{17}$$

The last step follows from $|u + \sqrt{u^2 - a^2}| = -u - \sqrt{u^2 - a^2}$, and $(-u - \sqrt{u^2 - a^2})(-u + \sqrt{u^2 - a^2}) = (-u)^2 - (u^2 - a^2) = a^2$.

75—RATIONAL FUNCTIONS

A rational fraction with real coefficients $f(x)$ has the form

$$f(x) = \frac{a_n x^n + a_{n-1} x^{n-1} + \cdots + a_1 x + a_0}{b_m x^m + b_{m-1} x^{m-1} + \cdots + b_1 x + b_0} = \frac{P(x)}{D(x)}. \tag{18}$$

Here n, m are positive integers or zero and the polynomials $P(x)$ and $D(x)$ have no common polynomial factors involving x If $n \geq m$, we may use long division to obtain

$$f(x) = Q(x) + \frac{R(x)}{D(x)}, \tag{19}$$

where $Q(x)$ is a polynomial and $R(x)$ is of lower degree than $D(x)$

The proper fraction $R(x)/D(x)$ may be integrated by first decomposing it into *partial fractions* as illustrated in the examples

EXAMPLE 1.   Evaluate

$$\int \frac{x^5 - 8}{x^3 - 4x}\, dx.$$

SOLUTION.   By division,

$$\frac{x^5 - 8}{x^3 - 4x} = x^2 + 4 + \frac{16x - 8}{x^3 - 4x}.$$

We next write

$$\frac{16x - 8}{x^3 - 4x} = \frac{A}{x} + \frac{B}{x - 2} + \frac{C}{x + 2}.$$

Clearing of fractions, we get $16x - 8 = A(x^2 - 4) + Bx(x + 2) + Cx(x - 2)$. Equating coefficients of like powers of x, we find that

$$A + B + C = 0 \qquad 2B - 2C = 16 \qquad -4A = -8.$$

From these we may deduce that $A = 2$, $B = 3$, $C = -5$, so that

$$\int \frac{x^5 - 8}{x^3 - 4x}\, dx = \int \left(x^2 + 4 + \frac{2}{x} + \frac{3}{x - 2} + \frac{-5}{x + 2} \right) dx$$

$$= \frac{x^3}{3} + 4x + 2 \ln |x| + 3 \ln |x - 2|$$

$$- 5 \ln |x + 2| + C$$

EXAMPLE 2.   Evaluate

$$\int \frac{4\, dx}{(x - 1)^3 (x^2 + 1)}.$$

SOLUTION. We first write

$$\frac{4}{(x-1)^3(x^2+1)} = \frac{A}{x-1} + \frac{B}{(x-1)^2} + \frac{C}{(x-1)^3} + \frac{Dx+E}{x^2+1}.$$

Clearing of fractions, we get $4 = A(x-1)^2(x^2+1) + B(x-1)(x^2+1) + C(x^2+1) + (Dx+B)(x-1)^3$. Equating like powers of x, we find that $A + D = 0$, $-2A + B - 3D + E = 0$, $2A - B + C + 3D - 3E = 0$, $-2A + B - D + 3E = 0$, $A - B + C - D = 4$. From these we may deduce that $A = 1$, $B = -2$, $C = 2$, $D = -1$, $E = 1$, so that the fraction equals

$$\frac{1}{x-1} + \frac{-2}{(x-1)^2} + \frac{2}{(x-1)^3} + \frac{-x+1}{x^2+1}.$$

Whence the integral equals

$$\ln|x-1| + \frac{1}{(x-1)^2} - \tfrac{1}{2}\ln(x^2+1) + \tan^{-1}x + C.$$

These examples illustrate that the real polynomial $D(x)$ may be written as the product of factors of the form $(x - a)$ and $(x^2 + bx + c)$, where a, b, c are real but $x^2 + bx + c$ does not have real first-degree factors. We omit the proof of the fact that the proper fraction $R(x)/D(x)$ always admits of a decomposition into partial fractions. There is a single fraction of the form $A/(x - a)$ for each simple factor $(x - a)$ of $D(x)$. There is a group of fractions of the form $A_1/(x - a) + A_2/(x - a)^2 + \cdots + A_r/(x - a)^r$ for each factor $(x - a)$ occurring r times in $D(x)$, where A_1, A_2, $\ldots$, A_r are real constants, any of which except A_r may be zero. There is a single fraction $(Bx + C)/(x^2 + bx + c)$ for each simple factor $(x^2 + bx + c)$ of $D(x)$, where B, C are real and not both zero. And there is a group of fractions $(B_1x + C_1)/(x^2 + bx + c) + (B_2x + C_2)/(x^2 + bx + c)^2 + \cdots + (B_rx + C_r)/(x^2 + bx + c)^r$ for each factor $(x^2 + bx + c)$ occurring r times in $D(x)$, where B_1, C_1, $\ldots$, B_r, C_r are real, with B_r and C_r not both zero.

If the complex roots of $x^2 + bx + c$ are $p \pm iq$, we may write

$$\int \frac{(Bx + C)\, dx}{(x^2 + bx + c)^r} = \frac{B}{2} \int \frac{(2x + b)\, dx}{(x^2 + bx + c)^r}$$

$$+ \left(C - \frac{bB}{2}\right) \int \frac{dx}{[(x - p)^2 + q^2]^r}. \quad (20)$$

The first integral on the right becomes $\int u^{-r}\, du$ if $u = x^2 + bx + c$. And we may use Eq. (14) with $m = 2r$ for the second integral.

PROBLEMS

Section 65

For each $f(x)$ find an equation of the curve having slope $dy/dx = f(x)$ and passing through the given point:

1. $2x$, $(0,5)$.
2. $\cos x$, $(0,1)$.
3. $6x^5$, $(1,1)$.
4. $2 \sin x$, $(0,2)$.

Find s in terms of t if $s = 0$ when $t = 0$, and at any time t the velocity is given by $v = f(t)$ for each given $f(t)$:

5. $4 \cos t$.
6. e^t.
7. $2t + 4$.
8. $5t^4$.

Section 66

Find the general integral of each given differential:

9. $(x^5 + 4x^2)\, dx$.
10. $(\sin x + \cos x)\, dx$.
11. $\dfrac{3t^2 + t + 2}{t^4}\, dt$.
12. $\dfrac{2t^2 + 3t + 2}{t}\, dt$.

Section 67

Evaluate each given indefinite integral:

13. $\int \sqrt{4x + 3}\, dx$.
14. $\int \cos 2x\, dx$.

15. $\int \dfrac{x\ dx}{x^2 + 2}$.

16. $\int x^3 \sqrt{x^4 + 1}\ dx$.

17. $\int e^{-4x}\ dx$.

18. $\int \dfrac{\sin x\ dx}{2 + 3 \cos x}$.

Section 68

For each $F(x,y)$ find an equation of the curve having slope $dy/dx = F(x,y)$ and passing through the given point:

19. $2xy^2$, $(1,1)$.

20. $\sin x/\cos y$, $(0,\ \pi/2)$.

21. x^2/y^2, $(1,2)$.

22. y^2/x^2, $(1,2)$.

Section 69

Verify each specified formula:

23. Formula 10.

24. Formula 13.

25. Formula 15.

26. Formula 16.

27. Formula 17.

28. Formula 18.

Section 70

Evaluate each given indefinite integral:

29. $\int \sin^3 x\ dx$.

30. $\int \sin^4 x\ dx$.

31. $\int \sec^4 x\ dx$.

32. $\int \sin x \cos 7x\ dx$.

33. $\int \csc^4 x \tan^3 x\ dx$.

34. $\int \cos^3 x \sin^2 x\ dx$.

Section 71

Evaluate each given indefinite integral:

35. $\int \sin^{-1} x\ dx$.

36. $\int x^4 \ln x\ dx$.

37. $\int \tan^{-1} x \, dx.$

38. $\int x^2 e^x \, dx.$

39. $\int x \cos x \, dx.$

40. $\int x \sec^2 x \, dx.$

41. $\int e^{ax} \cos bx \, dx = e^{ax} \dfrac{b \sin bx + a \cos bx}{a^2 + b^2} + C.$

42. $\int e^{ax} \sin bx \, dx = e^{ax} \dfrac{a \sin bx - b \cos bx}{a^2 + b^2} + C.$

43. $\int \cos (\ln x) \, dx.$

44. $\int \sin (\ln x) \, dx.$

45. Check Probs. 43 and 44 by putting $x = e^t$ and using the results of Probs. 41 and 42.

Derive each given reduction formula:

46. $\int x^n e^x \, dx = x^n e^x - n \int x^{n-1} e^x \, dx.$

47. $\int \tan^n x \, dx = \dfrac{\tan^{n-1} x}{n - 1} - \int \tan^{n-2} x \, dx.$

48. $\int \sec^n x \, dx = \dfrac{\sec^{n-1} x \tan x}{n - 1} - \dfrac{n - 2}{n - 1} \int \sec^{n-2} x \, dx.$

Section 72

Evaluate each given indefinite integral:

49. $\int \dfrac{dx}{x^2 - 4x + 13}.$

50. $\int \dfrac{dx}{\sqrt{7 - 6x - x^2}}.$

51. $\int \dfrac{x \, dx}{\sqrt{27 + 6x - x^2}}.$

52. $\int \dfrac{(8x - 8) \, dx}{4x^2 - 4x - 3}.$

53. $\int \dfrac{(2x - 1) \, dx}{\sqrt{4x^2 + 4x + 2}}.$

54. $\int \dfrac{dx}{x\sqrt{8 - 2x - x^2}}.$

Section 73

Evaluate each given indefinite integral:

55. $\int \dfrac{x^3 \, dx}{(x^2 + 4)^{3/2}}.$

56. $\int \dfrac{\sqrt{x^2 - 4}}{x}\, dx.$

57. $\int \dfrac{dx}{x^2\sqrt{4 - x^2}}.$

58. $\int x^3 \sqrt{x^2 + 1}\, dx.$

59. $\int \dfrac{x^2\, dx}{(x^2 + 4)^{5/2}}.$

60. $\int \dfrac{x^3\, dx}{\sqrt{x^2 + 9}}.$

61. $\int \dfrac{x^4\, dx}{(9 - x^2)^{5/2}}.$

62. $\int \dfrac{dx}{x^4\sqrt{25 + x^2}}.$

Section 74

Check each given evaluation:

63. $\int \dfrac{du}{a^2 - u^2} = \dfrac{1}{2a} \ln \left| \dfrac{u + a}{u - a} \right| + C = \dfrac{1}{a} \tanh^{-1} \dfrac{u}{a} + C, u \le a$ and $= \dfrac{1}{a} \coth^{-1} \dfrac{u}{a} + C,\, u \ge a.$

64. $\int \sqrt{u^2 + a^2}\, du = \frac{1}{2}\left(u\sqrt{u^2 + a^2} + a^2 \sinh^{-1} \dfrac{u}{a} \right) + C.$

65. $\int \sqrt{u^2 - a^2}\, du = \frac{1}{2}\left(u\sqrt{u^2 - a^2} - a^2 \cosh^{-1} \dfrac{u}{a} \right) + C.$

66. $\int \dfrac{du}{u\sqrt{a^2 + u^2}} = -\dfrac{1}{a} \sinh^{-1} \dfrac{a}{u} + C = -\dfrac{1}{a} \operatorname{csch}^{-1} \dfrac{u}{a} + C.$

67. $\int \dfrac{du}{u\sqrt{a^2 - u^2}} = -\dfrac{1}{a} \cosh^{-1} \dfrac{a}{u} + C = -\dfrac{1}{a} \operatorname{sech}^{-1} \dfrac{u}{a} + C.$

Section 75

Evaluate each given indefinite integral:

68. $\int \dfrac{(2x^2 - 10x + 10)\, dx}{(x - 1)(x - 2)(x - 3)}.$

69. $\int \dfrac{x^2 + x - 4}{x^2 - x^2}\, dx.$

70. $\int \dfrac{(2x + 4)\, dx}{(x - 1)(x - 3)(x - 4)}.$

71. $\int \dfrac{4\, dx}{(x^2 - 1)^2}.$

72. $\int \dfrac{x^2\,dx}{(x+1)(x^2+4)}$.

73. $\int \dfrac{2x^2 + x + 3}{(x^2+1)^2}\,dx.$

74. Show that

$$\int \frac{dx}{x(x+1)(x+2)\,\cdots\,(x+k)} = \sum_{r=0}^{k} \frac{(-1)^r}{r!\,(k-r)!}\ln|x-r|.$$

Hint: Put $x = r$ in the equation $1 = \displaystyle\sum_{r=0}^{k} B_r\, x(x+1)\,\cdots$

$(x+r-1)(x+r+1)\,\cdots\,(x+k).$

75. If the evaluation of

$$\int \frac{(4x + b)\,dx}{(x-2)^2(x^2+1)}$$

involves no logarithmic terms, verify that b must equal -3.

GEOMETRIC APPLICATIONS OF DEFINITE INTEGRALS

In this chapter we shall discuss reasonable definitions of a number of geometrical quantities such as area, volume, arc length, and moments. Our definition of each concept leads to an expression for it in terms of a definite integral. We shall also illustrate an efficient technique for setting up such integrals. Although this rests on the theory of Chap. 2, it avoids repetition of most of the details in individual computations.

76—AREA BETWEEN TWO CURVES

Consider the part of the plane $A = CDBA$ (Fig. 19) bounded by the arcs CD and AB and the straight-line segments CA, on which $x = a$, and DB, on which $x = b$. We assume that on $[a,b]$ CD is the graph of a continuous function f_1, and AB is the graph of a continuous function f_2, and that $f_2(x) \geq f_1(x)$ on $[a,b]$. Let the ordinate at x cut CD in P and AB in Q. Form a rectangle with height $PQ = f_2(x) - f_1(x) = y_2 - y_1$ and width dx. We call the area of this rectangle an *element of area* and denote it by dA. Thus we have

$$dA = (y_2 - y_1) \, dx. \tag{1}$$

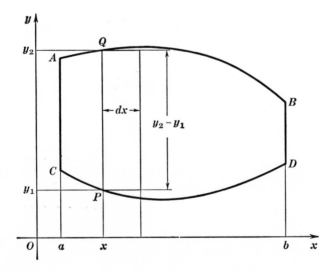

FIGURE 19

Now consider $(x, x + dx)$ as one of a finite set of intervals dividing the x axis between a and b. And let the element of area dA be formed for each such interval. Then, for the sums, we have

$$\Sigma \, dA = \Sigma (y_2 - y_1) \, dx. \tag{2}$$

Considerations like those used in Sec. 27 show that by taking the limit in an appropriate way we obtain

$$A_a{}^b = \int_a^b (y_2 - y_1) \, dx. \tag{3}$$

EXAMPLE 1.   Find the area bounded by the curves $y = x^2$ and $y = x^3$.

SOLUTION.   The curves intersect at $(0,0)$ and $(0,1)$. And on the interval $(0,1)$, we have $0 < x < 1$ so that $x^3 < x^2$. Hence we take $dA = x^2 - x^3$ and integrate from 0 to 1 to obtain

$$A = \int_0^1 (x^2 - x^3) \, dx = \left[\frac{x^3}{3} - \frac{x^4}{4} \right]_0^1 = \frac{1}{12}.$$

EXAMPLE 2.   For a particular function f, the area between the ordinates at $x = 0$ and $x = b$ which lies below the graph of $y = f(x)$ and above the x axis is $\ln (b + \sqrt{b^2 + 1})$ for positive values of b. Find $f(x)$.

SOLUTION.   By   Sec.   23, $(d/dx) \int_0^x f(u) \, du = f(x)$.   Here $\int_0^x f(u) \, du = \int_0^x f(x) \, dx = \ln (x + \sqrt{x^2 + 1})$.   And $f(x) = (d/dx) \ln (x + \sqrt{x^2 + 1}) = 1/\sqrt{x^2 + 1}$, for $x > 0$

EXAMPLE 3.   Find $\lim\limits_{n \to \infty} T_n$, where

$$T_n = \frac{1}{\sqrt{n^2}} + \frac{1}{\sqrt{n^2 - 1^2}}$$
$$+ \frac{1}{\sqrt{n^2 - 2^2}} + \cdots + \frac{1}{\sqrt{n^2 - (n - 1)^2}}.$$

SOLUTION.   The expression T_n can be written as

$$T_n = \sum_{i=1}^n \frac{1}{\sqrt{n^2 - (i - 1)^2}}.$$

With $f(x) = 1/\sqrt{1 - x^2}$, $\Delta x_i = 1/n$, $x_i = (i - 1)/n$, the sum is

$$\sum_{i=1}^{n} f(x_i) \; \Delta x_i.$$

Compare the example in Sec. 24, and Example 2 in Sec. 27. As the x_i here are u_i, the sum cannot exceed the area whose measure is the improper integral $\int_0^1 dx/\sqrt{1 - x^2}$. But it may be made arbitrarily close to this integral, so that the required limit of T_n is

$$\lim_{x \to 1-} \; \sin^{-1} x \; = \; \pi/2.$$

77—GENERAL DEFINITION OF VOLUME

Let S be any solid. Let E be the volume of any solid containing S in its interior and I be the volume of any solid contained in S. E and I may be made up of polyhedra, prisms, conical frusta, or any other figures for which the volume has already been defined.

Suppose that there exist sequences of exterior volumes E_n and interior volumes I_n such that, as $n \to \infty$,

$$\lim E_n = V \quad \text{and} \quad \lim I_n = V. \tag{4}$$

Then the common limit is called the *volume* of S.

By the argument given in Sec. 26, we may show that the value of V is independent of the choice of the exterior and interior figures.

78—SOLIDS OF REVOLUTION

Consider S_x, the volume generated by revolving the area $abBA$ described in Sec. 27 about the x axis.

Then rotation of the rectangle of height m_i about the x axis generates a figure composed of cylinders contained in S_x. And its volume is

$$I = \sum_{i=1}^{n} \pi \; m_i^2 \; \Delta x_i = \pi \sum_{i=1}^{n} [f(u_i)]^2 \; \Delta x_1. \tag{5}$$

Also (Fig. 20), rotation of the rectangles of height M_i about the x axis generates a figure composed of cylinders containing S_x. And its volume is

$$E = \sum_{i=1}^{n} \pi\, M_i^2\, \Delta x_i = \pi \sum_{i=1}^{n} [f(v_i)]^2\, \Delta x_i. \qquad (6)$$

It follows from Sec. 77, by reasoning as in Sec. 27, that for a suitable sequence of subdivisions, the sequences E_t and I_t will have a common limit,

$$V_a^b = \pi \int_a^b y^2\, dx. \qquad (7)$$

Here, as in Sec. 27, AB is the graph of $y = f(x)$.

In practice, we define an *element of volume* as the cylinder whose base is a circle of radius y and whose height is dx. Thus we have

$$dV = \pi\, y^2\, dx. \qquad (8)$$

And without repeating the argument in detail, we proceed directly from this to the expression for the volume in Eq. (7).

79—SOLIDS OF KNOWN CROSS SECTION

Let us take three perpendicular axes in space, Ox, Oy, Oz, and consider a solid (Fig. 21) lying between the two planes $x = a$ and $x = b$. For $a \le x \le b$, let the area of the cross section of this solid perpendicular to Ox, or parallel to the yz plane, be $A(x)$. We may form a

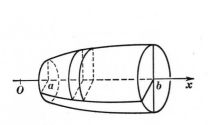

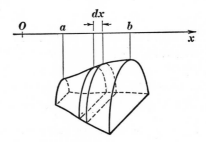

FIGURE 20   FIGURE 21

prism or cylinder (in general not circular) having this cross section as base and having dx as its altitude. We call the volume of the cylinder an *element of volume* and denote it by dV. Thus we have

$$dV = A(x)\, dx. \tag{9}$$

Assume that $A(x)$ defines a continuous function of x on $[a,b]$. And on any subinterval Δx_i, let $A(u_i)$ be the least, and $A(v_i)$ be the greatest, value of $A(x)$ on this subinterval. If ΔV_i is the volume of the solid between x_{i-1} and x_i, then

$$A(u_i)\, \Delta x_i \leq \Delta V_i \leq A(v_i)\, \Delta x_i. \tag{10}$$

For some solids, for example, a cone, this follows directly from the result of Sec. 77. In any case, it is true that the volume increases when $A(x)$ increases, so that Eq. (10) holds. From this, by reasoning as in Sec. 27, it follows that the volume $V_a{}^b$ is given by

$$V_a{}^b = \int_a^b A(x)\, dx. \tag{11}$$

EXAMPLE. For x on $[0,1]$, every section of a solid perpendicular to Ox is a rectangle. One of its sides is the ordinate of $y = 1 - x^2$ in the xy plane, and the other side is the ordinate of $z = x^3$ in the zx plane. Find the volume of the solid.

SOLUTION. The area of the rectangular section at distance x is $A(x) = x^3(1 - x^2) = x^3 - x^5$. Hence we have

$$V = \int_0^1 (x^3 - x^5)\, dx = \tfrac{1}{12}.$$

80—LENGTH OF A CURVE

To define the length of a curved arc AB, we make the following construction. We divide the arc AB into parts by successive points $P_1, P_2, \ldots, P_{n-1}$. Let $P_0 = A$ and $P_n = B$. Join P_{i-1} to P_i by a straight-line segment, and denote the length of this chord by ΔC_i. The length of the resulting inscribed polygonal line from A to B is $L_n = \sum_{i=1}^{n} \Delta C_i$. If, for every sequence of polygons with max $\Delta C_i \to 0$, as $n \to \infty$, the sequence S_n tends to the same limit, then the arc AB

is said to be *rectifiable,* and the common limit s is called its length.

Now assume that AB is that portion of the graph of the function f with x on $[a,b]$. Suppose further that, on this interval, the derivative f' is continuous. Let $P_i = (x_i, y_i)$, with $y_i = f(x_i)$. Then

$$\Delta C_i{}^2 = \overline{P_{i-1}P_i}{}^2 = (x_i - x_{i-1})^2 + (y_i - y_{i-1})^2$$
$$= \Delta x_i{}^2 + \Delta y_i{}^2. \tag{12}$$

By the mean-value theorem of Sec. 61, we have

$$\Delta y_i = f(x_i) - f(x_{i-1}) = f'(\xi_i)(x_i - x_{i-1})$$
$$= f'(\xi_i)\,\Delta x_i, \tag{13}$$

for some suitably chosen ξ_i between x_{i-1} and x_i.

It follows that

$$L_n = \Sigma\,\Delta C_i = \Sigma\sqrt{\Delta x_i{}^2 + \Delta y_i{}^2}$$
$$= \Sigma\sqrt{1 + [f'(\xi_i)]^2}\,\Delta x_i. \tag{14}$$

Since $\Delta x_i \le \Delta C_i$, $\delta_M = \max \Delta x_i \le \max \Delta C_i$. Hence, for any sequence of polygons with $\max \Delta C_i \to 0$, we shall have $\delta_M = \max \Delta x_i \to 0$, and by Sec. 18 the sum L_n will approach a limit. By the definition given above, this limit is the length $s_a{}^b$ of AB, so that

$$s_a{}^b = \int_a^b \sqrt{1 + [f'(x)]^2}\,dx. \tag{15}$$

EXAMPLE 1.   Find C, the length of the circumference of the circle whose equation is $x^2 + y^2 = a^2$.

SOLUTION.   By symmetry, the required length C is four times the length in the first quadrant. For this part of the circle, we have

$$0 \le x \le a \qquad \text{and} \qquad y = \sqrt{a^2 - x^2}.$$

And, for $0 \le x < a$,

$$f'(x) = \frac{-x}{\sqrt{a^2 - x^2}} \qquad \sqrt{1 + f'(x)^2} = \frac{a}{\sqrt{a^2 - x^2}}.$$

Hence we have

$$\frac{C}{4} = s_0{}^a = \int_0^a \frac{a\,dx}{\sqrt{a^2 - x^2}} = a\left[\sin^{-1}\frac{x}{a}\right]_0^a = \frac{\pi a}{2};$$

whence

$$C = 2\pi a.$$

Strictly speaking, since $f'(x)$ and the integrand become infinite when $x \to a$, we must consider $s_0{}^a$ as the limit of $s_0{}^x$ as $x \to a-$. But this is an improper integral as defined in Sec. 25. And when, as here, the indefinite integral is continuous in the closed interval of integration, we may compute this by merely substituting in the limits.

EXAMPLE 2.   Find an expression for arc length if the arc AB is the locus of the parametric equations $x = F(t)$, $y = G(t)$, as in Sec. 43.

SOLUTION.   We have $s_a{}^x = \int_a^x \sqrt{1 + [f'(x)]^2}\ dx$.   Hence, by Sec. 23, we have $ds_a{}^x/dx = \sqrt{1 + [f'(x)]^2}$. Let us write s for the arc length from any fixed point on the curve to the variable point (x,y) on AB. Then $s - s_a{}^x$ is constant, so that $ds/dx = ds_a{}^x/dx$. Also recall that $f'(x) = dy/dx$. Then we have

$$\frac{ds}{dx} = \sqrt{1 + \left(\frac{dy}{dx}\right)^2}, \qquad \text{or } dx^2 = dx^2 + dy^2. \tag{16}$$

This equation is easily remembered if it is thought of as expressing the fact that, like ΔC, Δx, Δy, the differentials ds, dx, dy form a right triangle. If the triangle is drawn with side dx parallel to the x axis and dy parallel to the y axis, as in Fig. 22, the angle opposite dy is ϕ, the slope angle of the curve. From Eq. (16) we have

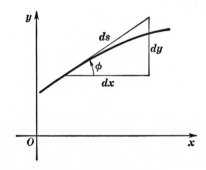

FIGURE 22

$$\left(\frac{ds}{dt}\right)^2 = \left(\frac{dx}{dt}\right)^2 + \left(\frac{dy}{dt}\right)^2 = [F'(t)]^2 + [G'(t)]^2,$$

so that $\qquad s_{t_1}{}^{t_2} = \displaystyle\int_{t_1}^{t_2} \sqrt{[F'(t)]^2 + [G'(t)]^2} \, dt.$ $\qquad\qquad$ (17)

We might have derived Eq. (17) from Eq. (15) by the method of Sec. 67, using the equations

$$f'(x) = \frac{G'(t)}{F'(t)} \qquad \text{and} \qquad dx = \frac{dx}{dt}\,dt = F'(t)\,dt.$$ $\qquad$ (18)

81—AREA OF A SURFACE OF REVOLUTION

If the curved arc AB of Sec. 80 is revolved about the x axis, it generates a surface. We assume that $y \geq 0$ for the whole interval $[a,b]$. For such a revolution (Fig. 23), each chord $P_{i-1}P_i$ generates the curved surface of a frustum of a cone, whose lateral area is $2\pi y_m \, \Delta C_i$, where (x_m, y_m) is the midpoint of the chord $P_{i-1}P_i$. Since $y_m = \frac{1}{2}(y_{i-1} + y_i)$ is between the greatest and the least value of $y = f(x)$ on (x_{i-1}, x_i), there is a point x_i^* on this interval such that $y_m = f(x_i^*)$, by the intermediate-value property of Sec. 13. From this and Eq. (13), it follows that S_n, the area of the figure generated by rotation of the polygonal line, is

$$S_n = \Sigma 2\pi \, f(x_i^*) \sqrt{1 + [f'(\xi_i)]^2} \, \Delta x_i.$$ $\qquad$ (19)

For any sequence of polygons with max $\Delta C_i \to 0$, $\delta_m = \max \Delta x_i \to 0$. And, by the Duhamel-Bliss theorem of Sec. 24, the sequence S_n approaches a limit S_a^b. This limit,

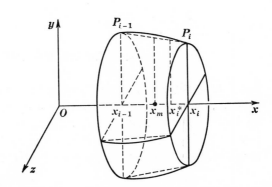

FIGURE 23

$$S_a{}^b = 2\pi \int_a^b f(x)\sqrt{1 + [f'(x)]^2}\, dx, \tag{20}$$

is defined to be the area of the surface of revolution.

Defining the arc length s as in Example 2 of Sec. 80 and proceeding as in that example, we find that

$$dS = 2\pi y \, ds \tag{21}$$

and that for $x = F(t)$, $y = G(t)$,

$$S_{t_2}{}^{t_1} = \int 2\pi y \, ds = \int_{t_1}^{t_2} 2\pi \, G(t)\sqrt{[F'(t)]^2 + [G'(t)]^2}\, dt. \tag{22}$$

The formula (21) may be recalled by thinking of the element of curved surface area as equal to that of a ribbon whose length is that of a circle of radius y and whose width is ds.

EXAMPLE.   Find the area generated by revolving the arc of the curve $x = a \cos^3 t$, $y = a \sin^3 t$, with $0 \le t \le \pi$, about the x axis.

SOLUTION.   From symmetry, the total area is twice that in the first quadrant. Here $0 \le t \le \pi/2$, $dx/dt = -3a \cos^2 t \sin t$, $dy/dt = 3a \sin^2 t \cos t$, and $ds^2 = dx^2 + dy^2 = 9a^2 \cos^2 t \sin^2 t$. Hence $dS = 2\pi y \, ds = 6\pi a^2 \cos t \sin^4 t \, dt$, so that $S/2 = \int_0^{\pi/2} 6\pi a^2 \cos t \sin^4 t \, dt = \frac{6}{5}\pi a^2$. Whence $S = \frac{12}{5}\pi a^2$.

Note that, if we had not made use of symmetry, it would have been necessary to observe that, for $\pi/2 < t \le \pi$, $ds = \sqrt{9a^2 \cos^2 t \sin^2 t} = 3a \, |\cos t| \sin t = -3a \cos t \sin t$, since $\cos t \le 0$ in this quadrant.

82—MEAN VALUE OF A VARIABLE

Let f be continuous in $[a,b]$. Divide this interval into n equal parts by points $x_i = a + i \, \Delta x_i$. Thus $x_0 = a$, $x_n = b$, and $\Delta x_i = (b - a)/n$. In each of the n intervals $[x_{i-1}, x_i]$ for $i = 1, 2, \ldots, n$, select any point ξ_i, $x_{i-1} \le \xi_i \le x_i$. And let $y_i = f(\xi_i)$. Then the arithmetic mean of the n numbers $y_1, y_2, \ldots, y_n$ is

$$\frac{y_1 + y_2 + \cdots + y_n}{n}. \tag{23}$$

As $n \to \infty$, this approaches a limit. To see this, note that, if we multiply the numerator and denominator by Δx, the new numerator $\Sigma y_i \, \Delta x$ satisfies $\Sigma y_i \, \Delta x \to \int f(x) \, dx$ by Sec. 18. And the new denominator $n \, \Delta x$ is equal to $b - a$. This proves that

$$\bar{y} = \lim_{n \to \infty} \frac{\Sigma y_i}{n} = \frac{1}{b - a} \int_a^b f(x) \, dx. \tag{24}$$

As we stated in Sec. 20, this limit is called the *average*, or *mean*, value of y with respect to x over the range (a,b). If the variable y is also expressible in terms of some other variable t, the mean value with respect to t is not ordinarily equal to that with respect to x.

EXAMPLE. For a falling body, we have $s = \frac{1}{2}gt^2$, $v = gt = \sqrt{2gs}$. Find the mean value of v with respect to t over the range $(0,2)$ and also with respect to s over the corresponding range $(0,2g)$.

SOLUTION. The first mean value is $\frac{1}{2} \int_0^2 gt \, dt = g$. The second mean value is $(1/2g) \int_0^{2g} \sqrt{2gs} \, ds = \frac{4}{3}g$.

83—MOMENTS OF AREA ABOUT THE y AXIS

Consider the area $A = abBA$ of Sec. 27 bounded by portions of the lines Ox, (ab), $x = a$ (aA), $x = b$ (bB), and the curved arc AB, which is the graph of $y = f(x)$. The element of area is

$$dA = y \, dx \tag{25}$$

by Eq. (1) of Sec. 76. This element approximates a portion of the area S, each of whose points is at nearly the same distance x from the y axis. We obtain the element for the *k*th *moment of area about the* y *axis* by multiplication by the kth power of this distance x. Thus the kth moment of A is defined by the equation

$$M_{kx} = \int_a^b x^k y \, dx = \int_a^b x^k f(x) dx. \tag{26}$$

For $k = 0$, the moment M_{0x} is the area A itself. And for $k = 1, 2,$ $3, \ldots$ $M_{kx}/A = (1/A)\int x^k \, dA$ is the average of the power x^k with respect to the area. In particular, M_{1x}/A is the mean value of x with respect to the area.

In statistics, we use idealized distribution functions so constructed that the area under the curve between two ordinates at x_1 and x_2 is equal to (or proportional to) the probability that x will lie between x_1 and x_2. In finding or discussing such functions, quantities closely related to the moments, particularly the first four, are often used.

EXAMPLE 1. Find the kth moment about the y axis, M_{kx}, for the area above Ox, and lying under the graph of $y = e^{-x}$, over the range $(0, \infty)$.

SOLUTION. The kth moment is $M_{kx} = \int_0^\infty x^k \, e^{-x} \, dx$. An integration by parts shows that

$$M_{kx} = \left[-x^k \, e^{-x} \right]_0^\infty + \int_0^\infty (kx^{k-1}) \, e^{-x} \, dx = k \, M_{(k-1)x}.$$

Since $M_{0x} = 1$, $M_{1x} = 1$, $M_{2x} = 2 \cdot 1$, by using mathematical induction we see that

$$M_{kx} = k(k - 1) \cdots 2 \cdot 1 = k!.$$

EXAMPLE 2. Find the kth moment M_{kx} about the y axis for the rectangle bounded by the lines $x = x_1$, $x = x_2$, $y = 0$, $y = h$.

SOLUTION. Here

$$M_{kx} = \int_{x_1}^{x_2} x^k \, h \, dx = \frac{h}{k + 1} \, (x_2^{k+1} - x_1^{k+1}).$$

84—MOMENTS OF AREA ABOUT THE x AXIS

The definition of the kth moment of area about *any* axis is analogous to that given in Sec. 83 for the y axis. For some areas the kth moment about the x axis could be calculated merely by interchanging x and y in the discussion of Sec. 83.

Let us, however, consider the area $A = CDBA$ of Sec. 76. For a rectangle bounded by $y = y_1$, $y = y_2$, $x = x_{i-1}$, $x = x_i = x_{i-1} + \Delta x_i$, the kth moment about the x axis will be

$$\Delta M_{ky} = \frac{1}{k+1} (y_2^{k+1} - y_1^{k+1}) \Delta x_i. \tag{27}$$

This follows from Example 2 of Sec. 83. But there are choices of ξ_i' and ξ_i'' in the equations $y_1 = f_1(\xi_i')$ and $y_2 = f_2(\xi_i'')$ which make ΔM_{ky} in Eq. (27) greater than the corresponding moment of the part of A which it approximates. And there are also choices which make it less. Hence the common limit of $\Sigma \, \Delta M_{ky}$ for any choice of ξ_i' and ξ_i'', which exists by the Duhamel-Bliss theorem of Sec. 24, is the kth moment of A about the x axis. Thus we have

$$M_{ky} = \int_a^b \frac{1}{k+1} (y_2^{k+1} - y_1^{k+1}) dx. \tag{28}$$

PROBLEMS

Section 76

Find the area between the lines $x = 0$ and $x = 1$, above the x axis and below the graph of each given equation:

1. $y = x \, e^x$.
2. $y^2(x^2 + 1) = 1$.
3. $y = \ln (x + 1)$.
4. $y^2(1 - x^2) = 1$.

Find the area bounded by each given pair of curves:

5. $y = x^3 - 3x$, $y = x$.
6. $y = x^2$, $y = 2 - x^2$.
7. $y^2 = x$, $x^2 = 8y$.
8. $x^2 = 4y$, $y(x^2 + 4) = 8$.
9. $y = x^3 + x^2$, $y = x^3 + 1$.
10. $y(x^2 + 4) = 8$ and $y = 0$, its asymptote.

Find $\lim_{n \to \infty} T_n$ for each of the expressions T_n:

11. $\dfrac{1}{\sqrt{n^2 + 1^2}} + \dfrac{1}{\sqrt{n^2 + 2^2}} + \cdots + \dfrac{1}{\sqrt{n^2 + n^2}}$.

12. $\dfrac{1}{\sqrt{n^2 + 2n}} + \dfrac{1}{\sqrt{n^2 + 4n}} + \cdots + \dfrac{1}{\sqrt{n^2 + 2n^2}}.$

13. $\dfrac{1}{n}\left(\sin\dfrac{\pi}{n} + \sin\dfrac{2\pi}{n} + \cdots + \sin\dfrac{n\pi}{n}\right).$

14. $n\left(\dfrac{1}{n^2 + 1^2} + \dfrac{1}{n^2 + 2^2} + \cdots + \dfrac{1}{n^2 + n^2}\right).$

15. $\dfrac{1}{n}\left[F'\left(\dfrac{b}{n}\right) + F'\left(\dfrac{2b}{n}\right) + \cdots + F'\left(\dfrac{nb}{n}\right)\right].$ Ans.: $\dfrac{1}{b}\,[F(b) - F(0)].$

16. Show that d^2y/dx^2 is proportional to y, and find the constant of proportionality, if $x = \int_0^y dt/\sqrt{a^2 + b^2 t^2}$.   *Hint:* Differentiate $dy/dx = \sqrt{a^2 + b^2 y^2}$ as in Example 2 of Sec. 50.

17. The continuous function f satisfies the conditions $f(ax) = a^2 f(x)$ for all a and all x, and $\int_0^1 f(x)\,dx = 2$. Show that $\int_0^a f(x)\,dx = 2a^3$. *Hint:* Put $x = at$ in the second integral.

18. Show that in Prob. 17, $f(x) = 6x^2$.   *Hint:* By Prob. 17, $\int_0^x f(t)\,dt = 2x^3$. Hence $(d/dx)\int_0^x f(t)\,dt = (d/dx)\,(2x^3)$.

Section 78

The area in the first quadrant bounded above by the given curve and below by Ox is revolved about Ox. Find the volume of the solid generated in each problem:

19. $y^2 = 4 - 2x.$

20. $y^2 = 4x - x^3.$

21. $y = 1 - x^2.$

22. $y = \sin x,\ 0 \le x \le \pi.$

Let V_0^b be the volume of the solid generated by rotating about the x axis the area bounded above by the graph of $y = f(x)$, below by Ox, and lying between $x = 0$ and $x = b$. Find $f(x)$ for $x > 0$, if, for all $b > 0$, V_0^b equals the given value in each problem:

23. $e^{2b} - 1.$

24. $b - \sin b \cos b.$

Section 79

Let A be the area in the first quadrant bounded above by the given curve and below by the x axis. Let CD be a variable ordinate of A

perpendicular to the x axis. In each problem find the volume of the solid whose plane section perpendicular to the x axis is a square with CD as one side:

25. $y^2 = -x^2 + 3x - 2$.
26. $y = 4 - x^2$.
27. $y^2 = 16x - x^3$.
28. $y = 3 - x$.
29. $x^2 + y^2 = 4$.
30. $y = \cos x$, $0 \leq x \leq \pi/2$.

Section 80

Find the length of arc of each given curve between the two points specified:

31. $y = x^{3/2}$, $(0,0)$, $(1,1)$.
32. $8y^2 = x^3$, $(0,0)$, $(2,1)$.
33. $y = x^3/6 + 1/2x$, points with $x = 1$, $x = 2$.
34. $y = (a/2)(e^{x/a} + e^{-x/a})$, points with $x = 0$, $x = h$. *Hint:* Use the form $y = a \cosh (x/a)$.
35. $y = \ln \sec x$, points with $x = 0$, $x = \pi/4$.
36. $x = t^2$, $y = t^3$, points with $t = 0$, $t = 1$.
37. $x = t^2$, $y = t$, points with $t = 0$, $t = 1$.
38. $x = e^t \cos t$, $y = e^t \sin t$, points with $t = 0$, $t = 2$.
39. $x = \cos t + t \sin t$, $y = \sin t - t \cos t$, points with $t = 0$, $t = \pi$.
40. $x = a(t - \sin t)$, $y = a(1 - \cos t)$, points with $t = 0$, $t = 2\pi$.

41. Find an equation for the curve which passes through $(0,1)$ and is such that the length s of the curve from $(0,1)$ to (x,y) is $s = e^x - y$.

Section 81

Find the area of the surface of revolution generated by revolving each given curved arc about Ox:

42. $y^2 = x$, from $(0,0)$ to $(4,2)$.
43. $y = x^3$, from $(0,0)$ to $(1,1)$.
44. $y = \cosh x$ between points with $x = 0$, $x = 1$.
45. $y = x^3/6 + 1/2x$ between points with $x = 1$, $x = 2$.
46. $x = \cos^3 t$, $y = \sin^3 t$ between points with $t = 0$, $t = \pi$.
47. $x = a \cos t$, $y = b + a \sin t$, $0 < a < b$, between points with $t = 0$, $t = 2\pi$.

Section 82

Find the mean value of $y = f(x)$ with respect to x for each given function and specified range:

48. $y = \sin x$, $0 \leq x \leq \pi$.
49. $y = \sin^2 x$, $0 \leq x \leq \pi$.
50. $y = e^{-x}$, $0 \leq x \leq a$.
51. $y = 1/(x^2 + 1)$, $0 \leq x \leq a$.

For the upper half of the circle $x = a \cos t$, $y = a \sin t$, $0 \leq t \leq \pi$, find the mean value of y:

52. With respect to t.
53. With respect to x.
54. With respect to the arc length $s = at$.

For the first arch of the cycloid $x = a(t - \sin t)$, $y = a(1 - \cos t)$, $0 \leq t \leq 2\pi$, find the mean value of y:

55. With respect to t.
56. With respect to x.
57. With respect to the arc length $s = 4a[1 - \cos (t/2)]$.

Section 83

For each given $f(x)$ and interval (a,b), find M_{3x} for the area bounded above by the graph of $y = f(x)$, below by Ox, and lying between $x = a$ and $x = b$:

58. $1 - x^2$, $(0,1)$.
59. $\ln x$, $(1,e)$.
60. e^x, $(0,1)$.
61. $\sin x$, $(0,\pi)$.

62. Show that the kth moment about Ox of the area of Sec. 76 is
$$M_{kx} = \int_a^b x^k (y_2 - y_1)\, dx.$$

63. If the area of Sec. 76 is rotated about Oy, show that the volume generated is $V_x = \pi M_{2x}$, where $M_{2x} = \int_a^b x^2 (y_2 - y_1)\, dx$ as in Prob. 62.

Section 84

Find M_{2y} for the area in each problem:
64. Problem 60.

65. Problem 61.

66. From symmetry, for the triangle bounded by Ox, Oy, and the line $x + y = a$, $a > 0$, we have $M_{kx} = M_{ky}$. Check this by using Eqs. (26) and (28) to give $M_{kx} = M_{ky} = a^{k+2}/[(k + 1)(k + 2)]$.

67. If the area of Sec. 76 is rotated about Ox, show that the volume generated is $V_y = \pi M_{2y}$, where $M_{2y} = \int_a^b \frac{1}{2}(y_2{}^3 - y_1{}^3)\, dx$ as in Eq. (28).

Find the volume generated when the area in the first quadrant bounded by $y^2 = 4ax$, $a > 0$, $x = a$, and Ox is revolved about the given line in each problem:

68. The y axis.
69. The line $x = a$.
70. The x axis.
71. The line $x = 2a$.

8

PHYSICAL APPLICATIONS OF
DEFINITE
INTEGRALS

In this chapter we shall discuss reasonable definitions of a number of physical terms such as center of gravity, moment of inertia, force due to pressure, and work.   Each definition leads to one or more expressions involving definite integrals.

85—MASS DISTRIBUTIONS IN A PLANE

Let m_1 be a mass or other quantity located at the point $P_1(x_1, y_1)$ in a plane.   Then the moment of m_1 about any line in the plane is the product $m_1 L$, where L is the distance from the line to P_1, considered positive on one side of the line and negative on the other side.

To find the moment of a mass distribution in a plane, we select an element of mass dm corresponding to a part each of whose points is at approximately the same distance L from the line.   Then the element of the moment is $L\, dm$ and the moment is $\int L\, dm$.

The full implication of this definition requires multiple sums and integrals like those discussed in Chap. 11.   In this chapter we consider only situations for which results can be found by the evaluation of simple integrals.

The *center of gravity* of any mass distribution in a plane is the point such that the moment of the system about any line in the plane would not be changed if the total mass were concentrated at the point.   It can be proved that there is such a point and that, in finding the moment of any figure about a line, the figure can be divided into parts and the total mass of each part can be considered as being concentrated at the center of gravity of that part.

Let (x_g, y_g) be the center of gravity of any plane distribution.   Let the center of gravity of each element dm be $(\bar{x}, \bar{y})$.   The moment of the element about the y axis is $\bar{x}\, dm$, giving $\int \bar{x}\, dm$ as the moment of the entire distribution.   The mass of the body is $M = \int dm$, and this mass at (x_g, y_g) would have a moment $x_g M$ about the y axis.   Hence we have

$$x_g M = \int \bar{x}\, dm \quad \text{and} \quad x_g = \frac{\int \bar{x}\, dm}{M} . \tag{1}$$

Similarly, by considering moments about the x axis, we find

$$y_o M = \int \bar{y} \, dm \qquad \text{and} \qquad y_o = \frac{\int \bar{y} \, dm}{M}. \tag{2}$$

For a mass distribution along an arc, we may take $dm = \rho \, ds$, where ρ is the mass per unit of length. For a distribution over an area, we may take $dm = \rho \, dA$, where ρ is the mass per unit area, and dA is an element corresponding to a part, each point of which has approximately the same density.

If the density is constant, the factor ρ may be brought in front of the integral sign and canceled in the expressions for x_o and y_o. In this case, the point (x_o, y_o) is often called the *centroid*.

If a mass distribution in a plane is symmetrical as to density and position with respect to a line, its moment about that line is zero. Thus the center of gravity must lie on such an axis of symmetry.

EXAMPLE 1.   Find the center of gravity of a thin wire bent into the quadrant of a circle of radius a, $y = \sqrt{a^2 - x^2}$, $0 \leq x \leq a$, if the cross section and material vary in such a way that the density per unit length is ky.

SOLUTION.   We have

$$\frac{dy}{dx} = \frac{-x}{\sqrt{a^2 - x^2}}, \; ds^2 = dx^2 + dy^2 = \frac{a^2 \, dx^2}{a^2 - x^2}.$$

Since $\rho = ky = k\sqrt{a^2 - x^2}$, and $ds = (a \, dx)/\sqrt{a^2 - x^2}$, we have $dm = \rho \, ds = ka \, dx$. Hence $M = \int_0^a ka \, dx = ka^2$. For the element ds, we have $(\bar{x}, \bar{y}) = (x, y)$. Hence $Mx_o = \int_0^a x \, dm = \int_0^a ka \, x \, dx = \frac{1}{2}ka^3$, and $x_o = a/2$. Also, $My_o = \int_0^a dm = \int_0^a ka\sqrt{a^2 - x^2} \, dx = (\pi/4) \, ka^3$, and $y_o = \pi a/4$.

EXAMPLE 2.   Derive formulas for the centroid of the area of Sec. 76.

SOLUTION.   Here ρ is constant. For the element of area dA, we have

$$dA = (y_2 - y_1) \, dx \qquad (\bar{x}, \bar{y}) = \left(x, \frac{y_1 + y_2}{2} \right),$$

since the centroid of a rectangle is at its center of symmetry.

Thus we have $M = \rho \int_a^b (y_2 - y_1)\, dx$, $Mx_g = \rho \int_a^b x(y_2 - y_1)\, dx$, and $My_g = (\rho/2) \int_a^b (y_2{}^2 - y_1{}^2)\, dx$. Since $A = \int_a^b (y_2 - y_1)\, dx$, we obtain

$$x_g = \frac{1}{A} \int_a^b x(y_2 - y_1)\, dx \qquad y_g = \frac{1}{A} \int_a^b \tfrac{1}{2}(y_2{}^2 - y_1{}^2)\, dx. \tag{3}$$

Note that the integral in x_g is the moment M_{1x} as defined in Sec. 83, and the integral in y_g is the moment M_{1y} of Eq. (28) in Sec. 84.

EXAMPLE 3.   Prove *Pappus's theorem on areas:* If an arc of a plane curve is revolved about a line in its plane which does not intersect the arc, the surface area generated by the arc is equal to its length times the distance traversed by its centroid (Pappus, ca. A.D. 300, Greek).

SOLUTION.   Take the axis of revolution as the x axis, with $y \geq 0$ on the arc. Then, by Sec. 81, we have

$$S = \int 2\pi y\, ds. \tag{4}$$

But the distance traversed by the centroid is $2\pi y_g$. And if the length of the arc is s, then $M = \int \rho\, ds = \rho s$, $My_g = \int \rho y\, ds$. Since ρ is constant, $\int y\, ds = sy_g$. Hence, from Eq. (4), we have $S = s(2\pi y_g)$, which proves the theorem.

EXAMPLE 4.   Prove *Pappus's theorem on volumes:* If a plane area is revolved about a line in its plane which does not intersect the area, then the volume generated by the area is equal to its area times the distance traversed by its centroid.

SOLUTION.   Take the axis of revolution as the x axis. Let the area be that of Example 2, with $y_2 \geq y_1 \geq 0$. Then, from Eq. (11) of Sec. 79, we have

$$V = \pi \int (y_2{}^2 - y_1{}^2)\, dx. \tag{5}$$

But the distance traversed by the centroid is $2\pi y_g$. And if the area is A, from Eq. (3) we have $2Ay_g = \int (y_2{}^2 - y_1{}^2)\, dx$. It follows from this and Eq. (5) that $V = A(2\pi y_g)$, which proves the theorem.

86—MASS DISTRIBUTIONS IN SPACE

Let m_1 be a mass located in space at the point $P_1(x_1,y_1,z_1)$. Then the moment of m_1 about any plane in space is the product m_1L, where L is the distance from the plane to P_1, considered positive on one side of the plane and negative on the other side.

To find the moment of a mass distribution in space, we select an element dm corresponding to a part each of whose points is at approximately the same distance L from the plane. Then the element of the moment is $L\,dm$ and the moment is $\int L\,dm$.

The *center of gravity* of any mass distribution in space is the point such that the moment of the system about any plane in space would not be changed if the total mass were concentrated at the point. It can be proved that there is such a point and that, in finding the moment of any figure about a plane, the figure can be divided into parts and the total mass of each part can be considered as being concentrated at the center of gravity of that part.

Let (x_g,y_g,z_g) be the center of gravity of any distribution of mass in space. And let the center of gravity of each element dm be $(\bar{x},\bar{y},\bar{z})$. The moment of the element about the yz plane is $\bar{x}\,dm$, giving $\int \bar{x}\,dm$ as the moment of the entire distribution. The mass of the body is $M = \int dm$, and this mass at (x_g,y_g,z_g) would have a moment x_gM about the yz plane. Hence we have

$$x_gM = \int x\,dm \qquad \text{and} \qquad x_g = \frac{\int \bar{x}\,dm}{M}. \qquad (6)$$

Similarly, by considering moments about the zx and xy planes, we find

$$y_g = \frac{\int \bar{y}\,dm}{M} \qquad z_g = \frac{\int \bar{z}\,dm}{M}. \qquad (7)$$

Let the distribution of mass be over a volume. Take such elements of volume, dV, that each element corresponds to a part each of whose points has approximately the same density per unit volume, ρ. Then we can take $dm = \rho\,dV$.

If the density is constant, the factor ρ may be brought in front of the integral sign and canceled in the expressions for x_g, y_g, and z_g. In this case the point (x_g,y_g,z_g) is often called the *centroid*.

If a mass distribution is symmetrical as to density and position with respect to a plane, its moment about that plane is zero. Thus the center of gravity must lie on any such plane of symmetry. Consequently, it must lie on an axis of symmetry, when there is one.

EXAMPLE. The density of a solid of revolution occupying the volume described in Sec. 78 is the same throughout each circular cross section, but varies with x in such a way that $\rho = D(x)$. Find its center of gravity.

SOLUTION. Here, by Eq. (8) of Sec. 78, we can take $dm = \rho \, dV = D(x) \, \pi y^2 \, dx$. Hence $M = \int_a^b D(x) \, \pi y^2 \, dx$. The center of gravity lies on the axis of symmetry, Ox, and its distance x_g along this is such that $Mx_g = \int_a^b x \, D(x) \, \pi y^2 \, dx$. Then $x_g = Mx_g/M$ can be computed from these two integrals.

87—MOMENT OF INERTIA

In complete analogy with the first moments about a line in a plane or those about a plane in space, discussed in Secs. 85 and 86, respectively, we could form second moments $M_2 = \int L^2 \, dm$, with elements $L^2 \, dm$.

For a mass m_1 concentrated at a point P_1 at distance r from a straight line taken as axis, the moment of inertia about the axis is $I = m_1 r^2$. Similarly, for any mass distribution, if dm is an element of mass corresponding to a part each of whose points is at approximately the same distance r from the axis, the *moment of inertia* about this axis is $I = \int r^2 \, dm$.

Let a thin uniform plate of constant density ρ cover the area described in Sec. 76. Then, since each point of the element given in Eq. (1) of Sec. 76 is at approximately the distance x from Oy, the moment of inertia about the y axis is

$$I_{Oy} = \rho \int_a^b x^2 (y_2 - y_1) \, dx. \tag{8}$$

The moment of inertia about the x axis, I_{Ox}, is $\rho \, M_{2y}$ and hence, by Eq. (28) of Sec. 84, with $k = 2$, is

$$I_{Ox} = \rho \int_a^b \tfrac{1}{3} (y_2{}^3 - y_1{}^3) \, dx. \tag{9}$$

If I_O is the moment of inertia about an axis through O perpendicular to the xy plane, we have

$$I_0 = \int(x^2 + y^2)\, dm = \int x^2\, dm + \int y^2\, dm = I_{oy} + I_{ox}. \qquad (10)$$

We sometimes call I_0 the moment of inertia about O, or the polar moment of inertia.

To find the moment of inertia, about its axis, of the solid of revolution of the example given in Sec. 86, we use the elements $dV = \pi y^2\, dx$. But by Example 1, below, the moment of inertia about its axis of a homogeneous circular cylinder of radius a and height h is $I = (\pi/2)\, \rho\, a^4 h$. Hence, for the element dV, we have $dI = (\pi/2) D(x)\, y^4\, dx$. Accordingly, we have

$$I = \int_a^b \frac{\pi}{2} D(x)\, y^4\, dx. \qquad (11)$$

The distance k from the axis at which all the mass could be considered as being concentrated without changing the moment of inertia of the system about that axis is called the *radius of gyration*. Hence

$$I = Mk^2 \quad \text{and} \quad k = \sqrt{\frac{I}{M}}, \qquad (12)$$

where M is the total mass of the system.

For mass distributions covering a length, area, or volume, we may consider $dm = \rho\, ds$, $dm = \rho\, dA$, or $dm = \rho\, dV$, as in Secs. 85 and 86. For $\rho = 1$, the resulting expression is referred to as the moment of inertia of the length, area, or volume itself.

EXAMPLE 1.   Show that the moment of inertia, about its axis, of a homogeneous circular cylinder of radius a, height h, and density ρ is $I = (\pi/2)\, \rho\, a^4 h$. Also show that its radius of gyration is $k = a/\sqrt{2}$.

SOLUTION.   The volume cut out of the cylinder of height h by two concentric circular cylinders of radius r and $r + \Delta r$ is $\Delta V = \pi h[(r + \Delta r)^2 - r^2] = 2\pi h(r + \Delta r/2)\, \Delta r = 2\pi h r^*\, \Delta r$. This suggests the element of volume $dV = 2\pi h\, r\, dr$, for which $dI = \rho\, r^2\, dV = 2\pi\, \rho\, h\, r^3\, dr$. Hence

$$I = \int_0^a 2\pi\, \rho\, h\, r^3\, dr = \frac{\pi}{2}\, \rho\, a^4 h. \qquad (13)$$

For the cylinder, we have $M = \pi \rho h a^2$, so that

$$\frac{I}{M} = \frac{a^2}{2} \qquad I = \frac{Ma^2}{2} = Mk^2 \qquad k = \frac{a}{\sqrt{2}}. \qquad (14)$$

EXAMPLE 2.   A homogeneous rectangular parallelepiped has as the lengths of its edges $OA = a$, $OB = b$, $OC = c$. Find the radius of gyration about the axis OC.

SOLUTION.   Take the x, y, z axes along OA, OB, OC, respectively. To find M_{2x}, we take elements $dV = bc\ dx$. Then $M_{2x} = \int x^2\ dV = \int_0^a bcx^2\ dx = bca^3/3$. Similarly, $M_{2y} = cab^3/3$. But $I_{OC} = \int (x^2 + y^2)\ dm = \rho\ (M_{2x} + M_{2y}) = (\rho\ abc/3)$ $(a^2 + b^2)$. Since $M = \rho\ abc$, we have $I_{OC}/M = (a^2 + b^2)/3$; whence $k = \sqrt{a^2 + b^2}/3$.

88—WORK

Suppose that a constant force F is applied to a particle. If the particle moves a distance s in the direction of F under the action of F, we say that the force does the work Fs.

If the particle moves in the opposite direction, we consider s and $W = Fs$ negative. And the positive quantity $F(-s)$ is the work done against F.

Suppose that a particle moves along the x axis from $x = a$ to $x = b$ under the action of a variable force $F(x)$. Divide $[a,b]$ into parts Δx_i, and select any value ξ_i in the ith interval. Then the sum $\Sigma F(\xi_i)\ \Delta x_i$ should be a reasonable approximation to the work done by the variable force. If the force function is continuous, when max $\Delta x_i \to 0$, each sequence of approximating sums will approach a common limit

$$W = \int_a^b F(x)\ dx, \qquad (15)$$

and this limit is defined as the *work* done by the variable force.

EXAMPLE 1.   The amount a spring is stretched is proportional to the force applied. If a force of P lb stretches a spring of length

L to a length $2L$, find the work done in stretching the spring from length L to length $1.2L$.

SOLUTION.   Let x be the amount stretched.   Then we have $F = kx$, $P = kL$, $k = P/L$.   Also, $dW = F\,dx = kx\,dx$; whence

$$W = \int_0^{0.2L} kx\,dx = 0.02\,kL^2 = 0.02\,PL \text{ ft-lb.}$$

EXAMPLE 2.   A tank (Fig. 24) has the form of the solid of revolution described in Sec. 78, with x axis pointing vertically downward. If it is full of liquid of weight w lb per ft³, how much work is required to pump all the liquid over the top of the tank?

SOLUTION.   The element of volume is given by $dV = \pi y^2\,dx$ by Eq. (8) of Sec. 78. It weighs $w\pi y^2\,dx$ lb, and the work done in lifting this to the top, $x = a$, or through a distance $(x - a)$, is

$$dW = \pi w(x - a)y^2\,dx. \tag{16}$$

Hence the total work is

$$W = \int_a^b \pi w(x - a)y^2\,dx. \tag{17}$$

EXAMPLE 3.   Let the total weight of liquid initially in the full tank of Example 2 be Mg. Show that the work done is $Mg(x_g - a)$,

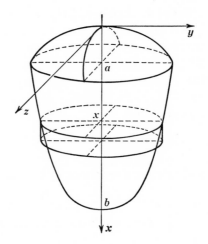

FIGURE 24

or the work of lifting this weight from the center of gravity to the top of the tank.

SOLUTION.   With $D(x) = w/g$, the equations of the example in Sec. 86 are $M = \int_a^b (w/g)\ \pi y^2\ dx$ and $Mx_g = \int_a^b x(w/g)\ \pi y^2\ dx$. It follows from these and Eq. (17) that $W = \int_a^b \pi wxy^2\ dx -$ $a\int_a^b \pi wy^2\ dx = gMx_g - agM = Mg(x_g - a)$, the desired result.

Note that either the expression for W in Example 2 or that in Example 3 could be interpreted directly as g times the first moment of the mass distribution of the liquid about the horizontal plane $x = a$ at the top of the tank.

89—FORCE DUE TO PRESSURE OF A FLUID

At a point below the surface of a fluid at rest, the intensity of the pressure, or force per unit area, is the same in every direction.   If the liquid weighs w lb per ft³ and we consider a horizontal flat plate at distance x ft below the surface, the pressure p is given by $p = wx$ lb per ft².

We wish to determine the force exerted by liquid pressure against one side of a vertical plate (Fig. 25) such as a gate in the face of a dam.   Let the gate cover the area described in Sec. 76, where the xy plane is vertical, with Oy in the surface of the fluid and Ox point-

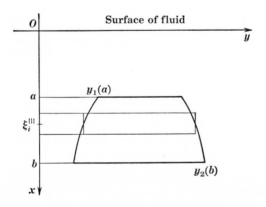

FIGURE 25

ing vertically downward. With ξ_i''' any point in the interval Δx_i, the sum $\Sigma w \xi_i''' [y_2(\xi_i') - y_1(\xi_i'')] \Delta x_i$ should be a reasonable approximation to the total force. Accordingly, the limit F of a sequence with max $\Delta x_i \to 0$,

$$F = \int_a^b wx(y_2 - y_1) \, dx \tag{18}$$

gives the force due to pressure on the vertical gate.

It follows from Eq. (3) that

$$F = wAx_g. \tag{19}$$

EXAMPLE.   The center of pressure of the gate is defined as the point (x_c, y_c) at which a single force F would have the same moments about any line in the plane of the gate as the separate forces due to fluid pressure.   Find this point.

SOLUTION. Taking   moments   about Oy,   we   find $Fx_c = \int_a^b wx^2(y_2 - y_1) \, dx = wM_{2x}$.   Taking moments about Ox, and reasoning as we did for Eq. (28) of Sec. 84, we find that $Fy_c = \int_a^b wx\frac{1}{2}(y_1{}^2 - y_2{}^2) \, dx$.   Then $x_c = Fx_c/F$ and $y_c = Fy_c/F$, where the numerators are to be found from their expressions as integrals.

It will be noted that x_c and y_c are the coordinates of the center of gravity of a thin plate covering the gate whose density is equal to wx.

PROBLEMS

Section 85

1. Show that for a triangle the distance of the centroid from the base is one-third of the altitude.

2. Show that for a quadrant of a circle of radius a, with the bounding radii as coordinate axes, $\bar{x} = \bar{y} = 4a/3\pi$.

Find the centroid of the area in the first quadrant bounded by the x axis and each given set of curves:

3. $y = 4x - x^2$.
4. $y = \sin x \qquad 0 \leq x \leq \pi$.
5. $y = x - x^3$.
6. $y = e^x \qquad x = 0, x = 1$.

A thin plate covers the region in the first quadrant bounded by $y^2 = x$, $x = 0$, and $x = 1$. In each problem find its center of gravity if the density is proportional to:

7. x.

8. x^2.

9. y.

10. Show that for the centroid of the arc of a quarter of a circle of radius a, with the limiting radii as coordinate axes, we have $\bar{x} = \bar{y} = 2a/\pi$.

In each problem find the center of gravity of a straight rod of length L if the density at a point at distance x from one end is proportional to the following:

11. x.

12. x^2.

13. e^x.

Find the centroid of the arc of each given curve between the two points indicated:

14. $9y^2 = 4x^3$, $(1, -\frac{2}{3})$, $(1, \frac{2}{3})$.
15. $y = \cosh x$, points with $x = -1$, $x = 1$.
16. $x = \cos^3 t$, $y = \sin^3 t$, points with $t = 0$, $t = \pi/2$.

Section 86

The area in the first quadrant bounded by the x axis and the given curve or set of curves is rotated about Ox. In each problem, find the x coordinate of the centroid of the *solid* thus generated:

17. $y^2 = 4ax \qquad x = a$.
18. $y = e^{-x} \qquad x = 0, x = 1$.
19. $x^2 + y^2 = a^2 \qquad x = 0$.
20. $xy = 4 \qquad x = 1, x = 4$.

The arc of the given curve between the two specified points is rotated about Ox. In each problem, find the x coordinate of the surface area generated:

21. $y = \cosh x$, points with $x = 0$, $x = 1$.

22. $y^2 = 4x$, points with $x = 0$, $x = 1$.

Section 87

Find I_{Ox}, I_{Oy}, and I_O for the area of the following:

23. The right triangle with vertices $(0,0)$, $(0,b)$, (a,b).

24. The rectangle with vertices $(0,0)$, $(a,0)$, (a,b), $(0,b)$.

25. The ellipse $x^2/a^2 + y^2/b^2 = 1$.

Find the moment of inertia about its axis of the volume of the solid of revolution of the following:

26. Problem 17.

27. Problem 18.

28. Problem 19.

29. Problem 20.

Section 88

30. The force required to stretch a spring is proportional to the elongation and is 3 lb when the extension is 1 in. Find the work done in stretching the spring from its natural length to a length 4 in. greater.

31. A negative electric charge at a fixed point O attracts a positively charged particle at P with a force inversely proportional to the square of the distance OP. If the force is 10^{-5} lb when OP is 1 in., find the work done in moving the charged particle from a point 2 in. from O to a point 50 in. from O.

32. A bucket weighing 100 lb is to be hoisted from the bottom to the top of a shaft 50 ft deep. If the cable weighs 0.2 lb/ft, find the work done.

33. A bag containing originally 100 lb of sand is hoisted up a distance 12 ft. The sand leaks out in such a way that the loss is proportional to the square of the height lifted, and is 25 lb at the maximum height of 12 ft. Find the work done in lifting the bag.

For water, $w = \frac{1}{32}$ ton per ft³. Find the work done in pumping all the water over the top from a full tank, if the tank is:

34. A circular cylinder of altitude 10 ft and radius 2 ft with its axis vertical.

35. A cylinder like that in Prob. 34 with its axis horizontal.

36. An inverted cone of height 4 ft and radius 3 ft.
37. A sphere of radius 3 ft.
38. The lower half of a sphere of radius 2 ft.

Section 89

For each of the following vertical wetted surfaces, find the force due to pressure on one side of the surface, and find the depth of the center of pressure:

39. A square 4 ft on a side, with the upper side parallel to and 10 ft below the surface of the liquid.
40. A circle 2 ft in radius, with center 10 ft below the surface of the liquid.
41. The upper half of the circle in Prob. 40.
42. The lower half of the circle in Prob. 40.

9

POLAR COORDINATES, CURVATURE

In Sec. 6 we defined the graph of a relation, or locus of an equation defining the relation, by using the one-to-one correspondence between ordered number pairs (x,y) and points in the cartesian plane which we described in Sec. 1.   In this chapter we shall introduce a polar number pair (r,θ), which is preferable for certain problems.

We shall also discuss the curvature of a curve, and find its expression for a curve which is the locus of an equation in rectangular coordinates, for a curve given in parametric form as in Sec. 43, or for a curve given as the locus of an equation in polar coordinates.

90—POLAR COORDINATES

As in Fig. 26, let a horizontal line Ox start at O and extend to the right.   Let the angle from Ox to OP, measured counterclockwise, be θ radians.   Denote the distance OP by r.   Then the ordered pair of numbers (r,θ) may be taken as *polar* coordinates of the point P.

To each pair (r,θ) there corresponds a single point.   But a point has many pairs of coordinates.   For example, $(r, \theta + 2\pi)$ and $(r, \theta - 2\pi)$ correspond to the same point as (r,θ).

We call O the *pole* of the system of polar coordinates and Ox the *polar axis*.   The line OP is called the *radius vector*.   The distance from O to P is positive when OP is the terminal side of θ.   The distance from O to P is negative when PO produced through O is the terminal side of θ.   Thus the pair $(-r, \theta + \pi)$, or $(-r, \theta - \pi)$ give the same point as (r,θ).

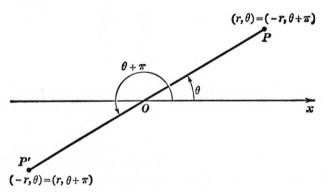

$$(r,\theta)=(-r,\theta+\pi)$$

$$(-r,\theta)=(r,\theta+\pi)$$

FIGURE 26

When polar coordinates are indicated by the context, we shall use the symbol (a,A) to mean the point with $r = a$ and $\theta = A$. And to show that the point is P, we write $P = (a,A)$ or $P(a,A)$. If (as in Sec. 42) $D = (180/\pi)A$, the number of degrees in A radians, we often write $D°$ in place of A, as in $P = (a,D°)$.

Let us superimpose a cartesian system with the radius vector $\theta = 0$ as the positive x axis and the radius vector $\theta = \pi/2$ as the positive y axis. Then, from elementary trigonometry, we find

$$x = r \cos \theta \qquad y = r \sin \theta. \tag{1}$$

From these equations we have

$$x^2 + y^2 = r^2 \qquad \frac{y}{x} = \tan \theta \qquad \text{or } r = \pm\sqrt{x^2 + y^2}$$

$$\theta = \tan^{-1} \frac{y}{x} \pm k\pi. \tag{2}$$

With $\tan^{-1}$ given its principal value, $k = 0$ or such an integer that Eq. (1) holds.

EXAMPLE.   Find a polar equation of a circle with center at the point $C = (a,0)$ and radius a.

SOLUTION.   The circle cuts the polar axis at $O = (0,0)$ and $A = (2a,0)$. For any point $P = (r,\theta)$ on the circle, the angle OPA is a right angle since OA is a diameter. Hence $\cos \theta = OP/OA = r/2a$, so that the coordinates of any point on the circle satisfy the equation $r = 2a \cos \theta$.

Conversely, note that, by Eqs. (2) and (1), $r^2 = 2ar \cos \theta$ (which is an equivalent equation since O is on the locus) becomes $x^2 + y^2 = 2ax$, so that any point whose coordinates satisfy $r = 2a \cos \theta$ lies on the circle.

91—TANGENT AT THE ORIGIN

If $OP = 0$, then P is at the origin O. Thus $O = (0,\theta)$ for any value of θ. Now consider the equation $r = f(\theta)$, with f a continuous function. And suppose that the locus of this equation is a smooth curve. Suppose, further, that $f(\theta_1) = 0$. Then, since $r = 0$, $\theta = \theta_1$ satisfies the equation $r = f(\theta)$, the origin is one point on the curve. And for θ in an interval including θ_1, the points (r,θ) in general make up an arc. Now let $\theta \to \theta_1$. Then the radius vector from 0 to (r,θ), a chord of the curve, approaches the tangent to the arc at the origin. Accordingly, this tangent is the radius vector with $\theta = \theta_1$. This proves the theorem:

If the locus of the equation $r = f(\theta)$ is a smooth curve, and $f(\theta_1) = 0$, then not only does the graph include an arc passing through the origin, but the radius vector with $\theta = \theta_1$ is tangent to this arc at the origin.

92—GRAPHS

In general, the locus of points (r,θ) whose polar coordinates satisfy a given equation $r = f(\theta)$ is a curve. We may plot an arc of the locus by tabulating a few pairs of values of r and θ which satisfy the equation and joining them by a smooth curve. The work is facilitated by using polar-coordinate paper, ruled with equidistant concentric circles and radius vectors for θ an even multiple of $15°$, or $\pi/12$.

It is often sufficient to consider θ as increasing (or decreasing) from some particular value, as 0, and determine intervals of θ in which r increases or decreases. We may then plot accurately the points where r is a maximum or minimum and through them draw a curve on which r increases or decreases as indicated.

EXAMPLE.   Sketch the locus of $r = 2a \cos \theta$.

SOLUTION.   Here r is a maximum for $\theta = 0$, $r = 2a$. And $|r|$ is a minimum for $\theta = \pi/2$ or $-\pi/2$, $r = 0$. Since $\cos \theta = \cos(-\theta) = -\cos(\theta + \pi)$, the curve consists of a single loop traversed once each time θ increases by π radians. This loop has a tangent perpendicular to the radius vector for $\theta = 0$, since r is a maximum there, and is tangent to the line $\theta = \pi/2$, $\theta = -\pi/2$ by the theorem of Sec. 91. The loop passes through $(\sqrt{2}a, \pm\pi/4)$ and looks like a circle. The example of Sec. 90 shows that it *is* a circle.

93—DIFFERENTIAL RELATIONS

Let s be the arc length of a curve C whose equation is $r = f(\theta)$, measured in such a direction that s increases as θ increases. We use the Greek letter ψ (psi) to denote the angle at a point P from the direction PR in which r increases to the tangential direction PT in which s increases (Fig. 27). Since the angle from the Ox direction to the PT direction is ϕ, the slope angle, and the angle from the Ox direction to the PR direction is $\theta \pm k\pi$, we have $\phi = \theta + \psi \pm k\pi$. It follows that $\psi = \phi - \theta \mp k\pi$; whence

$$\tan \psi = \tan (\phi - \theta) = \frac{\tan \phi - \tan \theta}{1 + \tan \phi \tan \theta}. \qquad (3)$$

From Eq. (1), we find that

$$dx = dr \cos \theta - r \sin \theta \, d\theta \qquad dy = dr \sin \theta + r \cos \theta \, d\theta. \qquad (4)$$

Since $\tan \phi = dy/dx$, we have

$$\tan \phi = \frac{dy}{dx} = \frac{r' \tan \theta + r}{r' - r \tan \theta}, \qquad (5)$$

where we have used Eq. (4), divided numerator and denominator by $\cos \theta \, d\theta$, and written r' for $dr/d\theta$. Insertion of this value of $\tan \phi$ in Eq. (3) leads to

$$\tan \psi = \frac{r(1 + \tan^2 \theta)}{r'(1 + \tan^2 \theta)} = \frac{r}{r'} = \frac{r \, d\theta}{dr}. \qquad (6)$$

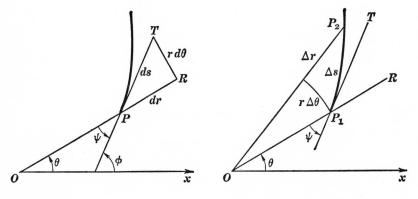

FIGURE 27

This result will not apply at the origin if we take an arbitrary value of θ. But for the θ_1 of Sec. 91, we shall always have $\lim_{\theta \to \theta_1} (r/r') = 0$ (even when $r' \to 0$), making $\psi = 0$ in agreement with the theorem of Sec. 91.

From Eq. (16) of Sec. 80, we have $ds^2 = dx^2 + dy^2$. From this and Eq. (4), we find that, in polar coordinates,

$$ds^2 = dr^2 + r^2 \, d\theta^2 \qquad \text{and} \qquad s'^2 = \left(\frac{ds}{d\theta}\right)^2 = r'^2 + r^2. \qquad (7)$$

This shows that the differentials dr, $r \, d\theta$, and ds may be used as the sides of a right triangle. And Eq. (6) shows that in this triangle the angle opposite $r \, d\theta$ is ψ. Thus we have the additional relations

$$\sin \psi = \frac{r \, d\theta}{ds} \qquad \cos \psi = \frac{dr}{ds}. \qquad (8)$$

All the Eqs. (6) to (8) may be read from a right triangle with straight sides dr from P in the direction PR, ds from P along PT, and third side $r \, d\theta$. This can be remembered by considering the curvilinear right triangle with hypotenuse Δs along an arc from P_1 to P_2, side $r \, \Delta\theta$ along a circle through P_1, and side Δr from this circle to P_2 on the radius vector OP_2. The angle of this triangle at P_1, opposite to Δr, is $\pi/2 - \psi$ (Fig. 27).

EXAMPLE 1. Find the tangent of the angle ψ for the curve $r = a(1 + \cos \theta)$.

SOLUTION. From $r = a(1 + \cos \theta) = 2a \cos^2 (\theta/2)$, $r' = dr/d\theta = -a \sin \theta = -2a \cos (\theta/2) \sin (\theta/2)$. And from Eq. (6) we get $\tan \psi = r/r' = -\cot (\theta/2) = \tan (\theta/2 \pm \pi/2)$. For $-\pi \leq \theta \leq \pi$, $\psi = \theta/2 + \pi/2$ gives the value of ψ in the first or second quadrant.

EXAMPLE 2. Find the arc length of the curve in Example 1.

SOLUTION. From Eq. (7) we find $s'^2 = r'^2 + r^2 = 2a^2(1 + \cos \theta) = 4a^2 \cos^2 (\theta/2)$ by using the value of r' found in Example 1. Hence $ds = 2a|\cos (\theta/2)| \, d\theta$, and $L = 2a \int_0^{2\pi} |\cos (\theta/2)| \, d\theta =$

$$2a \int_0^\pi \cos (\theta/2) d\theta - 2a \int_\pi^{2\pi} \cos (\theta/2) d\theta = 4a \left[\sin (\theta/2) \right]_{0,2\pi}^{\pi,\pi} =$$

$8a.$ Alternatively, from the symmetry, we have $L = 2 \int_0^\pi ds =$

$$4a \int_0^\pi \cos (\theta/2) d\theta = 8a.$$

94—CURVATURE

Let s be the arc length of a curve C measured from a fixed point P_0 to a variable point P on C. Then the slope angle ϕ at P depends on s. Since a change in ϕ measures the change in direction of the curve, the rate of change with respect to s or $d\phi/ds$ measures the change in direction per unit distance along the curve. This rate is called the *curvature* of the curve at P, and is denoted by the Greek letter κ (kappa). To calculate κ for the curve with equation $y = f(x)$, we have

$$\tan \phi = \frac{dy}{dx} = y' \qquad \phi = \tan^{-1} y' \qquad d\phi = \frac{y''}{1 + y'^2} dx. \qquad (9)$$

And from Eq. (16) of Sec. 80 we get

$$ds = \sqrt{dx^2 + dy^2} = \sqrt{1 + y'^2}\, dx. \qquad (10)$$

Hence for the curvature we find

$$\kappa = \frac{d\phi}{ds} = \frac{y''}{(1 + y'^2)^{3/2}} = \frac{d^2y/dx^2}{[1 + (dy/dx)^2]^{3/2}} . \qquad (11)$$

The quantity $\rho = 1/|\kappa|$ (for $\kappa \neq 0$) is called the *radius of curvature*. If P is a point on the curve, then the circle through P with radius ρ (Greek letter, rho) and center on the normal at P drawn on the concave side of the curve is the *circle of curvature* at P. It can be shown that the values of y, y', and y'' at P for this circle are the same as those for the curve and that this circle fits the curve at P closer than any other circle does.

As in Sec. 43, let a curve be given parametrically by a pair of equations

$$x = f(t) \qquad \text{and} \qquad y = g(t). \qquad (12)$$

Then, using primes for t derivatives, we have

$$dx = f'(t)dt \qquad dy = g'(t)dt \qquad \frac{dy}{dx} = \frac{g'}{f'}. \tag{13}$$

From this we also have

$$d\left(\frac{dy}{dx}\right) = \frac{g''f' - f''g'}{f'^2} dt \qquad \frac{d^2y}{dx^2} = \frac{g''f' - f''g'}{f'^3}. \tag{14}$$

On combining Eqs. (13) and (14) with Eq. (11), we find

$$\kappa = \frac{g''f' - f''g'}{(f'^2 + g'^2)^{3/2}} = \frac{\ddot{y}\dot{x} - \ddot{x}\dot{y}}{(\dot{x}^2 + \dot{y}^2)^{3/2}}, \tag{15}$$

as a more suggestive form, with the use of dots for differentiation with respect to the parameter.

For a curve given in polar coordinates we may consider

$$x = r \cos \theta \qquad y = r \sin \theta \qquad r = f(\theta) \tag{16}$$

as giving x and y in terms of θ as a parameter. Thus we have

$$\dot{x} = r' \cos \theta - r \sin \theta \qquad \ddot{x} = r'' \cos \theta - 2r' \sin \theta - r \cos \theta$$
$$\dot{y} = r' \sin \theta + r \cos \theta \qquad \ddot{y} = r'' \sin \theta + 2r' \cos \theta - r \sin \theta. \tag{17}$$

On combining these results with Eq. (15), we obtain

$$\kappa = \frac{-rr'' + 2r'^2 + r^2}{(r'^2 + r^2)^{3/2}}, \tag{18}$$

where the primes denote differentiation of $r = f(\theta)$ with respect to θ.

EXAMPLE 1.   Find the curvature of the catenary

$$y = \frac{a}{2}(e^{ax} + e^{-ax}) = a \cosh \frac{x}{a}.$$

SOLUTION.   From $y' = \sinh (x/a)$, $y'' = (1/a) \cosh (x/a)$, we find

$$1 + y'^2 = 1 + \sinh^2 \frac{x}{a} = \cosh^2 \frac{x}{a}$$

and, from Eq. (11),

$$\kappa = \frac{(1/a) \cosh (x/a)}{\cosh^3 (x/a)} = \frac{1}{a \cosh^2 (x/a)} = \frac{a}{y^2}.$$

EXAMPLE 2.   Verify by direct calculation that the radius of curvature of the circle $x = a \cos t$, $y = a \sin t$, is $\rho = a$.

SOLUTION.   Here $\dot{x} = -a \sin t$, $\dot{y} = a \cos t$, $\ddot{x} = -a \cos t$, $\ddot{y} = -a \sin t$.   Hence $\dot{x}^2 + \dot{y}^2 = a^2 (\sin^2 t + \cos^2 t) = a^2$, and $\dot{y}\ddot{x} - \ddot{x}\dot{y} = a^2 (\sin^2 t + \cos^2 t) = a^2$.   And from Eq. (15), $\kappa = a^2/(a^2)^{3/2} = 1/a$.   Thus $\rho = 1/|\kappa| = a$.

95—AREA IN POLAR COORDINATES

We sometimes wish to find the sectorial area bounded by a curve and two of its radius vectors.   Let the equation of the curve in polar coordinates be $r = f(\theta)$.   And let the two radius vectors (Fig. 28) be OD corresponding to $\theta = \alpha$ and OE corresponding to $\theta = \beta$.   Assume that for $\alpha \leq \theta \leq \beta$, f is continuous and $f(\theta) \geq 0$.

To find S, the sectorial area DOE of Fig. 28, we divide the angle DOE into n parts by radius vectors θ_i.   As in Sec. 15, we have

$$\alpha = \theta_0 < \theta_1 < \theta_2 < \cdots < \theta_{n-1} < \theta_n = \beta. \tag{19}$$

Also, in each sector corresponding to the interval $[\theta_{i-1},\theta_i]$ of length $\Delta\theta_i$, construct two circular sectors whose radii are $m_i = f(u_i)$ and $M_i = f(v_i)$, respectively the least and greatest values of $f(\theta)$ in the

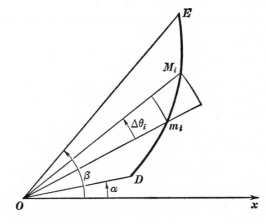

FIGURE 28 O

interval $[\theta_{i-1},\theta_i]$. We recall that the area of a circular sector of radius r and angle $\Delta\theta$ is

$$\Delta S = \tfrac{1}{2}r^2\ \Delta\theta. \tag{20}$$

Then the sum of the circular sectors with radii m_i constitutes a figure of known area I which is contained in S and whose area is

$$I = \sum_{i=1}^{n} \tfrac{1}{2}m_i{}^2\ \Delta\theta_i = \sum_{i=1}^{n} \tfrac{1}{2}[f(u_i)]^2\ \Delta\theta_i. \tag{21}$$

Similarly, the sum of the circular sectors with radii M_i constitutes a figure of known area E which contains S and whose area is

$$E = \sum_{i=1}^{n} \tfrac{1}{2}M_i{}^2\ \Delta\theta_i = \sum_{i=1}^{n} \tfrac{1}{2}[f(v_i)]^2\ \Delta\theta_i. \tag{22}$$

As in Eq. (7) of Sec. 15, and with $f(x)$ replaced by $\tfrac{1}{2}[f(\theta)]^2$, we may consider the u_i and v_i a special choice of the ξ_i. It follows from Sec. 18, and the continuity of f, that for any two sequences E_t and I_t with $\delta_M = \max\ \Delta\theta_i$ tending to zero as t tends to infinity, we have

$$\lim_{t\to\infty} E_t = \lim_{t\to\infty} I_t = \int_\alpha^\beta \tfrac{1}{2}[f(\theta)]^2\ d\theta. \tag{23}$$

Hence, by Sec. 26, this is the measure of the area S.

Equation (20) suggests that we define

$$dS = \tfrac{1}{2}r^2\ d\theta \tag{24}$$

as the element of sectorial area. By a procedure like that of Sec. 76, we may use this to recall that the area $S_\alpha{}^\beta$ between radius vectors $\theta = \alpha$ and $\theta = \beta$ is given by

$$S_\alpha{}^\beta = \tfrac{1}{2}\int_\alpha^\beta r^2\ d\theta = \tfrac{1}{2}\int_\alpha^\beta [f(\theta)]^2\ d\theta. \tag{25}$$

As the last form indicates, we must replace r by its value $f(\theta)$ in the integral.

EXAMPLE 1. Find the total area of the lemniscate, $r^2 = 2a^2 \cos 2\theta$.

SOLUTION. If we should naively calculate $\tfrac{1}{2}\int_0^{2\pi} 2a^2 \cos 2\theta\ d\theta$, we should get zero, because of the negative values of r^2 for $\pi/4 < \theta < 3\pi/4$, and $5\pi/4 < \theta < 7\pi/4$, which correspond to *imag-*

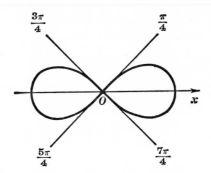

FIGURE 29

inary values of r. The curve (Fig. 29) consists of two loops and is symmetrical about $\theta = 0$ and $\theta = \pi/2$, since $\cos 2\theta = \cos 2(-\theta)$, and $\cos 2\theta = \cos 2(\pi - \theta)$. Hence we have $S/4 = \frac{1}{2}\int_0^{\pi/4} 2a^2\cos 2\theta\, d\theta = a^2/2\ [\sin 2\theta]_0^{\pi/4} = a^2/2$; whence $S = 2a^2$.

EXAMPLE 2.   Find the centroid of the sectorial area S in Fig. 28.

SOLUTION.   The element dS may be approximated by a circular sector of radius r and central angle $d\theta$ or an isosceles triangle of altitude r and base $r\, d\theta$. By Prob. 1 of Chap. 8, the centroid of this triangle is two-thirds of the way from the vertex to the base, and so has polar coordinates $(\frac{2}{3}r, \theta)$. Hence, for dS, $\bar{x} = \frac{2}{3}r \cos \theta$, $\bar{y} = \frac{2}{3}r \sin \theta$. With these values, $\rho = 1$, $M = S$, and $dm = dS$, Eqs. (1) and (2) of Sec. 85 give

$$Sx_g = \tfrac{1}{3}\smallint r^3 \cos \theta\, d\theta \qquad Sy_g = \tfrac{1}{3}\smallint r^3 \sin \theta\, d\theta. \tag{26}$$

Then $x_g = Sx_g/S$ and $y_g = Sy_g/S$, where the numerators are to be found from Eq. (26).

PROBLEMS

Section 90

Verify that each given polar equation has the same locus as the corresponding cartesian equation:

1. $r^2 = a^2 \cos 2\theta$, $(x^2 + y^2)^2 = a^2(x^2 - y^2)$.

2. $r = 4 \csc \theta + 2 \sec \theta$, $xy = 4x + 2y$.

3. $r = \tan\theta$, $x^4 + x^2y^2 = y^2$.

4. $r = a\sec\theta$, $x = a$.

5. $r - r\cos\theta = 2a$, $y^2 = 4a(x + a)$.

6. $r = a\sin 2\theta$, $(x^2 + y^2)^2 = 4a^2x^2y^2$.

7. Show that $r = eq/(1 - e\cos\theta)$ is the locus of a point P whose distance OP from the origin is given by $OP = e\,MP$, where MP is the perpendicular distance from the straight line $r\cos\theta = -q$ to P. *Hint:* At M, we have $x_1 = -q$, so that $MP = x - x_1 = r\cos\theta + q$.

8. Show that the cartesian equation of the locus of Prob. 7 is $y^2 = (e^2 - 1)x^2 + 2qe^2x + q^2$.

9. Show that the curves $r = \sin 2\theta$ and $r = \cos 2\theta$ have nine points of intersection. *Hint:* $\sin 2\theta = \cos 2\theta$, $\tan 2\theta = 1$ gives four points; $r_1 = \sin 2\theta_1$, $-r_1 = \cos 2(\theta_1 + \pi)$, $\sin 2\theta_1 = -\cos 2\theta_1$; $\tan 2\theta_1 = -1$ gives four more; and the origin is the ninth point. Thus $r = 0$, and $r = \frac{1}{2}\sqrt{2}$ with $\theta = \pm(k\pi/8)$ and $k = 1, 3, 5, 7$ may be taken as coordinates of the nine points.

10. Show that the equations $r = 1 + \sin\theta$ and $r = -1 + \sin\theta$ have the same locus. *Hint:* If $r_1 = 1 + \sin\theta_1$, then the point $r = -r_1$, $\theta = \theta_1 + \pi$ satisfies the second equation.

Section 91

Verify that, for n a positive integer, each of the n radius vectors $\theta_k = 2\pi k/n$, $k = 0, 1, 2, \ldots, (n - 1)$ is tangent at the origin to the locus of:

11. $r = a\sin n\theta$.

12. $r^2 = a^2\sin n\theta$.

Section 92

Verify that for n an even integer, the curve of:

13. Problem 11 has $2n$ loops.

14. Problem 12 has n loops.

Verify that for n an odd integer, the curve of:

15. Problem 11 has n loops.

16. Problem 12 has $2n$ loops.

Sketch the locus of each given equation:

17. $r = 1 - \cos \theta$.

18. $r = 1 - 2 \cos \theta$.

Section 93

Find $\tan \psi$ for each given curve:

19. $r = a \cos n\theta$.

20. $r^2 = a^2 \cos n\theta$.

21. $r = a \sin^n (\theta/n)$.

22. $r = a \sec^n (\theta/n)$.

23. $r = ae^{b\theta}$.

24. $r = a\theta$.

Find the length of the specified arc of each given curve:

25. $r = 1 - \cos \theta$, total curve.

26. $r = a \sin^3 (\theta/3)$, one loop.

27. $r = a \sec^2 (\theta/2)$ between points with $\theta = 0$, $\theta = \pi/2$.

28. $r = a\theta^2$ between points with $\theta = 0$, $\theta = 1$.

29. $r = ae^{b\theta}$ between points with $\theta = 0$, $\theta = 1/b$.

30. From Sec. 85, deduce that the rectangular coordinates $(\bar{x},\bar{y})$ of the centroid of an arc of the graph of $r = f(\theta)$ may be found from $L = \int ds$, $L\bar{x} = \int r \cos \theta \, ds$, $L\bar{y} = \int r \sin \theta \, ds$, by expressing r and $ds = \sqrt{r'^2 + r^2} \, d\theta$ in terms of θ.

Use Prob. 30 to find the centroid of the arc of:

31. Problem 25.

32. Problem 27.

Find the *area* of the surface of revolution generated when the graph of $r = a \sqrt{\cos 2\theta}$, $0 \le \theta \le \pi/4$, is rotated:

33. About Ox, or $\theta = 0$.

34. About Oy, or $\theta = \pi/2$.

For the arc of the semicircle $r = 2a \cos \theta$, $0 \le \theta \le \pi/2$, verify that:

35. The centroid $(\bar{x},\bar{y}) = (a, 2a/\pi)$.

36. The moments of inertia I_x, I_y, I_0 are given by $I_x = \pi a^3/2$, $I_y = 3\pi a^3/2$, $I_0 = 2\pi a^3$.

Section 94

Find the curvature of each given curve:

37. $3y = x^3$.

38. $y = \ln \sin x$.

39. $2y = x^2$.

40. $x^2/a^2 + y^2/b^2 = 1$.

41. $r = ae^{b\theta}$.

42. $r = a \sin^n (\theta/n)$.

43. $r = a\theta$.

44. $r = a \sec^n (\theta/n)$.

45. $x = a \cos^3 t$, $y = a \sin^3 t$.

46. $x = a(t - \sin t)$, $y = a(1 - \cos t)$.

47. $x = a \sec t$, $y = a \ln (\sec t - \tan t)$.

48. $x = a (\cos t + t \sin t)$, $y = a (\sin t - t \cos t)$.

Section 95

Find the sectorial area bounded by the lines $\theta = 0$, $\theta = \pi/4$, and each given curve:

49. $r = \theta$.

50. $r = \tan \theta$.

51. $r = e^\theta$.

52. $r = \sec^2 \theta$.

Find the area of that loop of each given curve which is bisected by the radius vector $\theta = 0$:

53. $r = \cos 5\theta$.

54. $r^2 = \cos 2\theta$.

55. $r = \cos^2 \theta$.

56. $r^2 = \cos 2\theta \cos \theta$.

57. $r = 1 - \cos \theta$.

58. $r = 2 + \cos 2\theta$.

59. For the curve $r = 1 + 2 \cos \theta$, calculate the area between the two loops.

60. Find that portion of the area inside one loop of the curve $r^2 = 2 \cos 2\theta$ which is outside the circle $r = 1$.

61. Find that portion of the area inside the circle $r = 3 \cos \theta$ which is outside the loop of the curve $r = 1 + \cos \theta$.

Find the centroid of the total area bounded by each given curve:

62. $r = a(1 - \cos \theta)$.

63. $r = 3 + 2 \sin \theta$.

64. By Example 1 of Sec. 87, the radius of gyration of the area of a circle of radius r, about its center, is $r/\sqrt{2}$. By symmetry, this is also the radius of gyration of any sector of this circle. Deduce that for dS we have $dI_o = (r/\sqrt{2})^2 \, dS = (r^4/4)d\theta$. And therefore that for the sectorial area S we have $I_o = \int \frac{1}{4} r^4 \, d\theta$.

65. Use Prob. 64 to verify that for the semicircular area bounded by $\theta = 0$ and $r = 2a \cos \theta$, $0 \leq \theta \leq \pi/2$, $I_o = \frac{3}{4}\pi a^4$, so that $k = \sqrt{I_o/S} = \sqrt{\frac{3}{2}} a$.

66. Show that for the area of a sector of a circle of radius a and central angle B, the centroid lies at a distance $(4a/3B) \sin (B/2)$ from the center of the circle on the radius which bisects the sector.

67. Show that for the length of arc of a circle of radius a which subtends an angle B at the center, the centroid lies at a distance $(2a/B) \sin (B/2)$ from the center of the circle on the radius which bisects the central angle.

68. By taking moments about Oy, or $\theta = \pi/2$, and using Prob. 66, verify that the centroid of the area between $\theta = -B/2$ and $\theta = B/2$ which lies inside $r = a + h$, and outside $r = a$, has coordinates

$$\bar{x} = \frac{4}{3B} \frac{(a + h)^3 - a^3}{(a + h)^2 - a^2} \sin \frac{B}{2} \qquad \bar{y} = 0.$$

Check Prob. 67 by taking the limit as $h \to 0$.

10

INFINITE SERIES

In this chapter we shall begin by defining the sum of a convergent infinite series of numerical terms. We shall then describe several tests for convergence. We shall also consider series with terms of the form $A_n(x - a)^n$ and methods of representing certain expressions $f(x)$ by series of this type.

96—SEQUENCES AND SERIES

If a set of numbers is so arranged that there is a first, a second, and so on, it constitutes a *sequence*. Thus a sequence is a function f, with domain the positive integers 1, 2, 3, ... We indicate a sequence by the general term in braces, $\{f(n)\}$. As examples of sequences we have

$$\{u_n\} : u_1, u_2, \ldots, u_n, \ldots ; \tag{1}$$

$$\left\{\frac{1}{2^n}\right\} : \frac{1}{2}, \frac{1}{4}, \ldots, \frac{1}{2^n}, \ldots ; \tag{2}$$

$$\left\{\frac{1}{n}\right\} : 1, \frac{1}{2}, \ldots, \frac{1}{n}, \ldots . \tag{3}$$

With any sequence $\{u_n\}$ we can associate an array

$$\Sigma u_n = u_1 + u_2 + u_3 + \cdots + u_n + \ldots, \tag{4}$$

called a *series*. If all but a finite number of terms, say, those with $n > N$, are equal to zero, then the array takes the form

$$\sum_{i=1}^{N} u_i = u_1 + u_2 + u_3 + \cdots + u_N. \tag{5}$$

This has a sum in the ordinary sense. And this sum is called the *value* of the finite series.

If there are an infinite number of nonzero terms in the array (4), we sometimes assign a value by a limiting process, to be explained presently.

97—CONVERGENCE AND DIVERGENCE

The nth *partial sum* of the infinite series (4), s_n, is defined as the sum of its first n terms.   That is,

$$s_n = \sum_{i=1}^{n} u_i = u_1 + u_2 + \cdots + u_n. \tag{6}$$

The partial sums s_n form a new sequence $\{s_n\}$.   If, as n increases and tends to infinity, the sequence of numbers s_n approaches a (finite) limit L, the series (4) *converges*.   As in Sec. 11, this means that $|L - s_n| \to 0$ and $s_n \to L$ as $n \to \infty$.   And we write

$$\lim_{n \to \infty} s_n = L. \tag{7}$$

We say that the infinite series converges to L and that L is the *value*, or *sum*, of the series.

If the sequence $\{s_n\}$ does not approach a limit, in any one of many ways, then the series (4) is *divergent* and we do not assign any value to it.

EXAMPLE 1.   Show that the geometric series $a + ar + ar^2 + \cdots + ar^{n-1} + \ldots$, with $a \neq 0$, in which $u_n = ar^{n-1}$, converges for $|r| < 1$ and diverges for $|r| \geq 1$.

SOLUTION.   By Prob. 5 of Chap. 3, $1 - r^n = (1 - r)(1 + r + r^2 + \cdots + r^{n-1})$.   For $r \neq 1$, we find from this that $s_n = a(1 - r^n)/(1 - r)$.   If $|r| < 1$, as $n \to \infty$, we have $r^n \to 0$ and $s_n \to a/(1 - r) = L$.   But if $|r| > 1$, then $r^n \to \infty$, so that s_n becomes infinite and therefore does not approach a limit.   If $r = -1$, $s_n = a$ for n odd and 0 for n even.   If $r = 1$, the formula for s_n does not apply, but we see directly that $s_n = na$.

EXAMPLE 2.   Show that the series with $u_n = 1/n^p$, or
$1 + 1/2^p + 1/3^p + \cdots + 1/n^p + \cdots$ diverges for $p \leq 1$.

SOLUTION.   If $p \leq 0$, then each $u_n \geq 1$.   Hence $s_n \geq n$ and $s_n \to \infty$ as $n \to \infty$.   For $0 < p \leq 1$, we have $n^p \leq n$, and $u_n = 1/n^p \geq 1/n$.

Hence $\sum_{i=1}^{n} (1/i^p) \geq \sum_{i=1}^{n} (1/i)$. Now insert parentheses in the last series as follows: $1 + (\frac{1}{2} + \frac{1}{3}) + (\frac{1}{4} + \cdots + \frac{1}{7}) + \cdots + [1/2^{k-1} + \cdots + 1/(2^k - 1)] + \cdots$. In the kth parentheses, each term exceeds the first term of the next parentheses, $1/2^k$. And there are 2^{k-1} terms in the parentheses. Hence the sum v_k in these parentheses satisfies the inequality $v_k > \frac{1}{2}$. It follows that the s_n for $p = 1$ satisfies $s_n > k/2$, if $n > 2^k$. This shows that $s_n \to \infty$ as $n \to \infty$ for $p = 1$. And the same is true of the larger partial sums for $0 < p < 1$. ∎

EXAMPLE 3.   Show that the series with $u_n = 1/n^p$, or $1 + 1/2^p + 1/3^p + \cdots + 1/n^p + \cdots$, converges for $p > 1$.

SOLUTION. Insert parentheses as in Example 2.   Here the terms in the kth parentheses are

$$v_k = \left(\frac{1}{2^{(k-1)p}} + \cdots + \frac{1}{(2^k - 1)^p} \right).$$

Since the first term is the largest and there are 2^{k-1} terms, it follows that

$$v_k < \frac{2^{k-1}}{2^{(k-1)p}} = \frac{1}{2^{(k-1)(p-1)}}.$$

For any n, take k such that $(2^k - 1) > n$.   Then we have

$$s_n = \sum_{i=1}^{n} \frac{1}{i^p} < \sum_{j=1}^{k} v_k < \sum_{j=1}^{k} \left(\frac{1}{2^{p-1}} \right)^{j-1} < \frac{1}{1 - \frac{1}{2}^{p-1}},$$

by Example 1.   Since the numbers s_n increase with n, and for all n remain less than a fixed bound, by Prob. 8 they must approach a limit L, and the series converges for $p > 1$.

98—A TEST FOR DIVERGENCE

Suppose that the series (4) converges.   Then, since $(n - 1) \to \infty$ when $n \to \infty$, we have

$$\lim_{n \to \infty} s_n = L \quad \text{and} \quad \lim_{n \to \infty} s_{n-1} = L. \tag{8}$$

But $s_n = s_{n-1} + u_n$, or $u_n = s_n - s_{n-1}$. Hence, as $n \to \infty$,

$$\lim u_n = \lim (s_n - s_{n-1}) = \lim s_n - \lim s_{n-1} = L - L = 0.$$
$$(9)$$

Hence, as $n \to \infty$, $u_n \to 0$ in any convergent series. Thus we have established the following result:

If u_n does not tend to zero as n becomes infinite, the series (4) is divergent.

This is the test which we set out to prove.

EXAMPLE 1. Show that the series with $u_n = n/(2n + 1)$, that is, the series $\frac{1}{3} + \frac{2}{5} + \frac{3}{7} + \cdots + n/(2n + 1) + \cdots$, diverges.

SOLUTION. Here

$$\lim_{n \to \infty} u_n = \lim_{n \to \infty} \frac{1}{2 + 1/n} = \frac{1}{2} \neq 0.$$

EXAMPLE 2. Show that the series with odd terms $(n + 1)/n$ and even terms $1/n$, namely, the series $2 + \frac{1}{2} + \frac{4}{3} + \frac{1}{4} + \cdots + m/(m - 1) + 1/m + (m + 2)/(m + 1) + \cdots$, diverges.

SOLUTION. Here, for large n, there are (odd) terms, $1 + 1/n$, near 1, and also (even) terms, $1/n$, near 0. Thus no limit is approached by u_n; the terms near 1 show that we cannot have $u_n \to 0$.

99—COMPARISON TESTS FOR POSITIVE SERIES

A *positive* series is one with each $u_n \geq 0$. We shall prove the following:

Let Σv_n be a positive series known to converge. If $0 \leq u_n \leq v_n$ for all n, then the series Σu_n converges.

Let s_n be the nth partial sum of Σu_n, and let s_n' be the nth partial sum of Σv_n. Since the latter series converges, as $n \to \infty$, s_n' tends to a finite limit L'. And, since the series is positive, $v_n \geq 0$, so that s_n' is a never-decreasing sequence, and for all n we have $s_n' \leq L'$. Now $u_n \leq v_n$ implies that $s_n \leq s_n'$ and hence $s_n \leq L'$ for all n. Further, we have $u_n \geq 0$. Hence s_n is a never-decreasing sequence. Since its sums are bounded by L', by Prob. 8, s_n must tend to a limit L. ■

We note that $0 \leq L \leq L'$.

Let V_n be a positive series known to diverge. If $u_n \geq V_n$ for all n, then the series Σu_n diverges.

Let s_n be the nth partial sum of Σu_n, and let s_n'' be the nth partial sum of ΣV_n. As a never-decreasing sequence, the V_n would approach a limit if their values stayed within any bound. But ΣV_n diverges, so that as $n \to \infty$, $s_n'' \to \infty$. Now $u_n \geq V_n$ implies that $s_n \geq s_n''$, so that $s_n \to \infty$. Hence Σu_n diverges. ■

100—THE RATIO TEST FOR POSITIVE SERIES

For a positive series Σu_n, let us define the test ratio $t_n = u_{n+1}/u_n$. Suppose that, as $n \to \infty$, $t_n \to T$. Then the ratio test asserts the following:

For a positive series Σu_n, with $\lim\limits_{n \to \infty} (u_{n+1}/u_n) = T$, the series converges if $T < 1$. And the series diverges if $T > 1$.

From the value $T = 1$, no conclusion can be drawn.

To establish the test, suppose first that $T < 1$, and let r be any number such that $T < r < 1$. Then, since $u_{n+1}/u_n \to T$, there is a number N such that

$$\frac{u_{n+1}}{u_n} < r \qquad \text{if } n \geq N. \tag{10}$$

From this we conclude that

$$u_{N+1} < r u_N \qquad u_{N+2} < r u_{N+1} < r^2 u_N, \; \ldots$$
$$u_{N+k} < r u_{N+k-1} < r^k u_N. \tag{11}$$

The infinite series with nth term $r^n u_N$ converges by Example 1 of Sec. 97, since $r < 1$. If its sum is S, the series

$$u_1 + u_2 + \cdots + u_N + r u_N + r^2 u_N + \cdots + r^{n-N} u_N + \cdots \tag{12}$$

converges to the sum $s_N + S$. But, by Eq. (11), each term of Σu_n is less than or equal to the corresponding term of the series (12). Since both series are positive, the first comparison test of Sec. 99 shows that Σu_n converges.

Next suppose that $T > 1$, and let R be any number such that $T > R > 1$. Then, since $u_{n+1}/u_n \to T$, there is a number N such that

$$\frac{u_{n+1}}{u_n} > R \qquad \text{if } n \geq N. \tag{13}$$

By reasoning as in Eq. (11), we conclude from this that $u_{N+k} > R u_{N+k-1} > R^k u_N$. Consequently, since $R > 1$, we have

$$u_n > R^{n-N} u_N > u_N \qquad \text{for } n \geq N. \tag{14}$$

Since $u_n > u_N > 0$, we cannot have $u_n \to 0$, and so u_n diverges by the test of Sec. 98. ∎

In applying the ratio test, we can use u_{n+K+1}/u_{n+K} with K any fixed positive or negative integer, in place of u_{n+1}/u_n, since $n + K \to \infty$ when $n \to \infty$.

EXAMPLE 1.   Test the series with $u_n = (n - 1)!/n^{n-1}$ for convergence. (Note that $u_1 = 1$, since $0! = 1$.)

SOLUTION.   The test ratio is

$$t_n = \frac{u_{n+1}}{u_n} = \frac{n!}{(n + 1)^n} \frac{n^{n-1}}{(n - 1)!}$$

Since $n! = n(n - 1)!$, we have

$$t_n = \left(\frac{n}{n + 1} \right)^n = \frac{1}{(1 + 1/n)^n} \cdot$$

It follows from Sec. 39 that $t_n \to 1/e = 1/2.7+ < 1$. Hence the series converges.

EXAMPLE 2.   Show that the ratio test is not applicable to the p series, with $u_n = 1/n^p$.

SOLUTION.   For this series we have

$$t_n = \frac{u_{n+1}}{u_n} = \frac{n^p}{(n+1)^p} = \left(1 + \frac{1}{n}\right)^{-p}.$$

Hence $t_n \to 1$, and no conclusion is implied.   By Examples 2 and 3 of Sec. 97, the series diverges for $p = 1$ and converges for $p = 2$.   This illustrates that for $t_n \to 1$, either case is possible.

EXAMPLE 3.   Test the series with $u_n = \sqrt{2n+1}/(3n^2 - 2n)$ for convergence.

SOLUTION.   This series has some resemblance to a p series.   In fact, we have

$$\frac{n^2}{\sqrt{n}} u_n = \frac{\sqrt{2 + 1/n}}{3 - 2/n},$$

so that

$$\lim_{n\to\infty} \frac{u_n}{n^{-3/2}} = \frac{\sqrt{2}}{3}.$$

From this and the calculation of Example 2, it follows that $t_n \to 1$, so that the ratio test is not useful here.   However, from the limiting relation just found, for any fixed number $K > \sqrt{2}/3$ (for example, $K = 2$) and for n sufficiently large, say, $n \geq N$, we have $u_n < Kn^{-3/2}$.   For $n > N$, the partial sum s_n of Σu_n may be decomposed into a fixed sum s_N, and a part less than $K(s'_n - s'_N)$, where s'_n is the nth partial sum of the series $\Sigma 1/n^{3/2}$. This p series, with $p = \frac{3}{2} > 1$, converges by Example 3 of Sec. 97.   Hence the given series converges, by the comparison test.

EXAMPLE 4.   Let ΣU_n be a series some of whose terms may be negative.   Show that if the positive series $\Sigma |U_n|$ converges, then the series ΣU_n converges.

SOLUTION.   Let S_n be the nth partial sum of ΣU_n, let s'_n be the nth partial sum of $\Sigma |U_n|$, and let s_n be the nth partial sum of the series Σu_n, where $u_n = U_n + |U_n|$. Thus $s_n = S_n + s'_n$. Since $\Sigma|U_n|$ converges, we have $s'_n \to L'$ as $n \to \infty$. Hence $\Sigma 2|U_n|$ converges. But $u_n \geq 0$, and $u_n \leq 2|U_n|$, so that Σu_n converges by the comparison test. If its sum is L, when $n \to \infty$, $s_n \to L$. Then, since $S_n = s_n - s'_n$, when $n \to \infty$, we have $\lim S_n = L - L'$ and ΣU_n converges. ∎

101—ABSOLUTE CONVERGENCE

Consider a series with general term u_n, which may be positive, zero, or negative. Then, with Σu_n, we associate the positive series $\Sigma|u_n|$, obtained by taking absolute values. If this latter series converges, the first series is said to *converge absolutely*. It follows from Example 4 of Sec. 100 that:

An absolutely convergent series is necessarily convergent.

Since the series of absolute values is a positive series, its convergence can be investigated by the comparison or ratio test.

If the series of absolute values diverges, the original series may still converge, and in this case it is said to *converge conditionally*.

102—ALTERNATING SERIES

A series whose terms alternate in sign is said to be *alternating*. Thus, if $p_n > 0$, then

$$p_1 - p_2 + p_3 - \cdots + (-1)^n p_n + \cdots \tag{15}$$

is an alternating series.

If, in addition, $p_n \leq p_{n-1}$ and $p_n \to 0$ as $n \to \infty$, then the alternating series converges.

To prove this, we first consider partial sums with even indices, and write

$$s_{2n} = (p_1 - p_2) + (p_3 - p_4) + \cdots + (p_{2n-1} - p_{2n}), \qquad (16)$$
$$s_{2n} = p_1 - (p_2 - p_3) - \cdots - (p_{2n-2} - p_{2n-1}) - p_{2n}. \qquad (17)$$

Because $p_n \leq p_{n-1}$ or $p_k \geq p_{k+1}$, each set of parentheses satisfies the inequality $(p_k - p_{k-1}) \geq 0$. Thus, from Eq. (16), the sequence s_{2n} is never-decreasing. Further, Eq. (17) shows that s_{2n} never exceeds the bound p_1. Hence, as $n \to \infty$, we have $s_{2n} \to L$, a finite limit.

For the partial sums with odd indices, we can write

$$s_{2n+1} = s_{2n} + p_{2n+1}. \qquad (18)$$

Since $p_n \to 0$ as $n \to \infty$, so does p_{2n+1}. Since $s_{2n} \to L$, it now follows that

$$\lim_{n \to \infty} s_{2n+1} = L. \qquad (19)$$

Since the odd and even partial sums approach the same limit L, as $n \to \infty$, we have $s_n \to L$ and the series converges. ∎

EXAMPLE. Show that, for $0 < p \leq 1$, the series $1 - 1/2^p + 1/3^p - \cdots + (-1)^{n+1}/n^p + \cdots$ is conditionally convergent.

SOLUTION. Since the signs alternate, $1/n^p < 1/[(n-1)^p]$, and $1/n^p \to 0$ as $n \to \infty$, it follows that the alternating series converges. But the absolute values give the p series with $u_n = 1/n^p$, which, by Example 2 of Sec. 97, diverges for $p \leq 1$.

103—TAYLOR'S THEOREM WITH THE REMAINDER

Let the function f possess derivatives of all orders in the interval $[a,b]$. Then it is possible to represent $f(b)$ as a sum of terms of the form $A_m(b - a)^m$ plus a remainder term. To obtain the expansion, we first write

$$\int_0^{b-a} f'(b - x)\, dx = [-f(b - x)]_0^{b-a} = f(b) - f(a). \qquad (20)$$

We next integrate the left-hand member by parts, to obtain

$$\int_0^{b-a} f'(b - x)\, dx = [x\, f'(b - x)]_0^{b-a} + \int_0^{b-a} x\, f''(b - x)\, dx$$
$$= (b - a)\, f'(a) + \int_0^{b-a} x\, f''(b - x)\, dx. \qquad (21)$$

We integrate the new integral by parts, and repeat this procedure. After n integrations by parts, we find that

$$f(b) = f(a) + (b - a) f'(a) + \frac{(b - a)^2}{2!} f''(a) + \cdots$$
$$+ \frac{(b - a)^n}{n!} f^{(n)}(a) + \int_0^{b-a} \frac{x^n}{n!} f^{(n+1)}(b - x) \, dx. \quad (22)$$

The last term in Eq. (22) is called the *remainder*. We denote it by R_n. Since $f^{(n+1)}$ is differentiable, it is continuous, and hence it has a maximum M and a minimum m on the interval $[a,b]$. From the inequalities

$$m \leq f^{(n+1)}(b - x) \leq M \qquad \text{for } 0 \leq x \leq b - a, \quad (23)$$

we deduce that for the remainder R_n, unless $m = M$,

$$\int_0^{b-a} \frac{x^n}{n!} m \, dx < R_n < \int_0^{b-a} \frac{x^n}{n!} M \, dx. \quad (24)$$

This shows that if $R_n = K(b - a)^{n+1}/(n + 1)!$, then $m < K < M$. Since K is between m and M, it is equal to $f^{(n+1)}(t)$ for a suitable value of t on (a,b). Thus

$$R_n = \frac{(b - a)^{n+1}}{(n + 1)!} f^{(n+1)}(t). \quad (25)$$

Let us insert this in place of the last term in Eq. (22), and then replace b by x. The result is

$$f(x) = f(a) + (x - a) f(a) + \frac{(x - a)^2}{2!} f''(a) + \cdots$$
$$+ \frac{(x - a)^n}{n!} f^{(n)}(a) + \frac{(x - a)^{n+1}}{(n + 1)!} f^{(n+1)}(t), \quad (26)$$

for a suitable value of t between a and x. This is *Lagrange's* form of *Taylor's theorem* with the *remainder*.

By reasoning similar to that just used, but based on the maximum and minimum values of the continuous function $x^n f^{(n+1)}(b - x)$, we can show that

$$f(x) = f(a) + (x - a) f'(a) + \frac{(x - a)^2}{2!} f''(a) + \cdots$$
$$+ \frac{(x - a)^n}{n!} f^{(n)}(a) + \frac{(x - a)(x - t)^n}{n!} f^{(n+1)}(t), \quad (27)$$

for a suitable value of t between a and x. This is *Cauchy's* form of *Taylor's theorem* with the *remainder*.

For simplicity, we have referred to the interval $[a,b]$, which assumes $a < b$, and $a < x < b$. If $b < a$ and $b < x < a$, Eq. (22) still applies. Except for a reversal of inequality signs in Eq. (23) when $(b - a)$ is negative, the reasoning used to derive Eqs. (26) and (27) is still valid. Thus these results hold for $a > b$.

Let us put $x = a + h$, and note that any value t between a and x can then be written $x = a + \theta h$, with $0 < \theta < 1$. Then we can transform Eq. (26) into

$$f(a + h) = f(a) + h f'(a) + \frac{h^2}{2!} f''(a) + \cdots$$
$$+ \frac{h^n}{n!} f^{(n)}(a) + \frac{h^{n+1}}{(n+1)!} f^{(n+1)}(a + \theta h), \quad (28)$$

for a suitable value of θ with $0 < \theta < 1$.

104—TAYLOR'S SERIES

Let the function f possess derivatives of all orders for $x = a$. Then the right-hand member of Eq. (26) suggests that we form the infinite series

$$\sum_{n=0}^{\infty} u_n \quad \text{with } u_0 = f(a) \text{ and } u_n = \frac{(x - a)^n}{n!} f^{(n)}(a) \quad \text{for } n \geq 1.$$

In any case such that, for a given x, the remainder term R_n tends to zero as $n \to \infty$, the series will necessarily converge and have a sum equal to $f(x)$. At least for values sufficiently near a, this is true for many simple functions. And for such functions we have

$$f(x) = f(a) + f'(a) (x - a) + \frac{f''(a)}{2!} (x - a)^2 + \cdots$$
$$+ \frac{f^{(n)}(a)}{n!} (x - a)^n + \cdots . \quad (29)$$

This is known as *Taylor's series* (B. Taylor, 1685–1731, English).

When $a = 0$, the series takes the form

$$f(x) = f(0) + f'(0)\, x + \frac{f''(0)}{2!}\, x^2 + \cdots$$

$$+ \frac{f^{(n)}(0)}{n!}\, x^n + \cdots \cdot \quad (30)$$

This special form is known as *Maclaurin's series* (C. Maclaurin, 1698–1746, Scotch).

EXAMPLE 1.   Determine the Maclaurin's series for e^x and show that it represents the function for all values of x.

SOLUTION.   Here $f(x) = e^x$, $f'(x) = e^x$, $f^{(n)}(x) = e^x$.   Since $e^0 = 1$, we have $f(0) = f'(0) = f^{(n)}(0) = 1$.   Hence Eq. (30) becomes

$$e^x = 1 + x + \frac{x^2}{2!} + \cdots + \frac{x^n}{n!} + \cdots \cdot \quad (31)$$

The remainder term of Eq. (26) with $a = 0$ is

$$\frac{x^{n+1}\, e^t}{(n+1)!} \cdot$$

For any fixed x, with t between 0 and x, we have $e^t < 1$ if $x < 0$, and $e^t < e^x$ if $x > 0$.   Then e^t is bounded, $e^t < B$.   Further,

$$v_n = \frac{|x|^{n+1}}{(n+1)!}$$

is the nth term of a series which converges by the ratio test. Hence, by Sec. 98, $v_n \to 0$, and therefore so does R_n, since $|R_n| < Bv_n$. ∎

EXAMPLE 2.   Prove that e is irrational.

SOLUTION.   Suppose that $e = p/q$.   Since $2.5 < e < 3$, we must have $q > 2$.   Further, $p/q = e = 1 + 1 + 1/2! + \cdots + 1/q! + e^t/(q+1)!$ with $e^t < e$, by Example 1, with $x = 1$ and $n = q$.   Multiplication by $q!$ gives $I_1 = I_2 + e^t/(q+1)$, with I_1 and I_2 each integers.   But $e^t < e < 3$, $q + 1 > 3$, so that $0 < e^t/(q+1) < 1$.   Since $0 < I_1 - I_2 < 1$ is impossible, $e \neq p/q$. ∎

Any infinite series of the form

$$A_0 + A_1(x - a) + A_2(x - a)^2 + \cdots + A_n(x - a)^n + \cdots \tag{32}$$

is called a *power series*. If we call the first term u_0, we may write it

$$\sum_{n=0}^{\infty} u_n(x) \qquad \text{where } u_n(x) = A_n(x - a)^n. \tag{33}$$

Let us suppose that the absolute value of the ratio of successive coefficients, $|A_{n+1}/A_n|$, approaches a finite limit L, not zero, as $n \to \infty$. Thus

$$\lim_{n \to \infty} \left| \frac{A_{n+1}}{A_n} \right| = L \neq 0. \tag{34}$$

Then *the series* (33) *converges absolutely for any x such that*

$$|x - a| < \frac{1}{L}. \tag{35}$$

PROOF. This makes the limit of the ratio of the numerical values of successive terms in the series (33)

$$\lim_{n \to \infty} \left| \frac{A_{n+1}(x - a)^{n+1}}{A_n(x - a)^n} \right| = L\,|x - a| < 1. \tag{36}$$

Hence the positive series with general term $|A_n(x - a)^n|$ converges by the ratio test, and the series (33) converges absolutely.

We can show that the series (33) diverges for any x_1 such that $|x_1 - a| > 1/L$, as follows. Noting that $L|x_1 - a| > 1$, let R be any number such that $L|x_1 - a| > R > 1$. Then, for $x = x_1$, the limit of the numerical values of ratios of successive terms in the series (33) is $L|x_1 - a| > R$. Hence, by the reasoning that led to Eqs. (13) and (14), we have

$$|u_n(x_1)| = U_n > R^{n-N}U_N > U_N \qquad \text{for } n \geq N. \tag{37}$$

Since $|u_n(x_1)| = U_n > U_N$, we cannot have $|u_n(x_1)| \to 0$.

Hence $u_n(x_1)$ cannot tend to zero, and by Sec. 98, the series (33) diverges.

Thus, when the relation (34) holds, the power series (33) converges absolutely inside the open interval (35), with a its midpoint, and the series diverges outside the corresponding closed interval.

If in Eq. (34) the limit in the left-hand member is zero, the series (33) converges absolutely for all x.

It may be shown that, whether $|A_{n+1}/A_n|$ approaches a limit or not, every power series of the form (33) either converges for no value of x except $x = a$, converges absolutely for all values of x, or has an open interval of absolute convergence with a as its midpoint. The series diverges outside the corresponding closed interval. The series may or may not converge at one or both end points of the closed interval.

Reasoning similar to that used for Eq. (32) shows that if the power series has certain terms missing and the terms after the pth are

$$A_p(x - a)^p + A_{p+m}(x - a)^{p+m} + A_{p+2m}(x - a)^{p+2m} + \cdots \quad (38)$$

and

$$\lim_{n \to \infty} \left| \frac{A_p + (n + 1)m}{A_p + nm} \right| = L_m, \quad (39)$$

then the series (38) converges for all x if $L_m = 0$, and for

$$|x - a| < \left(\frac{1}{L_m}\right)^{1/m} \quad (40)$$

if $L_m \neq 0$. And the series diverges for values of x such that the inequality of Eq. (40) is reversed.

EXAMPLE.   Find the open interval of absolute convergence of the power series $x + x^2/2 + x^3/3 + \cdots + x^n/n + \cdots$.

SOLUTION.   Here

$$\left| \frac{x^{n+1}/(n + 1)}{x^n/n} \right| = \frac{n|x|}{n + 1} = \frac{|x|}{1 + (1/n)} \to |x|.$$

Thus the interval of absolute convergence is $|x| < 1$, or $-1 < x < 1$, that is, $(-1,1)$. We note that the series is divergent for $x = 1$, and conditionally convergent at $x = -1$, by the example of Sec. 102.

106—OPERATIONS WITH POWER SERIES

For any two convergent series

$$\sum_{n=0}^{\infty} u_n = U \quad \text{and} \quad \sum_{n=0}^{\infty} v_n = V, \tag{41}$$

the series may be added term by term and

$$\sum_{n=0}^{\infty} (u_n + v_n) = U + V. \tag{42}$$

It is not necessarily true that the product series, with general term w_n, where

$$w_n = u_0v_n + u_1v_{n-1} + u_2v_{n-2} + \cdots + u_nv_0, \tag{43}$$

converges, or if it does converge that its sum is UV. But this is always true if both series converge absolutely, and hence applies to two power series, each involving powers of $(x - a)$, for any x inside the smaller interval of convergence.

Similarly, if the divisor series is not zero at $x = a$, the series arising from term-by-term division of two power series converges to the quotient for values of x sufficiently near to a.

107—COMPUTATION BY MEANS OF POWER SERIES

The values of many functions are most easily found for particular numerical values by using appropriate power series. Series are sometimes preferable to Simpson's rule (Sec. 29) as a means of evaluating definite integrals.

For precise arguments, the error can be evaluated by using the Lagrange or Cauchy form of the remainder term. For the alternating series of Sec. 102, the error made in stopping at any point is always numerically less than the last term used.

In practical computation, however, power series are usually employed only where they converge relatively rapidly, for example, like a geometric progression with ratio of the order of magnitude of

$\frac{1}{2}$ or less. In such cases, to get a three-place decimal approximation, we use all terms which contribute something to the fourth place and round off to three places in the final result. We thus obtain a number not likely to be in error by more than 2 in the third place.

108—FUNCTIONS WITH COMPLEX-NUMBER DOMAINS

We recall that a *complex number* is an expression of the form $a + bi$, determined by an ordered pair of real numbers a and b. For the imaginary unit determined by the ordered pair 0 and 1, we often write

$$i = \sqrt{-1} \quad \text{and} \quad i^2 = -1. \tag{44}$$

For the most part, the rules for manipulating the ordered pairs may be recalled by applying the rules for real numbers to $a + bi$. One useful principle is that, if a, b, a', and b' are all real numbers, then the equation

$$a + bi = a' + b'i$$

is equivalent to $$\tag{45}$$

$$a = a' \quad \text{and} \quad b = b'.$$

Thus, in any equation simplified to this form, we may equate the real and imaginary parts separately.

For a complex variable $z = x + iy$, the power function is defined by $w(z) = Az^n = A(x + iy)^n$. The value $w(z)$ can be found by repeated multiplication. From this, by addition, we may evaluate polynomials and convergent power series with real or complex coefficients.

The functions exp, sin, and cos are defined for a complex domain by the following infinite power series:

$$\exp z = e^z = 1 + z + \frac{z^2}{2!} + \cdots + \frac{z^n}{n!} + \cdots, \tag{46}$$

$$\sin z = z - \frac{z^3}{3!} + \frac{z^5}{5!} - \cdots$$

$$+ (-1)^{n+1} \frac{z^{2n-1}}{(2n-1)!} + \cdots, \tag{47}$$

$$\cos z = 1 - \frac{z^2}{2!} + \frac{z^4}{4!} - \cdots + (-1)^n \frac{z^{2n}}{(2n)!} + \cdots . \qquad (48)$$

These series are similar to the Maclaurin's series which represent the functions for all real values of x. Thus, when $y = 0$, so that $z = x + iy = x$, the values obtained from the new definitions will agree with those previously used.

The series (46) to (48) converge for all values of z. Series of this type may be added and multiplied by the procedure described in Sec. 106. It follows that

$$e^{z_1} e^{z_2} = e^{z_1 + z_2}, \qquad (49)$$

$$\sin (z_1 + z_2) = \sin z_1 \cos z_2 + \cos z_1 \sin z_2, \qquad (50)$$

$$\cos (z_1 + z_2) = \cos z_1 \cos z_2 - \sin z_1 \sin z_2. \qquad (51)$$

109—EULER'S EXPRESSIONS

Let us replace z by iz in Eq. (46). In view of $i^2 = -1$, we find

$$e^{iz} = 1 + (iz) + \frac{(iz)^2}{2!} + \cdots + \frac{(iz)^n}{n!} + \cdots$$

$$= \left(1 - \frac{z^2}{2!} + \frac{z^4}{4!} - \cdots \right) + i\left(z - \frac{z^3}{3!} + \frac{z^5}{5!} - \cdots \right). \qquad (52)$$

From this and Eqs. (47) and (48) we obtain

$$e^{iz} = \cos z + i \sin z. \qquad (53)$$

This is called *Euler's relation* (L. Euler, 1707–1783, Swiss).

Since Eq. (47) makes $\sin (-z) = -\sin z$, and Eq. (48) makes $\cos (-z) = \cos z$, it follows that

$$e^{-iz} = \cos z - i \sin z. \qquad (54)$$

By solving Eqs. (53) and (54) for $\sin z$ and $\cos z$, we find

$$\sin z = \frac{e^{iz} - e^{-iz}}{2i} \qquad \cos z = \frac{e^{iz} + e^{-iz}}{2} . \qquad (55)$$

Equations (53) to (55) are collectively referred to as *Euler's* expressions.

110—COMPUTATION OF e^z, sin z, cos z

If $z = x + iy$, we find, from Eqs. (49) and (53), that

$$e^z = e^{x+iy} = e^x e^{iy} = e^x \, (\cos y + i \sin y)$$
$$= e^x \cos y + i \, e^x \sin y. \tag{56}$$

This enables us to compute the value of e^z from tables of values of e^x, cos y, and sin y, with y in radian measure.

To compute sin z and cos z, from Eqs. (50) and (51) we have

$$\sin z = \sin (x + iy) = \sin x \cos iy + \cos x \sin iy,$$
$$\cos z = \cos (x + iy) = \cos x \cos iy - \sin x \sin iy. \tag{57}$$

But, from Eq. (55) and Sec. 46, we have

$$\sin iy = \frac{e^{-y} - e^y}{2i} = i \sinh y \qquad \cos iy = \frac{e^{-y} + e^y}{2} = \cosh y. \tag{58}$$

This leads to

$$\sin z = \sin x \cosh y + i \cos x \sinh y,$$
$$\cos z = \cos x \cosh y - i \sin x \sinh y. \tag{59}$$

These equations enable us to compute sin z and cos z by use of tables of trigonometric and hyperbolic functions for real arguments.

PROBLEMS

Section 97

1. Let $u_n = f(n) - f(n + 1)$. Show that $s_n = f(1) - f(n + 1)$. If, as $n \to \infty$, $f(n) \to L_1$, show that the infinite series Σu_n converges and that its sum is $L = f(1) - L_1$.

Use Prob. 1 to show that the series with each given u_n is convergent and has the indicated sum:

2. $u_n = \sin \dfrac{\pi}{2n} - \sin \dfrac{\pi}{2(n + 1)}$, $L = 1$.

3. $u_n = \dfrac{1}{2^n}$, $L = 1$. *Hint:* $f(n) = \dfrac{1}{2^{n-1}}$.

4. $u_n = \dfrac{1}{n(n + 1)}$, $L = 1$. *Hint:* $f(n) = \dfrac{1}{n}$.

5. Let $u_n = f(n) - f(n + 1)$. If, as $n \to \infty$, $f(n) \to \infty$, show that Σu_n diverges. *Hint:* Use the s_n of Prob. 1.

Use Prob. 5 to show that the series with each given u_n is divergent:

6. $u_n = \dfrac{1}{\sqrt{n} + \sqrt{n + 1}} \cdot$ *Hint:* $f(n) = -\sqrt{n}$.

7. $u_n = \ln (1 + 1/n)$. *Hint:* $f(n) = -\ln n$.

8. Show that if a sequence of numbers a_n increases with n, and for all n remains less than a fixed bound B, then $a_n \to L$, a finite limit, as $n \to \infty$. *Hint:* Suppose that the Cauchy convergence criterion of Sec. 14 is *not* satisfied for some particular η. Then, for this η, no t_η exists such that $|a_{n_2} - a_{n_1}| \le \eta$ for $n_1 > t_\eta$, $n_2 > t_\eta$. Hence, if $a_j - a_i > \eta$, another pair with $a_{j'} - a_{i'} > \eta$ can be found with $j' > i' > j > i$. If N pairs are selected in this way, we have $a_{j(N)} - a_i > N\eta$. But this contradicts $a_{j(N)} < B$, if $N > (B - a_i)/\eta$.

9. Show that if Σu_n converges, so does $\Sigma(k u_n)$.

10. Show that if Σu_n converges, so does Σu_{n+k}, and vice versa. Hence, in applying any test for convergence, we may omit or disregard $u_1 + u_2 + \cdots + u_k$, a finite number of terms.

Section 98

Show that the series with each given u_n is divergent:

11. $u_n = \dfrac{3n^2 + n}{n^2} \cdot$

12. $u_n = \dfrac{4n + 5}{2n + 3} \cdot$

13. $u_n = 2 + 3^{-n}$.

14. $u_n = \dfrac{3 + 2(-1)^n}{100} \cdot$

15. $u_n = \dfrac{n + 1}{\ln (n + 1)} \cdot$

16. $u_n = \dfrac{\ln (n + 1)}{\ln (2n + 3)} \cdot$

For the series with partial sums s_n, use the Cauchy criterion of Sec. 14 to show that:

17. If as $n \to \infty$, $(s_{n+k} - s_{n-1}) \to 0$ for all k, then the series converges.

18. If, as $n \to \infty$, $(s_{n+k} - s_{n-1})$ does not tend to zero, for any choice of k constant or $k = f(n)$, then the series diverges. For $k = 0$, this is the theorem of Sec. 98.

Section 99

By Example 3 of Sec. 97, the p series $\Sigma(1/n^p)$ converges for $p > 1$. By comparison with this for a suitable value of p, show that the series with each given u_n converges:

19. $u_n = 1/(n^2 + 1)$.
20. $1/(2n + 1)^2$.
21. $u_n = 2/\sqrt{n^3}$.
22. $4n/(n^4 + 1)$.
23. $u_n = \sqrt{n}/(n^2 + 1)$.
24. $\dfrac{\sqrt{n+1} - \sqrt{n}}{\sqrt{n}}$.

By Example 2 of Sec. 97, the harmonic series $\Sigma(1/n)$ diverges. Use this to deduce the divergence of the series with each given u_n:

25. $u_n = 2/(3n - 5)$.
26. $u_n = (n^2 + 1)/n^3$.
27. $u_n = 1/\sqrt{2n + 1}$.
28. $u_n = \sqrt{n}/(4n + 1)$.
29. $u_n = (\ln n)/n$.
30. $u_n = (\ln n)/\sqrt{n}$.
31. $u_n = \dfrac{1}{\ln (n + 1)}$. See hint to Prob. 32.

32. $u_n = \dfrac{1}{[\ln (n + 1)]^5}$.

Hint: For $q > 0$, by L'Hôpital's rule, as $x \to \infty$, $(\ln x)/x^q \to 0$. Hence, for any q, there is an N_q such that for $n \geq N_q$, $\ln n < n^q$. See Prob. 10, and use $q = 1$ for Prob. 31 and $q = \frac{1}{5}$ for Prob. 32.

33. *Integral test.* Let f be continuous for all real $x \geq N$. And for $x \geq N$, let $f(x)$ be positive and always decreasing as x increases. Prove that the series with $u_n = f(n)$ converges if the improper integral $\int_N^\infty f(x) \, dx$ converges, and that the series diverges if the integral diverges. *Hint:* From $u_{n+1} \leq f(x) \leq u_n$ for $n \leq x \leq n + 1$, deduce that

$$u_{n+1} \leq \int_n^{n+1} f(x) \, dx \leq u_n \qquad \text{and}$$

$$\sum_{i=N+1}^n u_i \leq \int_N^n f(x) \, dx \leq \sum_{i=N}^{n-1} u_i.$$

Hence, $s_n \leq s_N + \int_N^\infty f(x) \, dx$ in the convergent case. Similarly, $s_n \geq s_{N-1} + \int_N^n f(x) \, dx$, so that $s_n \to \infty$ when $\int_N^n f(x) \, dx \to \infty$ in the divergent case.

34. Use Prob. 33 to check the conclusions of Examples 2 and 3 of Sec. 97 concerning the p series $\Sigma(1/n^p)$.

35. Use Prob. 33 to show that

$$\sum \frac{1}{n \, (\ln n)^p}$$

converges if $p > 1$ and diverges if $p \leq 1$.

36. Let s_n be the nth partial sum of the harmonic series with $u_n = 1/n$. Deduce from Prob. 33 that $\int_1^{n+1} (dx/x) \leq s_n \leq 1 + \int_1^n (dx/x)$. In particular, if A is the sum to 10^6 terms, show that $13.81 < A < 14.82$.

Section 100

With each given u_n, test the series for convergence:

37. $u_n = 2^n/n!$.

38. $u_n = n!/5^n$.

39. $u_n = n/3^n$.

40. $u_n = (n!)^2/(2n)!$.

41. $u_n = (n^3 + 1)/n!$.

42. $u_n = 2^n/n^4$.

43. $u_n = (4n^2 + 2)/(6n^4 + n)$.

44. $u_n = (5n + 2)/(2n + 1)^{3/2}$.

Section 101

Show that the series with each given n is absolutely convergent:

45. $u_n = (\cos n)/2^n$.

46. $u_n = (\sin n)/n^2$.

47. $u_n = 5(-\frac{2}{3})^n$.

48. $u_n = (-2)^n/n!$.

49. $u_n = (-1)^n/n^{5/2}$.

50. $u_n = \dfrac{\ln (4 \sin^2 n^{-1})}{n^{3/2}}$.

Section 102

Verify that the series with each given u_n is a conditionally convergent alternating series:

51. $u_n = \dfrac{(-1)^{n+1}}{2n\,(n+1)}$.

52. $u_n = \dfrac{(-1)^{n+1}}{\sqrt{n}}$.

53. $u_n = \dfrac{(-1)^{n+1}}{\ln (n+1)}$.

54. $u_n = \dfrac{(-1)^{n+1}}{\ln (n+1)^2}$.

55. Check the convergence of the series of Probs. 47 to 49 by the theorem on alternating series.

For each given u_n, alternating in sign, verify that $|u_n| > |u_{n+1}|$, but nevertheless show that the series with this u_n diverges:

56. $u_n = (-1)^{n+1}\dfrac{2n+3}{3n-1}$.

57. $u_n = (-1)^{n+1}\dfrac{2^{1/n}}{5}$.

Section 103

Each given $f(x)$ is expanded in powers of x. Verify the value of the given term and of the remainder after this term:

58. $\sin x$, $(-1)^{n+1}\dfrac{x^{2n-1}}{(2n-1)!}$, $R_{2n} = (-1)^n \dfrac{\cos \theta x \; x^{2n+1}}{(2n+1)!}$.

59. $\cos x$, $(-1)^{n+1}\dfrac{x^{2n}}{(2n)!}$, $R_{2n+1} = (-1)^{n+1}\dfrac{\cos \theta x \; x^{2n+2}}{(2n+2)!}$.

60. $\dfrac{1}{1-x}$, x^n, $R_n = (n+1)\dfrac{(1-\theta)^n \, x^{n+1}}{(1-\theta x)^{n+2}}$.

61. $\ln (1-x)$, $-\dfrac{x^n}{n}$, $R_n = -\dfrac{(1-\theta)^n \, x^{n+1}}{(1-\theta x)^{n+1}}$.

62. Show that $e^x = 1 + x + x^2/2$ to within 0.001 for $|x| < 0.18$.

63. Use Prob. 58 to show that $\sin x = x - x^3/6$ to within 0.001 for $|x| < 0.65$.

64. Use Prob. 59 to show that $\cos x = 1 - x^2/2 + x^4/24$ to within 0.001 for $|x| < 0.94$.

Section 104

65. Use Prob. 58 to show that, for all values of x, $\sin x = x - x^3/3! + x^5/5! - x^7/7! + \cdots$.

66. Use Prob. 59 to show that, for all values of x, $\cos x = 1 - x^2/2! + x^4/4! - x^6/6! + \cdots$.

67. Show that, for $|x| < 1$, $0 < \theta < 1$, we have $(1 - \theta)/(1 - \theta x) < 1$, so that, in Prob. 60,

$$|R_n| < \frac{(n + 1)\,|x|^{n+1}}{(1 - |x|)^2}.$$

Hence show that

$$\frac{1}{1 - x} = 1 + x + x^2 + x^3 + \cdots \qquad \text{for } -1 < x < 1.$$

68. For $|x| < 1$ and $0 < \theta < 1$, by Prob. 67, we may conclude that $(1 - \theta)/(1 - \theta x) < 1$. Deduce that, in Prob. 61,

$$|R_n| < \frac{|x|^{n+1}}{1 - |x|}$$

and that, for $-1 < x < 1$,

$$\ln(1 - x) = -x - \frac{x^2}{2} - \frac{x^3}{3} - \frac{x^4}{4} - \cdots.$$

Verify the given terms in each of the following Taylor's series:

69. $e^{a+h} = e^a + e^a h + \dfrac{e^a}{2!} h^2 + \dfrac{e^a}{3!} h^3 + \cdots$.

70. $\sin(a + h) = \sin a + h \cos a - (h^2/2!) \sin a - (h^3/3!) \cos a + \cdots$.

71. $\cos(a + h) = \cos a - h \sin a - (h^2/2!) \cos a + (h^3/3!) \sin a + \cdots$.

72. $\ln(a + h) = \ln a + h/a - h^2/2a^2 + h^3/3a^3 - \cdots, a > 0$.

73. $(a + h)^m = a^m + ma^{m-1}h + \dfrac{m(m - 1)}{2!} a^{m-2}h^2$

$+ \dfrac{m(m - 1)(m - 2)}{3!} a^{m-3}h^3 + \cdots , \ a > 0.$

Section 105

74. Show that the series of Eq. (31), and those of Probs. 65 and 66, converge for all values of x.

75. From Prob. 74, deduce that the series of Probs. 69 to 71 converge for all values of h.

76. Show that the series of Probs. 72 and 73 converge for $|h| < a$.

Find the open interval of absolute convergence for the power series $\displaystyle\sum_{n=1}^{\infty} u_n(x)$ for each given $u_n(x)$:

77. $u_n(x) = \dfrac{(x - 3)^n}{n}.$

78. $u_n(x) = \dfrac{n^2}{3^n} (x - 2)^n.$

79. $u_n(x) = \dfrac{(-2)^n}{n^2} (x + 1)^n.$

80. $u_n(x) = \dfrac{n}{8^n} (x - 4)^{3n+2}.$

81. $u_n(x) = \dfrac{(-4)^n}{n(n + 1)} (x + 2)^{2n}.$

82. $u_n(x) = n! \left(\dfrac{x}{n}\right)^n.$

Section 106

From the series of Eq. (31) and Probs. 65 and 66, deduce that:

83. $\sinh x = \dfrac{e^x - e^{-x}}{2} = x + \dfrac{x^3}{3!} + \dfrac{x^5}{5!} + \cdots .$

84. $\cosh x = \dfrac{e^x + e^{-x}}{2} = 1 + \dfrac{x^2}{2!} + \dfrac{x^4}{4!} + \dfrac{x^6}{6!} + \cdots .$

85. $e^x \sin x = x + x^2 + x^3/3 - x^5/30 + \cdots .$

86. $\tan x = x + x^3/3 + \frac{2}{15}x^5 + \frac{17}{315}x^7 + \cdots .$

87. $\sec x = 1 + x^2/2 + \frac{5}{24}x^4 + \cdots .$

88. For $-1 < x < 1$, deduce from Prob. 68 that

$$\ln \frac{1+x}{1-x} = 2\left(x + \frac{x^3}{3} + \frac{x^5}{5} + \frac{x^7}{7} + \cdots\right).$$

89. Let

$$\frac{1}{1 - x - x^2} = A_0 + A_1 x + \cdots + A_n x^n + \cdots.$$

Then $1 = (1 - x - x^2)(A_0 + A_1 x + \cdots + A_n x^n + \cdots)$. By equating coefficients of like powers of x, deduce that $A_0 = A_1 = 1$, and $A_n = A_{n-1} + A_{n-2}$ for $n > 1$.   These relations define the A_n in succession.   They are the Fibonacci numbers (Leonardo Fibonacci, ca. 1170, Italian).

90. If $r_1 = (-1 + \sqrt{5})/2$ and $r_2 = (-1 - \sqrt{5})/2$, show that

$$\frac{1}{1 - x - x^2} = \frac{1}{\sqrt{5}}\left(\frac{1}{x - r_2} - \frac{1}{x - r_1}\right).$$

By expanding the simple fractions in powers of x, show that the nth Fibonacci number of Prob. 89 is $A_{n-1} = (1/\sqrt{5})(r_1^{-n} - r_2^{-n}) = (1/\sqrt{5})(r_2^{n} - r_1^{n})$.

Section 107

For the problems in this section, show that the answers are accurate to the number of decimal places given.

91. Use Prob. 88, with $x = \frac{1}{3}$ and $x = \frac{1}{9}$, to verify that $\ln 2 = 0.69316$ and $\ln \frac{5}{4} = 0.2231$.

92. From the values found in Prob. 91, deduce that $\ln 10 = 2.3026$ and that $\log_{10} 2 = 0.3010$.

Use the series of Probs. 65 and 66 to verify that

93. $\sin 0.5 = 0.4794$.

94. $\cos 0.5 = 0.5463$.

95. $\sin 10° = 0.1736$.

96. $\cos 10° = 0.9848$.

97. By integrating the series for $1/(1 + x^2)$, deduce that $\tan^{-1} x = x - x^3/3 + x^5/5 - x^7/7 + \cdots$.   Use this to show that $\pi/4 = 2 \tan^{-1} \frac{1}{3} + \tan^{-1} \frac{1}{7} = 0.7854$.

98. Show that

$$\int_0^x e^{-x^2}\, dx = x - \frac{x^3}{3} + \frac{1}{2!}\frac{x^5}{5} - \frac{1}{3!}\frac{x^7}{7} + \cdots,$$

and use this to verify that $\int_0^1 e^{-x^2}\, dx = 0.7468$.

99. Show that

$$\int_0^x \frac{\sin x}{x}\, dx = x - \frac{1}{3!}\frac{x^3}{3} + \frac{1}{5!}\frac{x^5}{5} - \cdots,$$

and use this to verify that

$$\int_0^{0.5} \frac{\sin x}{x}\, dx = 0.4931.$$

100. Show that

$$\int_0^x \sqrt{1 - x^4}\, dx = x - \frac{1}{2}\frac{x^5}{5} + \frac{1}{2\cdot 4}\frac{x^9}{9} + \cdots,$$

and use this to verify that $\int_0^{0.5} \sqrt{1 - x^4}\, dx = 0.5315$.

Section 108

For the complex variable z, we have $(d/dz)\,(az^n) = anz^{n-1}$. Further, convergent power series may be differentiated term by term. From this and the series definitions, show that:

101. $(d/dz)\, e^z = e^z$.
102. $(d/dz)\, \sin z = \cos z$.
103. $(d/dz)\, e^{kz} = ke^{kz}$.
104. $(d/dz)\, \cos z = -\sin z$.

105. From Prob. 103, show that $y = e^{mx}$ is a solution of $d^2y/dx^2 + B\,(dy/dx) + Cy = 0$ if $m^2 + Bm + C = 0$. For a and b real, deduce from this that $y = c_1 e^{ax} + c_2 e^{bx}$ is a solution of $d^2y/dx^2 - (a + b)\,(dy/dx) + aby = 0$. And also show that $y = c_1 e^{ax} \cos bx + c_2 e^{ax} \sin bx = \frac{1}{2}(c_1 - ic_2)\, e^{(a+bi)x} + \frac{1}{2}(c_1 + ic_2)\, e^{(a-bi)x}$ is a solution of $d^2y/dx^2 - 2b\,(dy/dx) + (a^2 + b^2)y = 0$.

Section 109

106. Show that $\cos^2 z + \sin^2 z = 1$ is a consequence of Eqs. (55) and (49).

107. Use Euler's expressions to show that $\cos^4 z = \frac{1}{8}(\cos 4z + 4 \cos 2z + 3)$, and use this identity to evaluate the indefinite integral $\int \cos^4 x \, dx$.

Section 110

Verify each of the following numerical evaluations, to the number of decimal places given in Probs. 110 to 113:

108. $e^{\pi i} = -1$.

109. $e^{\pi i/2} = i$.

110. $\cos 4i = 27.31$.

111. $\sin 3i = 10.021$.

112. $e^{1-\pi i/4} = 1.967 - 1.967i$.

113. $\sin (1 + i) = 1.298 + 0.635i$.

11

PARTIAL DERIVATIVES, MULTIPLE INTEGRALS

In this chapter we shall consider functions of more than one variable. And we shall develop the processes of differentiation and integration for such functions.

111—FUNCTIONS OF TWO VARIABLES

Let X,Y be an arbitrary set of ordered pairs of two real numbers, and Z an arbitrary set of single real numbers. Suppose that a rule is given which assigns to each elementary pair x,y of X,Y a single element z of Z. Then the set f of ordered triplets $(x,y;z)$ thus generated is called a function of two variables. And we write

$$f:X,Y \to Z \qquad \text{or} \qquad f:(x,y;z), \tag{1}$$

read "the function f which maps X,Y onto Z" or "the function f whose elements are $(x,y;z)$", respectively.

The *domain of definition* of the function f is the set of pairs X,Y. The range of the function f is the set Z. The numbers x and y, elements of X and Y, are called the *independent variables*. The number z, an element of the range Z, is called the *dependent variable*. For any pair x,y, the corresponding z is called the *value of the function f at x,y*. It is denoted by $f(x,y)$, read "f of x and y".

Let the domain be a region R of the xy plane. Let $P_0 = (x_0,y_0)$ be a fixed point of R. And let $P = (x,y)$ be a variable point of R. If $f(x,y)$ tends to $f(x_0,y_0)$ when P tends to P_0, that is, for a given $\epsilon > 0$ there is a $\delta > 0$ such that $|f(x_1y) - f(x_0,y_0)| < \epsilon$ for all (x,y) satisfying $\sqrt{(x - x_0)^2 + (y - y_0)^2} < \delta$, then the function f is *continuous* at P_0 or at (x_0,y_0). This definition involves all the points in a circle of radius δ, so that continuity in x and y separately is necessary, but not sufficient for continuity in both variables taken together.

The equation $z = x^2 + y^2$ defines a function f with domain all possible pairs x,y and range all values on nonnegative axis $z \geq 0$. The equation $x^2 + y^2 + z^2 = 1$ may be satisfied by two continuous functions, defined by $z = \sqrt{1 - x^2 - y^2}$ and $z = -\sqrt{1 - x^2 - y^2}$, respectively. For each of these the domain consists of pairs with $x^2 + y^2 \leq 1$ and the range is $0 \leq z \leq 1$ for the first and $-1 \leq z \leq 0$ for the second.

The definitions of functions of more than two variables, and of continuity for such functions, are similar to those just given.

A function of two or more variables which is continuous through-out a closed region is uniformly continuous there and possesses an extreme-value property analogous to that discussed in Secs. 13 and 56 for the one-variable case.

112—GRAPHS OF FUNCTIONS OF TWO VARIABLES

Let us take x and y axes at right angles in a horizontal plane, as in Sec. 2. And let a z axis be drawn vertically through O perpendicular to this plane. Associate a positive value of z to distance above the plane, a zero z to points in the plane, and a negative value of z to distance below the plane. Then each point in space corresponds to one and only one triplet (x,y,z). We may think of each coordinate as the signed distance from an appropriate coordinate plane to this point.

With such a coordinate system, we may visualize the locus of any relation between x, y, and z. Thus the locus of the equation $x^2 + y^2 + z^2 = a^2$ is a sphere of radius a with center at the origin. The upper half of this sphere is the graph of the function defined by $z = \sqrt{a^2 - x^2 - y^2}$. The graph of the function defined by $z = Ax + By$ is a plane. The locus of $z = f(x)$, regarded as defining a function of x and y, is the surface of a cylinder (in general *not* circular) with linear elements parallel to the y axis, and directrix or base curve the graph of $z = f(x)$ in the xz plane. The linear elements extend in-definitely in both directions. The locus of $z = f(x^2 + y^2)$ is a surface of revolution whose axis is the z axis. This follows from the fact that, if $b = f(a^2)$, all the points on the circle $x^2 + y^2 = a^2$ in the plane given by $z = b$ lie on the surface.

113—PARTIAL DERIVATIVES

Consider the function f defined by $z = f(x,y)$. If we give y a fixed value, this equation defines a function of one independent variable x. The derivative of this function, with value

$$\lim_{\Delta x \to 0} \frac{f(x + \Delta x, y) - f(x,y)}{\Delta x} \qquad (2)$$

is the *partial derivative* of z with respect to x.   We denote its value by

$$\frac{\partial z}{\partial x}, \frac{\partial}{\partial x} f(x,y), \frac{\partial f}{\partial x}, f_x(x,y). \tag{3}$$

Thus the partial derivative defines a new function f_x of the two independent variables x and y.

Similarly, if we give x a fixed value, the equation $z = f(x,y)$ defines a function of one independent variable y.   And the derivative of this function, with value

$$\lim_{\Delta y \to 0} \frac{f(x,\, y + \Delta y) - f(x,y)}{\Delta y}, \tag{4}$$

is the partial derivative of z with respect to y.   We denote its value by

$$\frac{\partial z}{\partial y}, \frac{\partial}{\partial y} f(x,y), \frac{\partial f}{\partial y}, f_y(x,y). \tag{5}$$

This defines a new function f_y of the two independent variables x and y.

These partial derivatives have a simple relation to slopes obtained from the locus of $z = f(x,y)$.   Let $P_0 = (x_0, y_0, z_0)$ be a point on the locus.   Then the plane given by $y = y_0$ cuts this locus in a curve (Fig. 30).   The equation of this curve in the plane given by $y = y_0$ parallel to the xz plane is $z = f(x, y_0)$.   The tangent line to this curve makes an angle with any line parallel to the x axis equal to $\tan^{-1} f_x(x_0, y_0)$.   Similarly, the tangent line to the curve in which the plane

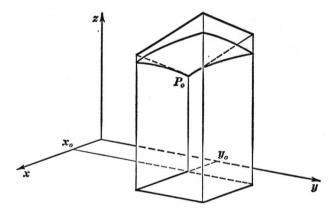

FIGURE 30

given by $x = x_0$ cuts the locus of $z = f(x,y)$ makes an angle with any line parallel to the y axis equal to $\tan^{-1} f_y(x_0,y_0)$. It follows that

$$z - f(x_0,y_0) = f_x(x_0,y_0)\ (x - x_0) + f_y(x_0,y_0)\ (y - y_0) \tag{6}$$

is an equation of the plane tangent to the locus of $z = f(x,y)$ at $P_0(x_0,y_0,z_0)$, with $z_0 = f(x_0,y_0)$.

Except for keeping in mind which variable is held constant and which varies, the calculation of partial derivatives is similar to the calculation of ordinary derivatives.

EXAMPLE.   Find an equation of the plane tangent to the locus of $z = x^2 + 2xy + 3y^2$ at the point with $x = 2$, $y = 3$.

SOLUTION.   With y constant, we have $\partial z/\partial x = 2x + 2y$, while with x constant, we obtain $\partial z/\partial y = 2x + 6y$. For $x = 2, y = 3$, we have $f(2,3) = 43$, $f_x(2,3) = 10$, $f_y(2,3) = 22$. Hence, from Eq. (6), an equation of the tangent plane is $z - 43 = 10(x - 2) + 22(y - 3)$, or $z = 10x + 22y - 43$.

114—TOTAL DIFFERENTIALS

In Sec. 48, for a function of one variable, we defined $dy = f'(x)\ dx$, with dx arbitrary. For $z = f(x,y)$ we define the differential in terms of two arbitrary numbers dx and dy. To lead up to the appropriate expression, we begin by considering the increment

$$\Delta z = f(x + \Delta x, y + \Delta y) - f(x,y). \tag{7}$$

To simplify the discussion, put $\Delta x = h$, $\Delta y = k$. Then

$$\begin{aligned}\Delta z &= f(x + h, y + k) - f(x,y) \\ &= f(x + h, y + k) - f(x, y + k) + f(x, y + k) - f(x,y).\end{aligned} \tag{8}$$

By the mean-value theorem of Sec. 61, this is

$$\Delta z = h\,f_x(x + \theta_1 h, y + k) + k\,f_y(x, y + \theta_2 k), \tag{9}$$

where $0 < \theta_1 < 1$ and $0 < \theta_2 < 1$.

Assume that f_x and f_y are each continuous functions. Then as $h \to 0$ and $k \to 0$, the values in Eq. (9) approach those at (x,y). Accordingly, we have

$$\Delta z = h\, f_x(x,y) + k\, f_y(x,y) + \epsilon_1 h + \epsilon_2 k \tag{10}$$

where $\epsilon_1 \to 0$ and $\epsilon_2 \to 0$ as $h \to 0$ and $k \to 0$. Thus, unless $f_x(x,y)$ and $f_y(x,y)$ are both zero for the particular (x,y) considered, the dominant part of Δz is

$$h\, f_x(x,y) + k\, f_y(x,y) = \Delta x\, f_x(x,y) + \Delta y\, f_y(x,y). \tag{11}$$

This leads us to define the differential as

$$
\begin{aligned}
dz &= f_x(x,y)\, dx + f_y(x,y)\, dy \\
&= \frac{\partial z}{\partial x}\, dx + \frac{\partial z}{\partial y}\, dy.
\end{aligned} \tag{12}
$$

This definition makes $\Delta z/dz$ approximate unity when $\Delta x = dx$ and $\Delta y = dy$ are both small and $dz \neq 0$. And it makes $\Delta z/dz \to 1$ as Δx and Δy each tend to zero.

In particular, let x and y each be functions of t. Then we could find dz/dt by dividing each member of Eq. (10) by Δt and letting $\Delta t \to 0$. The terms in ϵ_1 and ϵ_2 would drop out in the limit, and we should find

$$\frac{dz}{dt} = \frac{\partial z}{\partial x}\frac{dx}{dt} + \frac{\partial z}{\partial y}\frac{dy}{dt}. \tag{13}$$

This, and similar results for partial derivatives, may be written directly by dividing each member of Eq. (12) by dt and interpreting dz/dt, dx/dt, dy/dt as all either total derivatives, as in Eq. (13), or partial derivatives taken on the same basis. Thus, if x and y, and hence z, were each functions of u and v, we should find

$$\frac{\partial z}{\partial u} = \frac{\partial z}{\partial x}\frac{\partial x}{\partial u} + \frac{\partial z}{\partial y}\frac{\partial y}{\partial u}. \tag{14}$$

115—DERIVATIVES OF HIGHER ORDER

Let $z = f(x,y)$ define a differentiable function of two independent variables. Then f_x and f_y also define functions of two independent variables. Hence we may take their partial derivatives. Thus we find

$$\frac{\partial}{\partial x}\left(\frac{\partial z}{\partial x}\right), \ \frac{\partial}{\partial y}\left(\frac{\partial z}{\partial x}\right), \ \frac{\partial}{\partial x}\left(\frac{\partial z}{\partial y}\right), \ \frac{\partial}{\partial y}\left(\frac{\partial z}{\partial y}\right). \tag{15}$$

It can be shown that when all these exist and define continuous functions, the order of differentiation makes no difference. Thus there are only three second-order derivatives,

$$\frac{\partial^2 z}{\partial x^2}, \ \frac{\partial^2 z}{\partial y \, \partial x} = \frac{\partial^2 z}{\partial x \, \partial y}, \ \frac{\partial^2 z}{\partial y^2}. \tag{16}$$

Similarly, we may find third- and higher-order partial derivatives.

116—DOUBLE INTEGRALS

By a method similar to that used for the integral of a continuous function of one variable, we may prove the following theorem.

Let S denote a region of the xy plane. And let F be a continuous function of the two variables x and y in S. Divide the region S into a finite number of smaller regions, each of which can be enclosed in a circle of radius δ_M (Fig. 31). Let ΔS denote any one of these parts and also its area. And let (x,y) denote any point in ΔS. Then, when δ_M tends to zero, the sum $\Sigma F(x,y) \, \Delta S$ approaches a definite limit. The value of this limit is independent of the method of partition of S. We omit the proof of these results. The details are more complicated, but the argument is somewhat like that in Sec. 18.

We represent this limit by $\int_S F$ or $\int_S F(x,y) \, dS$. We call it the *double integral* of F over the region S.

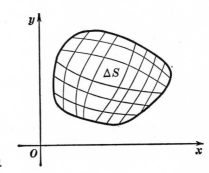

FIGURE 31

117—EVALUATION OF A DOUBLE INTEGRAL

Let S be the region $CDBA$ described in Sec. 76. We shall show that
the double integral described in Sec. 116 may be calculated as

$$\int_S F(x,y)\ dS = \int_a^b \left[\int_{f_1(x)}^{f_2(x)} F(x,y)\ dy \right] dx. \tag{17}$$

To prove this, we proceed as follows. Let $[x_i,x_{i+1}]$, with length
Δx_i, be one of a finite set of intervals constituting a partition of interval $[a,b]$ of the x axis (Fig. 32). Let $[y_j,y_{j+1}]$, with length Δy_j, be
one of a finite set of intervals constituting a partition of interval
$[m_1,M_2]$ of the y axis, where m_1 is the minimum value of f_1, and M_2 is
the maximum value of f_2, on $[a,b]$. Form a set of rectangles by draw-
ing in the lines given by $x = x_i$, $y = y_j$. Call δ_M the radius of the
largest circle circumscribed about a rectangle with sides Δx_i and Δy_j.
Note that when δ_M tends to zero, so does the largest Δx_i and Δy_j.

The region S is now subdivided into rectangles, ΔS_{ij}, and parts of
rectangles, ΔT_{ij}. Let H be the maximum value of Δx_i, and M the
maximum absolute value of F in S. Then, by considering separately
the N intervals in which f_1 and f_2 each always increase or always

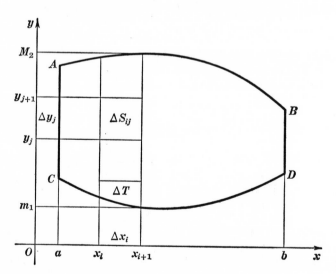

FIGURE 32

decrease, we note that the sum $\Sigma F(x,y) \Delta T_{ij}$ has a numerical value not exceeding $2NMH(M_2 - m_1)$. This tends to zero when δ_M, and hence H, tends to zero. Hence the contributions of the parts of rectangles may be neglected. And summing over complete rectangles in S only, we have

$$\int_S F(x,y) \, dS = \lim \Sigma F(x,y) \, \Delta S_{ij}. \tag{18}$$

Let ξ_i be any point in the interval $[x_i, x_{i+1}]$ and let η_j be any point in the interval $[y_j, y_{j+1}]$. Then (ξ_i, η_j) is a point in one of the complete rectangles ΔS_{ij} of area $\Delta x_i \, \Delta y_j$. And let M_{ij} be the maximum, and m_{ij} the minimum, value of F in this rectangle. Then we have $m_{ij} \leq F(\xi_i, \eta_j) \leq M_{ij}$. Multiply by Δy_j and sum on j. This leads to

$$\sum_j m_{ij} \, \Delta y_j \leq \sum_j F(\xi_i, \eta_j) \, \Delta y_j \leq \sum_j M_{ij} \, \Delta y_j. \tag{19}$$

For the sum in the middle, i and hence ξ_i are constant. Hence, by Sec. 18, the limit of this sum as max Δy_j tends to zero is equal to $\int_{f_1(\xi_i)}^{f_2(\xi_i)} F(\xi_i, y) \, dy$. This limit satisfies the same inequalities, since $\Sigma m_{ij} \, \Delta y_j \leq$ its limit and $\Sigma M_{ij} \, \Delta y_j \geq$ its limit. Thus after multiplication by Δx_i, and summing on i, we find that

$$\sum_{i,j} m_{ij} \, \Delta x_i \, \Delta y_j \leq \sum_i \Delta x_i \int_{f_1(\xi_i)}^{f_2(\xi_i)} F(\xi_i, y) \, dy \leq \sum_{i,j} M_{ij} \, \Delta x_i \, \Delta y_j. \tag{20}$$

But, in Eq. (18) we may take the (x,y) in ΔS_{ij} in such a way that $F(x,y) = M_{ij}$, or $F(x,y) = m_{ij}$. This shows that the first and last sums in Eq. (20) have as their limit the double integral $\int F(x,y) \, dS$. And, by Sec. 18, the middle term in Eq. (20) tends to

$$\int_a^b \left[\int_{f_1(x)}^{f_2(x)} F(x,y) \, dy \right] dx. \quad \text{Thus Eq. (17) holds.} \quad \blacksquare$$

We may rewrite Eq. (17) as

$$\int_S F(x,y) \, dS = \int_a^b dx \int_{y_1}^{y_2} F(x,y) \, dy = \int_a^b \int_{y_1}^{y_2} F(x,y) \, dy \, dx, \tag{21}$$

where the brackets are understood in the third expression. The second expression is more explicit, particularly since some writers interchange dx and dy in the third expression, on the principle that the first differential goes with the first integral sign.   In these forms we have written y_1 for $f_1(x)$ and y_2 for $f_2(x)$ to save space.

EXAMPLE 1.   The base of a cylinder with elements parallel to the z axis is the area between the loci of $y = x^2$ and $y = 2x$ in the xy plane.   The cylinder lies between the planes $z = 0$ and $z = y$.   Find the volume of the cylinder.

SOLUTION.   The volume (Fig. 33) is the limit of sums of prisms each with base ΔS and height $z = y$.   Hence we have $dV = z\,dS = z\,dx\,dy = y\,dx\,dy$.   To find the points of intersection of the curves, we note that, if $y = 2x$ and $y = x^2$, then $2x = x^2$ and $x(x - 2) = 0$, so that $x = 0$ or 2.   Hence the required volume is $\int_0^2 dx \int_{x^2}^{2x} y\,dy$.   The inner integral is $[y^2/2]_{x^2}^{2x} = \frac{1}{2}(4x^2 - x^4)$.   And the outer integral is $\int_0^2 \frac{1}{2}(4x^2 - x^4)\,dx = \frac{1}{2}[4x^3/3 - x^5/5]_0^2 = \frac{32}{15}$.

EXAMPLE 2.   Solve Example 1 by interchanging the roles of x and y and considering the equations $x = \sqrt{y}$, $x = y/2$.

SOLUTION.   Here we again have $dV = y\,dx\,dy$.   And if $x = \sqrt{y}$, $x = y/2$, then $\sqrt{y} = y/2$, $y^2 = 4y$, and $y = 0$ or 4.   Thus $V = \int_0^4 dy \int_{y/2}^{\sqrt{y}} y\,dx$.   The inner integral is $[yx]_{y/2}^{\sqrt{y}} = y^{3/2} - y^2/2$.   And the outer integral is $\int_0^4 (y^{3/2} - y^2/2)\,dy = [\frac{2}{5}y^{5/2} - y^3/6]_0^4 = \frac{32}{15}$, as in Example 1.

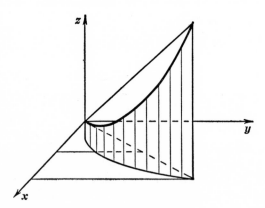

FIGURE 33

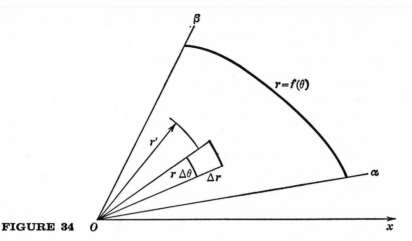

FIGURE 34

EXAMPLE 3.   Find the volume bounded below by the paraboloid of revolution given by $z = x^2 + y^2$ and above by the plane given by $z = 4$.

SOLUTION.   If we introduce polar coordinates in the xy plane, the two equations become $z = r^2$, $z = 4$.   (In space, r, θ, z are known as *cylindrical coordinates*.)   In the xy plane, for polar coordinates, we take as ΔS small keystone-shaped figures approximately rectangles of dimensions Δr and $r\,\Delta\theta$ (Fig. 34). The exact area of ΔS is $r'\,\Delta\theta\,\Delta r$, with $r' = r + \frac{1}{2}\Delta r$.   Since r'

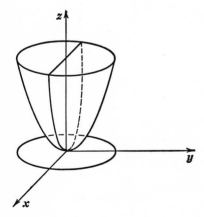

FIGURE 35

belongs to a point in ΔS, for a continuous F we have $\Sigma F(r'',\theta'')r' \, \Delta r \, \Delta\theta \to \iint F(r,\theta) \, r \, dr \, d\theta$. Hence, in polar coordinates, we can take $dS = r \, dr \, d\theta$ and evaluate

$$\int_S F(r,\theta) \, dS = \int_\alpha^\beta d\theta \int_0^{f(\theta)} F(r,\theta) \, r \, dr, \tag{22}$$

where S is the sectorial area discussed in Sec. 95. For Example 3, we get $dV = (z_2 - z_1) \, dS = (4 - r^2)r \, dr \, d\theta$. If $z = r^2$ and $z = 4$, then $r^2 = 4$ and $z = 2$ or -2. Since $r = 2$, $0 \le \theta \le 2\pi$ gives the entire circle of intersection (Fig. 35) and we get $V = \int_0^{2\pi} d\theta \int_0^2 (4 - r^2)r \, dr$. The inner integral is $[2r^2 - r^4/4]_0^2 = 4$, and the outer integral is $[4\theta]_0^{2\pi} = 8\pi$.

118—TRIPLE INTEGRALS

Let $w = F(x,y,z)$ define a continuous function F in R, a region of space. Then a triple integral $\int_V F \, dV$ can be defined in a manner similar to that described in Sec. 116. Let the volume (Fig. 36) be bounded below by a surface which is the locus of $z = g_1(x,y)$ and above by a surface which is the locus of $z = g_2(x,y)$. And either let these surfaces intersect in a curve whose projection on the xy plane is the boundary of a region $S = CDBA$ like that of Sec. 117, or let

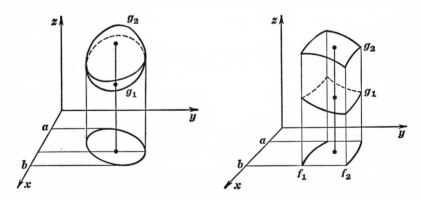

FIGURE 36

it be specified that the volume is bounded by a cylinder with elements parallel to the z axis having such a boundary $CDBA$ as its projection on the xy plane. Then we have

$$\int_V F(x,y,z)\, dV = \int_a^b dx \int_{f_1(x)}^{f_2(x)} dy \int_{g_1(x,y)}^{g_2(x,y)} F(x,y,z)\, dz. \qquad (23)$$

EXAMPLE.   Assuming a, b, c positive, use triple integration to find the volume of the tetrahedron bounded by the coordinate planes and the plane given by $x/a + y/b + z/c = 1$.

SOLUTION.   Here the surfaces are given by $z = 0$ and $z = c(1 - x/a - y/b)$. These intersect in the line $z = 0$, $x/a + y/b = 1$. And the area S in the plane lies between the loci of $y = 0$ and $y = b(1 - x/a)$. These intersect in the point given by $x = a$, $y = 0$. And for the area S, we have $0 \le x \le a$. Hence $V = \int_0^a dx \int_0^{b(1-x/a)} dy \int_0^{c(1-x/a-y/b)} dz$. The inside integral is $c(1 - x/a - y/b)$. The next integral is

$$c\left[\left(1 - \frac{x}{a}\right)y - \frac{y^2}{2b}\right]_0^{b(1-x/a)} = \frac{bc}{2}(1 - x/a)^2.$$

And the final integral is

$$\frac{bc}{2}\left[\left(\frac{-a}{3}\right)\left(1 - \frac{x}{a}\right)^3\right]_0^a = \frac{abc}{6}.$$

PROBLEMS

Section 113

Find $\partial z/\partial x$ and $\partial z/\partial y$ for the function defined by each given equation:

1. $z = 4x^2 + 3xy + y^2$.
2. $z = e^{-x^2} - 2y^2$.
3. $z = (x - y)/(x + y)$.
4. $z = 1/(2x^2 + y^2)$.
5. $z = e^{2x} \cos 3y$.
6. $z = \sin(x^2 + xy)$.
7. $z = \tan^{-1}(y/x)$.
8. $z = \ln \sqrt{x^2 + y^2}$.

Find an equation for the plane tangent to each given surface at the specified point, after verifying that this point lies on the surface:

9. $z = x^2 + y^2$, $(1,1,2)$.

10. $z = 3xy$, $(1,2,6)$.

11. $z = \sqrt{x^2 + y^2}$, $(3,4,5)$.

12. $z = \sqrt{x^2 - y}$, $(2,3,1)$.

Section 114

For each given set of equations, find dz/dt:

13. $z = 2x^2y + 3xy^2$, $x = 2t$, $y = 3t$.

14. $z = x^2y$, $x = e^t$, $y = e^{-t}$.

At a certain instant of time, $t = t_0$, we have $x = 3$, $y = 4$, $dx/dt = 2$, $dy/dt = -2$. Find dz/dt at $t = t_0$ if:

15. $z = \sqrt{x^2 + y^2}$.

16. $z = x^3y^2$.

Two measured lengths were recorded as $x = 12 \pm 0.03$ ft and $y = 5 \pm 0.02$ ft. Find the approximate error in the computed value of:

17. x/y.

18. $\sqrt{x^2 + y^2}$.

19. Let $z = f(x,y)$ define a differentiable function which makes $F(x,y,z) = 0$. Then

$$\frac{\partial F}{\partial x} + \frac{\partial F}{\partial z}\frac{\partial f}{\partial x} = 0 \quad \text{and} \quad \frac{\partial F}{\partial y} + \frac{\partial F}{\partial z}\frac{\partial f}{\partial y} = 0.$$

Therefore $\partial f/\partial x = -F_x/F_z$ and $\partial f/\partial y = -F_y/F_z$. Deduce that if $z_0 = f(x_0,y_0)$, an equation of the plane tangent to the locus of $F(x,y,z) = 0$ at (x_0,y_0,z_0) is $F_x(x_0,y_0,z_0)(x - x_0) + F_y(x_0,y_0,z_0)(y - y_0) + F_z(x_0,y_0,z_0)(z - z_0) = 0$.

20. Use the method of Prob. 19 to show that for suitable restrictions on the functions, if $F(x_0,y_0) = 0$, an equation of the line tangent to the curve $F(x,y) = 0$ at (x_0,y_0) is $F_x(x_0,y_0)(x - x_0) + F_y(x_0,y_0)(y - y_0) = 0$.

21. Use Prob. 19 to show that if $Ax_0^2 + By_0^2 + Cz_0^2 = D$, then an equation for the plane tangent to the locus of $Ax^2 + By^2 + Cz^2 = D$ at (x_0,y_0,z_0) is $Axx_0 + Byy_0 + Czz_0 = D$.

22. Use Prob. 20 to show that if $x_0y_0 = Ay_0 + B$, then an equation for the line tangent to the curve $xy = Ay + B$ at (x_0,y_0) is $y_0x + x_0y = Ay + Ay_0 + 2B$.

Section 115

Find $\partial^2 z/\partial x^2$, $\partial^2 z/\partial y^2$, and verify that $\partial^2 z/(\partial y\ \partial x) = \partial^2 z/(\partial x\ \partial y)$, for the function defined by each given equation:

23. $z = x^2 + 4xy - y^2$.
24. $z = xe^y$.
25. $z = \sin(2x + 3y)$.
26. $z = y \ln x$.
27. $z = e^{xy}$.
28. $z = \ln x^3 y^4$.

Section 117

Sketch the area which leads to each of the following double integrals, and set up an equivalent integral with dx and dy in reverse order. Evaluate both forms:

29. $\displaystyle\int_0^2 dx \int_0^{2x} dy$.

30. $\displaystyle\int_0^3 dy \int_0^{3-y} dx$.

31. $\displaystyle\int_0^1 dx \int_{x^3}^{x} dy$.

32. $\displaystyle\int_0^1 dy \int_y^{\sqrt{y}} dx$.

Sketch the area in the xy plane over which each of the given integrals is taken. Then set up an equivalent integral in polar coordinates and evaluate it:

33. $\displaystyle\int_0^2 dx \int_0^{\sqrt{4-x^2}} dy$.

34. $\displaystyle\int_0^4 dy \int_0^{\sqrt{4y-y^2}} (x^2 + y^2)\ dx$.

Use double integration to find the volume bounded below by the xy plane, which is represented by the equation $z = 0$ and bounded above by the surface which is the locus of each given equation:

35. $z = 1 - x^2 - y^2$.
36. $36z = 72 - 9x^2 - 4y^2$.

37. $z = 3 - x$, and inside $x^2 + y^2 = 4$.

38. $z = x^2 + y^2$, and inside $x^2 + y^2 = 1$.

39. $z = xy$, and with $0 \le x \le 1$, $0 \le y \le 1$.

Verify the given formulas for the moments of Sec. 83 and 84:

40. $M_{kx} = \int_a^b dx \int_{y_1}^{y_2} x^k \, dy = \int_a^b x^k (y_2 - y_1) \, dx$.

41. $M_{ky} = \int_a^b dx \int_{y_1}^{y_2} y^k \, dy = \int_a^b \frac{1}{k+1} (y_2{}^{k+1} - y_1{}^{k+1}) \, dx$.

Section 118

Evaluate each given triple integral:

42. $\int_0^2 dx \int_0^x dy \int_0^{x+y} xyz \, dz$.

43. $\int_0^1 dx \int_0^{\sqrt{1-x^2}} dy \int_0^{\sqrt{1-x^2-y^2}} z(x^2 + y^2) \, dz$

$= \int_0^{2\pi} d\theta \int_0^1 dr \int_0^{\sqrt{1-r^2}} r^3 z \, dz$.

44. Use the equation $V\bar{x} = \int x \, dV$ and the similar expressions for $\bar{y}$ and $\bar{z}$ to show that the centroid of the tetrahedron of the example in Sec. 118 is $(a/4, b/4, c/4)$.

45. The volume of a solid sphere of radius a is $V = \frac{4}{3}\pi a^3$. Check this by evaluating each of the following expressions:

$$\int_0^{2\pi} d\theta \int_0^a dr \int_{-\sqrt{a^2-r^2}}^{\sqrt{a^2-r^2}} r \, dz \qquad \int_{-a}^a dz \int_0^{2\pi} d\theta \int_0^{\sqrt{a^2-z^2}} r \, dr.$$

46. Verify that the volume of the solid of revolution bounded by the locus of $r = f(z)$ which lies between the planes given by $z = a$ and $z = b$ is

$$V = \int_a^b dz \int_0^{2\pi} d\theta \int_0^{f(z)} r \, dr = \pi \int_a^b [f(z)]^2 \, dz.$$

47. Let the density of the solid of Prob. 46 be $D(z)$, depending on z only. Verify that:

$$M = \int_a^b dz \int_0^{2\pi} d\theta \int_0^{f(z)} D(z) \, r \, dr = \pi \int_a^b D(z)[f(z)]^2 \, dz.$$

$$M\bar{z} = \int_a^b dz \int_0^{2\pi} d\theta \int_0^{f(z)} D(z) \, zr \, dr = \pi \int_a^b z \, D(z)[f(z)]^2 \, dz.$$

$$I = \int_a^b dz \int_0^{2\pi} d\theta \int_0^{f(z)} D(z) \, r^3 \, dr = \int_a^b \frac{\pi}{2} D(z) \, [f(z)]^4 \, dz.$$

48. Use Prob. 47 to show that, for the centroid of a solid hemisphere of radius a, with $r = f(z) = \sqrt{a^2 - z^2}$, we have

$$V\bar{z} = \pi \int_0^a z(a^2 - z^2)\, dz = \frac{\pi}{4}\, a^4 \qquad \text{and} \qquad \bar{z} = \tfrac{3}{8}a.$$

49. Use Prob. 47 to show that, for a homogeneous solid sphere of radius a, with $r = \sqrt{a^2 - z^2}$, we have

$$I = \int_{-a}^a \frac{\pi}{2}\, (a^2 - z^2)^2\, dz = \tfrac{8}{15}\pi a^5 \qquad \text{and} \qquad k = \sqrt{\frac{I}{V}} = \sqrt{\tfrac{2}{5}}\,a.$$